The structur
the Craven I
areas

C000079053

During the exploration of northern England for oil and gas in the 1980s, numerous seismic reflection surveys were carried out. These provide the principal means of investigating the geological structure and to some extent the stratigraphy of Carboniferous rocks below the levels that can be reliably predicted from outcrops, mine workings and most boreholes. In this book, such data have been integrated with all available geological information to produce an account which details the geological evolution of the region during Carboniferous and later times together with a series of structure-contour and preserved-thickness maps at a scale of 1:625 000 which illustrate present-day structure, and distribution of rock units.

Carboniferous basin development in the region can be divided broadly into two main phases. In early Carboniferous times, rapidly subsiding, fault-controlled, extensional basins developed between structurally elevated emergent blocks. More regional subsidence followed, which was characterised by a general lack of major fault-control, leading to submergence and depositional onlap of the earlier structural highs. In later Dinantian times platform carbonates developed on the former highs, whilst argillaceous sedimentation dominated in basinal areas. In Namurian times, a delta system prograded across the region, dominantly from the north and east, and infilled remaining topography resulting in rapid thickness and facies variations. During the Westphalian, thickness variations were less marked with a more uniform distribution of facies. Basin inversion occurred towards the end of Carboniferous times which led locally to strong folding and partial reversal of some of the earlier basin controlling normal faults. Deposition ceased with regional uplift, and widespread erosion ensued. A period dominated by extensional faulting from Permian to early Cretaceous times was followed by regional subsidence until early Palaeocene. Regional uplift with superimposed basin inversion then commenced, and triggered a period of erosion which has probably continued onshore to the present day.

Cover photograph

Gordale Scar, Malham [view point SD 9143 6300] (L2704).
Photographer: K E Thornton.

BRITISH GEOLOGICAL SURVEY

G A KIRBY
H E BAILY
R A CHADWICK
D J EVANS
D W HOLLIDAY
S HOLLOWAY
A G HULBERT
T C PHARAOH
N J P SMITH
N AITKENHEAD
B BIRCH

The structure and evolution of the Craven Basin and adjacent areas

Subsurface memoir

London: The Stationery Office 2000

ISBN 0 11 884536 5

Bibliographical reference

KIRBY, G A, BAILY, H E, CHADWICK, R A, EVANS, D J, HOLLIDAY, D W, HOLLOWAY, S, HULBERT, A G, PHARAOH, T C, SMITH, N J P, AITKENHEAD, N, and BIRCH, B. 2000. The structure and evolution of the Craven Basin and adjacent areas. *Subsurface Memoir of the British Geological Survey.*

Authors

G A Kirby, BSc, PhD
H E Baily, BA, PhD
R A Chadwick, MA, MSc, CGeol
D J Evans, BSc, PhD
D W Holliday, MA, PhD, CGeol
S Holloway, BA, PhD, CGeol
A G Hulbert
T C Pharaoh, BSc, PhD, CGeol
N J P Smith, MSc
N Aitkenhead, BSc, PhD, CGeol
B Birch, BSc
British Geological Survey
Keyworth

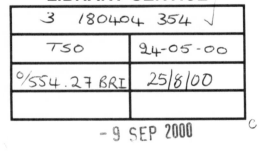

Printed in the UK for the Stationery Office
TJ000845   C6   03/00

Other publications of the Survey dealing with this and adjoining districts

BOOKS

Memoirs
See Appendix 1

Subsurface Memoir
The structure and evolution of the Northumberland–Solway Basin and adjacent areas

British Regional Geology
Northern England (4th edition)
The Pennines and adjacent areas (3rd edition)
Eastern England from the Tees to the Wash (2nd edition)

Offshore Regional Report
The Irish Sea
The southern North Sea

MAPS

1:1000 000
Geological map of the United Kingdom, Ireland and the continental shelf, Solid, 1991
Pre-Permian geology of the United Kingdom (South)

1:625 000
Geological map of Great Britain, Sheet 1, Solid, 3rd edition, 1979
Bouguer anomaly map of the British Isles, Southern Sheet 1986
Aeromagnetic map of Great Britain, South Sheet 1965

1:250 000
53 04W Liverpool Bay, Solid Geology, 1978
53 02W Humber/Trent, Solid Geology, 1983
54 04W Lake District, Solid Geology, 1980
54 02W Tyne-Tees, Solid Geology, 1981

Aeromagnetic (A) and Bouguer (B) anomaly maps
53 04W Liverpool Bay (A) 1978, (B) 1977
53 02W Humber/Trent (A) 1977, (B) 1977
54 04W Lake District (A) 1977, (B) 1986
54 02W Tyne-Tees (A) 1985, (B) 1978

1:50 000 and 1:63 360
See Appendix 1

CONTENTS

FIGURES

NB Two-way travel-time scales on seismic displays have been shifted to a common datum (OD).

TABLES

CROSS-SECTIONS

MAPS

ACKNOWLEDGEMENTS

NOTES

The interpretation of the seismic data, and the production of the structure contour maps was carried out by Dr H E Baily, Mr R A Chadwick, Dr D J Evans, Dr S Holloway, Mr A G Hulbert, Dr G A Kirby, Dr T C Pharaoh and Mr N J P Smith. These personnel also prepared the written account in conjunction with Dr N Aitkenhead and Dr D W Holliday. Regional maps were compiled by Dr H Baily and data digitisation and manipulation was undertaken by Ms B Birch and Mr A G Hulbert. The book was compiled by Dr G A Kirby and edited by Drs. A A Jackson and G A Kirby and Mr R A Chadwick.

Amoco Oil Company, British Gas Exploration and Production, BP Exploration Operating Company Ltd, Enterprise Oil plc, Teredo Resources, and Ultramar Oil Company are thanked for permission to display seismic data. These companies together with Amoco, Candecca Resources, Clyde Petroleum plc, Edinburgh Oil and Gas, Fina Exploration Ltd, Pentex Oil Company and North West Water Geological Services are also thanked for their permission to publish the structure contour and preserved thickness maps.

Throughout this book the word 'region' equates with the area shown on Maps 1 to 9. The word 'district' refers to the area of a specified 1:50 000 geological sheet.

National Grid references are given in square brackets.

PREFACE

Traditional methods of geological surveying do not always provide reliable indicators of subsurface structure. Nor is any deep borehole necessarily a good guide to what might be found at depth at other nearby localities. To overcome such difficulties, seismic reflection profiling methods have been developed and refined in recent decades. Such exploration methods are of particular importance to the oil industry, and the application of these and other basin analysis techniques to the sedimentary basins of the United Kingdom has significantly increased the economic resources of the nation, and greatly enhanced knowledge of the structure and geological evolution of both the land area and of the adjoining continental shelf.

Many recent maps and memoirs of the British Geological Survey have made use of seismic reflection profiles, but generally only in a limited way. This book is based on exhaustive use of such data, and aims to present a concise review of the tectonic and sedimentary history of the Carboniferous rocks of the Craven Basin and adjacent areas. It is the second in a series of subsurface memoirs relating to Upper Palaeozoic basins, and forms a sequel to a previously published account of the adjacent Northumberland–Solway Basin.

This account is essentially regional in scope, dealing particularly with the deeper, concealed parts of the Carboniferous succession and associated structures not considered in earlier publications. The results of the study are largely contained in the accompanying 1:625 000 scale structure contour and preserved thickness maps and associated palaeogeographical maps. The accompanying written account is intended both as a regional review, as an explanation and partial amplification of these maps, and as a summary of basin evolution and tectonic history.

This book provides an up-to-date summary and distillation of information obtained during the search for, and extraction of, mineral and energy resources of the region. It will also serve as a basic reference source when economic conditions change or new commodities are required, or when new exploration models are developed which once again result in new interest in the region by the exploration industry.

David A Falvey, PhD
Director

British Geological Survey
Kingsley Dunham Centre
Keyworth
Nottingham
NG12 5GG

ONE

Introduction

This memoir presents a review of the tectonic and sedimentary history of a significant part of northern England, encompassing the Craven Basin and surrounding areas, (Figures 1, 2 and 3) with an emphasis on Carboniferous rocks. In the account the term Craven Basin is defined as the series of basins and tilt blocks to the south of the Askrigg and Lake District blocks and to the north of the Central Lancashire High (Figures 1, 14). It forms a sequel to similar, previously published subsurface studies of the Mesozoic basins of England and Wales (Whittaker 1985), and of the Carboniferous rocks of the Northumberland–Solway Basin (Chadwick et al., 1995); it is the second book to be published in the Subsurface Memoir series of the British Geological Survey (BGS).

The region, in particular the Askrigg Block and the Craven Basin, includes many classic localities and areas of major importance in the development of British geology. The surface and near-surface geology have been described in BGS 1:50 000 Series maps and memoirs (Appendix 1). This account examines the deeper, concealed parts of the Carboniferous succession not considered in earlier publications. The results of the study are largely contained in the accompanying 1:625 000 scale structure contour and isopach maps (Maps 1 to 9), and associated text figures. This account is intended both as a regional review and as an explanation and amplification of these maps and figures.

The region includes both areas of high urban population density and remote mountainous and moorland

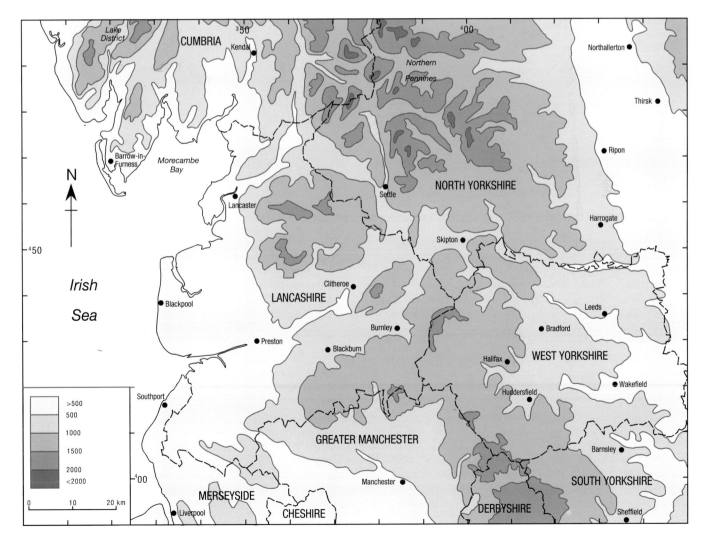

Figure 1   Location map of the region showing urban areas and county boundaries.

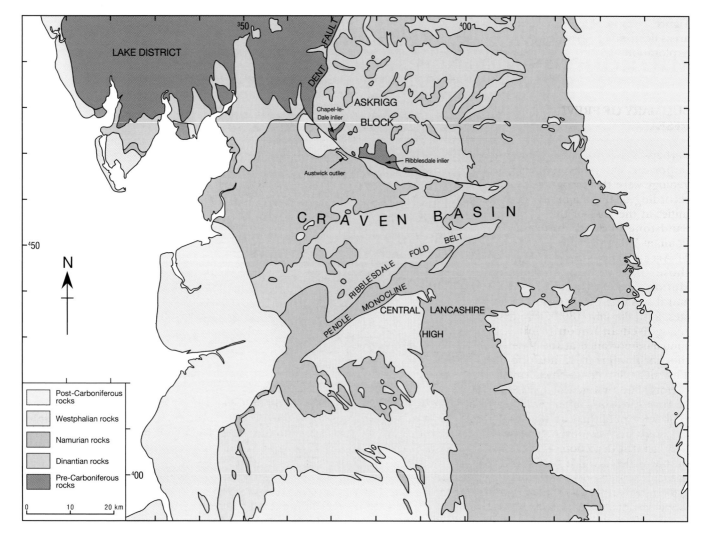

Figure 2 Simplified geological map of the region.

countryside. The main urban and industrial centres are located in west Yorkshire, centred on Leeds, and in central and southern Lancashire together with Manchester and Liverpool (Figure 1). Elsewhere, much of the lower-lying land is rural, but in the centre of the region, and more generally in the north, the land rises to the high open moorland of the Pennines. In the north-west lies the higher mountainous area of the English Lake District.

The Carboniferous rocks of the region have long been of economic significance. Coal, ore-minerals, building stone, aggregate, limestone, ironstone and ceramic materials have been worked in the past. Prior to the 1980s, only limited investigation of the concealed geology was possible, mainly through coal exploration and extraction, and from scientific drilling and geophysical surveys. More recently the region has been actively explored for hydrocarbons (Figure 3). This has provided an extensive network of commercial seismic reflection profiles, and some new deep boreholes, which for the first time have allowed elucidation of the detailed structure of the Carboniferous

strata beneath much of northern England. This account relies heavily on these data.

Good-quality seismic reflection data have been acquired in many parts of the region where Carboniferous rocks are exposed at the surface, or occur beneath a thin cover of Quaternary deposits. In such areas the entire Upper Palaeozoic basin fill is generally resolved. However, data quality commonly deteriorates in areas where Permo-Triassic rocks crop out, most notably in the west (Figure 2), and also in areas of thick drift. There are no seismic data over the Lake District and the Askrigg Block, and in the area around Leeds and Huddersfield.

Stratigraphical calibration of the seismic data is provided by the scatter of deep boreholes over the region. These are augmented by surface exposures, except in the west, and to a lesser extent in the east, where there is an extensive cover of Permo-Triassic rocks. The very thick early Carboniferous deposits which form the lower part of the sedimentary fill of the Craven and Harrogate basins, are neither penetrated by boreholes nor are satisfactorily exposed at surface.

Figure 3 Borehole locations and areas licensed for hydrocarbon exploration.

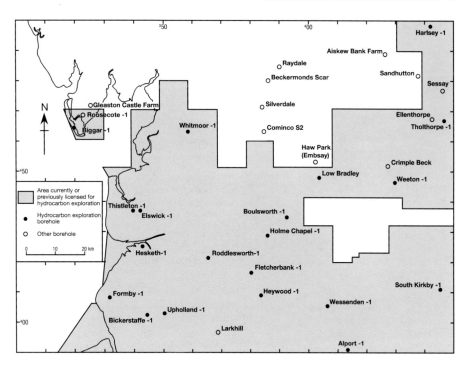

SUMMARY OF PREVIOUS RESEARCH

Perhaps the most perceptive and important early observations in geology were the recognition and recording of the major unconformities at the base of the Old Red Sandstone in Scotland at Siccar Point, at Jedburgh, and on the Isle of Arran. The man who made those observations was James Hutton (see Craig, et al., 1978), and it was one of his close associates, John Playfair (1802), who first recognised an unconformity of similar importance at the base of the Carboniferous Limestone at Thornton Force in the Craven region. The first geological maps of Yorkshire by William Smith, and of Lancashire by E Hall, were published in 1821 and 1832, respectively. The maps are primitive even by early standards, for example they lack any depiction of faults, but they do show a recognition of the general lithostratigraphical succession. In particular, Smith, possibly following either William Phillips (1818), or Farey (1811), recorded that the 'Mountain' (or 'Metalliferous') Limestone was overlain by 'Millstone Grit' (or 'Moorstone'). It was also about this time that the term 'Carboniferous' was formally proposed by Coneybeare and Phillips (1822). These authors also proposed the name 'Penine', soon changed to 'Pennine', for the range of hills which dominates the region (see Kendall and Wroot, 1924, p.227). A few years later in 1836, William Smith's nephew, John Phillips published the first major written work on the northern part of the region. This included the recognition and naming of the Craven Faults system, and use of the terms 'block' and 'basin' to distinguish the area of flat-lying limestones to the north of this system from the area with a thick, folded, argillaceous sequence to the south. He also recognised a number of folds in the basin and noted that these had a similar north-east to south-west axial trend; he named the extensive area where these occurred, the 'Ribblesdale Foldbelt'. Farther south, for the Rossendale and Manchester districts, much of the early stratigraphical observations are to be found in the publications by Binney (for example 1841a and 1841b). Other early papers by Binney and those of contemporary researchers on the geology of these districts, are listed in the Rossendale Anticline and Manchester memoirs (Wright et al., 1927 and Tonks et al., 1931).

The next major phase in the acquisition of geological knowledge of the region was largely due to the systematic primary geological mapping carried out by the Geological Survey in the middle part of the 19th century. This resulted in the publication, between 1852 and 1892, of a series of geological maps covering the entire region at a scale of one inch to one mile. These and the published memoirs which described the geology of much of the mapped area, except for parts of the Askrigg Block and Craven Basin, provided a foundation and stimulus for further research for several following decades. Published memoirs include the Burnley Coalfield (Hull et al., 1875), and the Yorkshire Coalfield (Green et al., 1878. Perhaps the most significant non-Survey contribution during this period was that of Sorby (1859) whose work on the cross-bedding and petrography of the Millstone Grit sandstones showed that they were formed from sand that had been derived from a crystalline terrain lying to the north-east. This study was subsequently greatly extended by Gilligan (1920) who suggested that the sediments were deposited in a large river delta.

In the early part of the present century, great advances were made in stratigraphical palaeontology (biostratigraphy). Of special note are the publications of Garwood (1913) and Garwood and Goodyear (1924), working on the coral/brachiopod faunas of the shelf/platform limestones of the Askrigg Block and Southern Lake District High, and those of Bisat (1924). Bisat's goniatite (ammonoid) zonation has provided the framework for most of the advances in understanding the stratigraphy and sedimentology of the latest Dinantian to Silesian succession. This was supplemented in the mainly non-marine Westphalian sequence by the use of bivalve zonation (for example Wray and Trueman, 1931).

These advances in biostratigraphy were put to good use when economic pressures stimulated a new phase of Geological Survey mapping in the Lancashire and Yorkshire coalfields and intervening Pennine areas in the 1920s and 30s. Memoirs describing this work include those of

Wright et al., 1927; Wray et al., 1930; Tonks et al., 1931; Bromehead et al., 1933 and Jones et al., 1938.

Working in the Craven Basin and Askrigg Block areas farther north, other researchers, notably Chubb and Hudson, (1925), Hudson (for example 1924, 1930, 1937, 1938a, and 1938b), Hudson and Mitchell, (1937), Parkinson (for example 1926, 1935, 1936 and 1944) and Turner (1927), were also greatly advancing knowledge of Dinantian and Namurian stratigraphy. The Survey was able to build on these and other studies, notably by Moseley, (1956), when, after the war, it resumed systematic but intermittent resurvey of the Craven Basin area, including the Clitheroe district (Earp et al., 1961), the Settle district (Arthurton et al., 1988), the Garstang district (Aitkenhead et al., 1992) and the Lancaster district (Brandon et al., 1998). Some useful general reviews were also produced (Wray, 1936, and Edwards and Trotter, 1954; Rayner, 1953), as well as works dealing specifically with areas of economic significance, for example the Yorkshire Coalfield (Edwards, 1951) and the Askrigg Block part of the Northern Pennine Orefield (Dunham and Wilson, 1985).

In the last three decades, more specialist research in biostratigraphy, sedimentology, structural geology and applied geophysics has been carried out both within the region and as part of wider studies. The use of biostratigraphy in subdividing and helping to define the Carboniferous succession is illustrated in many publications, for example Calver (1968), George et al. (1976), Ramsbottom et al. (1978), Conil et al. (1980), Metcalfe (1981) and Riley (1990, 1993) as well as in contributions to the Geological Survey memoirs referred to above.

There have been few detailed sedimentological studies made of the Dinantian rocks of the region. The enigmatic but scenically attractive and well-exposed limestone 'reefs' (variously termed reef knolls, knoll reefs, carbonate banks, Waulsortian reefs, build-ups and mud mounds) have long received much attention including both those within the basin (Tiddeman, 1889; Parkinson, 1926; Black, 1954; Bathurst, 1959; Lees and Miller, 1985; Miller, 1986), and those at the block or shelf margins. (Tiddeman, 1899; Hudson, 1930, 1932; Bond, 1950; Mundy, 1978, Arthurton et al., 1988; and Horbury, 1992). Only in the last 25 years has a methodology been developed for properly working out the genesis and palaeoenvironmental significance of these various 'reefs'.

Such sedimentological work as has been done on the Askrigg Block, summarised by Wilson (in Dunham and Wilson, 1985, pp.17–19), includes the recognition of deltaic facies in the Yoredale sandstones by Moore (1959, 1960). However, most work has been concerned with describing, defining and interpreting the remarkable succession of cyclothemic sequences noted earlier by Hudson (1924). In the Southern Lake District High, which forms the north-western margin of the Craven Basin, detailed research by Adams et al. (1990) and Horbury (1987, 1989) has demonstrated the broad oscillations of facies between submarine slope, ramp and emergent shelf. Farther south in the Bowland Basin, Gawthorpe (1986) showed that a ramp-to-slope transition had occurred from late Courceyan to Brigantian times.

Modern sedimentological research on the Namurian rocks was much stimulated by the classic synthesis of Reading (1964) in which he demonstrated the progressive fill of the Central Pennines Basin by the various facies of the Millstone Grit. The sedimentology of particular stratigraphical intervals within the region has been published by several authors, Collinson and Banks (1975); Collinson et al.(1977); McCabe (1978); Chisholm (1981), Okolo (1983); Bristow (1988); and Maynard (1992). Much important work remains unpublished, however, mostly in academic theses (Baines, 1977; and Sims, 1988), or published only in outline (Benfield, 1969). Sedimentological studies of more extended Namurian rock successions in particular parts of the region have been made by Steel (1988) for the Gainsborough Trough, and Martinsen (1990a) for the Askrigg Block and adjacent areas to the west and south, (see also Martinsen, 1990b, and Brenner and Martinsen, 1990).

There has been relatively little sedimentological research on the Westphalian rocks in this particular part of the Pennine Basin as can be seen from the comprehensive overview of the basin by Guion and Fielding (1988). A few papers deal with particular aspects, for example Broadhurst and Loring (1970), Broadhurst and France (1986), and certain localities, for example Scott (1984). Only Chisholm (1990) has provided a detailed regional synthesis of one cyclic sequence.

Much detail of surface geological structures accrued before and during the first half of the present century from work outlined above, supplemented locally by an abundance of data from underground coal workings. Structural syntheses are given in the various memoirs but structural contour maps are only to be found for the relatively uncomplicated coalfield districts east of the Pennines (Wray et al., 1930; Bromehead et al., 1933; Edwards et al., 1940; Mitchell et al., 1947 and Edwards, 1951). Broader regional syntheses were produced by Fearnsides (1933), Turner (1936, 1949), Edwards and Trotter (1954) and Moseley (1972). The Craven Fault and Dent Fault belt has received particular attention, and is reviewed by Dunham and Wilson (1985) and locally reassessed in detail by Arthurton et al.(1988) and Underhill et al. (1988).

It was not until the 1960s with the application of geophysical techniques that a picture of the deeper geological structure of parts of the region began to be revealed. Gravity and magnetic surveys (Bott, 1961, 1967; Myers and Wardell, 1967), and, in particular, seismic reflection profiling and seismic refraction surveys, have not only greatly extended the limited knowledge previously gained from interpolating surface evidence downwards but have been interpreted to suggest the presence of hitherto unknown features. Some of these, such as the Wensleydale Granite and nearby magnetic Ordovician strata, have been subsequently proved by drilling (Dunham, 1974; Wilson and Cornwell, 1982). In the last decade, geophysical studies (for example Gawthorpe, 1987; Lee, 1988; Cornwell and Walker, 1989; Smith and Smith, 1989) have automatically become part of any geological study of a district (for example Arthurton et al., 1988; Aitkenhead et al., 1992) or region (for example Plant and Jones, 1989; Holliday et al., 1999).

This greatly improved sedimentological and structural knowledge combined with the application of plate tectonic theory has led to a number of important works on block and basin evolution and controls on sedimentation to a large extent stimulated by the needs of the hydrocarbons industry. These include Johnson (1967), Anderton et al. (1979), Dewey (1982), Leeder (1982), Grayson and Oldham (1987), Leeder and McMahon (1988), Collinson (1988), Steele (1988), Gawthorpe et al. (1989), Horbury (1989) and Fraser et al. (1990).

Eustatic sea-level oscillations have also long been held to be an important control on sedimentation (Ramsbottom, 1973; 1977; Holdsworth and Collinson, 1988; Maynard and Leeder, 1992). In recent years the prolonged debate on the relative importance of these effects and those of tectonism may be moving towards being resolved by the application of the concept of sequence stratigraphy (Fraser and Gawthorpe, 1990; Ebdon et al., 1990; Read, 1991; Maynard, 1992; Martinsen, 1993).

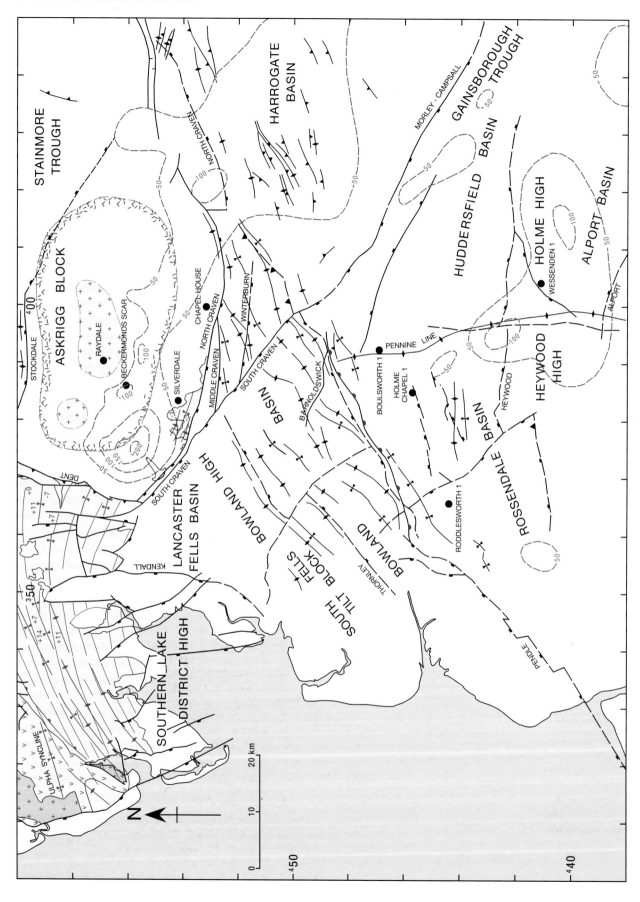

Figure 4   Generalised pre-Carboniferous structure map to show known and inferred structures of the Caledonide basement of the region. Incorporates structural mapping from Soper et al. (1987) and Arthurton et al. (1988). Values of cleavage/fold transection angle (from Soper et al. 1987) shown as positive or negative values. Aeromagnetic anomalies (M) depicted at +50nT and +100nT values.

TWO

Pre-Carboniferous basement

Rocks of early Palaeozoic age crop out in the Lake District and also in the Craven inliers, at Chapel le Dale (Ingleton) and Ribblesdale (Horton), adjacent to the North Craven Fault, at the southern edge of the Askrigg Block (Figures 2 and 4). These strata are folded and cleaved as a consequence of Caledonian deformation. A number of boreholes penetrating the relatively thin Carboniferous cover of the Askrigg Block provide further information on the early Palaeozoic strata and intrusions of granite and microdiorite emplaced into them. Elsewhere direct evidence for the composition and structural history of the Caledonian basement underlying the region is scant.

The Caledonian basement of the region is inferred to comprise two domains (Figure 4). The north-eastern domain, north of the South Craven Fault, is underlain by crust characterised by a strong positive north-west-trending regional magnetic anomaly, the Furness–Ingleborough–Norfolk Magnetic Anomaly, which includes the granite-underpinned Askrigg Block. The anomaly

belt has previously been interpreted as a product of metamorphism, and granite emplacement in early Devonian times. Structural and geochemical evidence are presented here which suggest that the Wensleydale Granite and microdiorite intrusions within the Askrigg Block may have been emplaced somewhat earlier, in Ordovician time, in a possible continuation of the Borrowdale (Lake District) volcanic arc. This domain is delimited by the north-west-trending South Craven Fault, and its inferred continuation, the Morley–Campsall Fault. While both structures can only be demonstrated to have large Dinantian syndepositional throws, they are inferred to be reactivated fundamental basement features.

The south-western basement domain is characterised by a few, discrete magnetic anomaly highs. Two deep boreholes penetrated cleaved metasedimentary rocks, with affinities closer to the concealed Caledonide basement of eastern England than to the Craven inliers. Following the interpretation of the north-eastern domain as a possible Ordovician arc complex, the south-western domain may represent a back-arc region. Major Dinantian structures in this domain are arcuate in trend, mirroring the pattern seen in the exposed early Palaeozoic rocks of the Craven inliers. In the west, major Dinantian structures trend south-west, comparable to other Caledonian lineaments such as the Menai Straits Fault System. In the east, major Dinantian structures trend north-west to south-east, and are most likely 'inherited' from the Caledonian basement, representing the reactivation of old orogenic lines of weakness such as thrust faults and shear zones.

CALEDONIAN STRUCTURES (After Soper et al. 1987)

Anticline, axial plane trace
Syncline, axial plane trace
Monocline, axial trace
Trace of cleavage (S₁)
+7 Sub-areas with transection angle (T) in degrees clockwise

CALEDONIAN ROCKS

Exposed granite
Concealed granite cupola
Limit of granite batholith (inferred)
Exposed volcanic rocks (Borrowdale Volcanic Group)
Sedimentary rocks

SUB-SURFACE INFORMATION

Positive aeromagnetic anomaly contoured at intervals of 50nt
Borehole location

VARISCAN STRUCTURES (This report)

Anticline, axial plane trace
Syncline, axial plane trace
Monocline, axial trace
Major Carboniferous basin controlling fault
Minor fault
Variscan thrust or reverse fault

PLATE TECTONIC SETTING

In early Palaeozoic times, the region lay near the northern edge of the microcontinent of 'Avalonia' (Soper, 1986), encompassing parts of what are presently New England, Maritime Canada, southern Ireland, southern Britain and Belgium (Figure 5). This crust was generated in Neoproterozoic times by the accretion of primitive volcanic arc and marginal basin complexes (Thorpe et al., 1984; Pharaoh et al., 1987) onto the oceanward margin of the Gondwana Continent (Ziegler, 1982).

The separation of Avalonia from Gondwana (and Armorica) is inferred to have occurred in early Ordovician times (Ziegler, 1990). Palaeomagnetic reconstructions have documented the northward drift of Avalonia from high southerly latitudes (about 60°S) to about 30°S by early Silurian times (Torsvik and Trench, 1991; Scotese and McKerrow, 1991; Trench et al., 1992), while Gondwana remained essentially stationary at high southerly latitudes. Studies of faunal provinciality (Cocks and

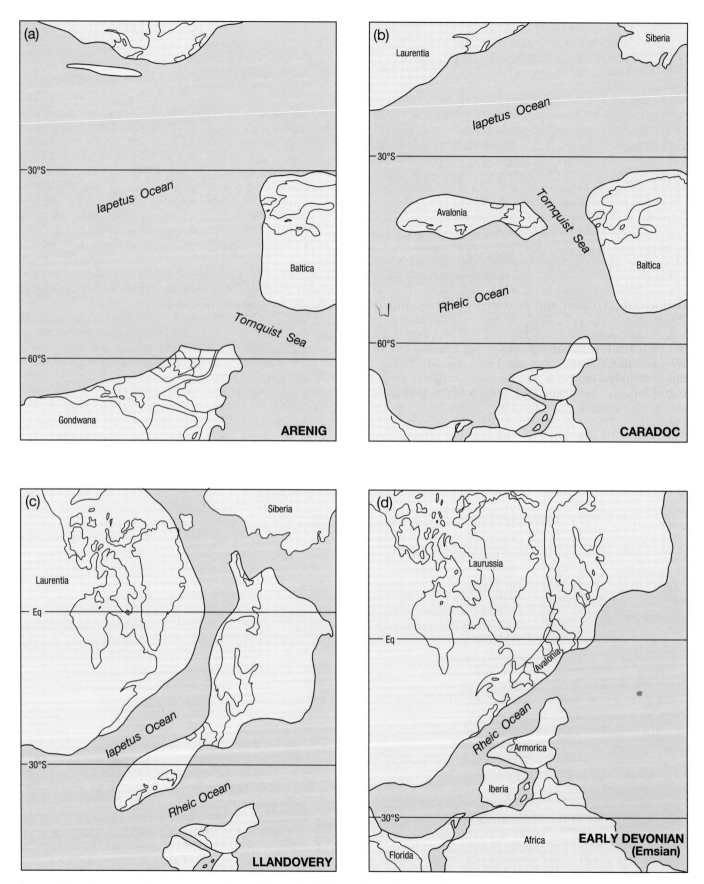

Figure 5   Diagrammatic representation of the early Palaeozoic evolution of northern England, to illustrate the plate-tectonic setting of the region. Reproduced from Cocks (1993).

Fortey, 1982) and sediment provenance (Thorogood, 1990) suggest that the microplate was isolated from other continental masses, for example Laurentia, Baltica and Gondwana (including Armorica), during this oceanic drift.

In early Ordovician (Tremadoc) times, subduction was initiated along the northern margin of Avalonia, marked by the onset of subduction-related magmatism in Wales (Kokelaar et al., 1984). The turbiditic Skiddaw and Ingleton groups (Tremadoc–Llanvirn) were deposited along this active margin, in northern England (Cooper et al., 1993). The early Ordovician strata form the eroded substrate for arc-related volcanic rocks of the Eycott and Borrowdale Volcanic groups (Llanvirn–Caradoc). Subduction-magmatism in southern Britain ceased in Ashgill times (Leat and Thorpe, 1989), coincident with the end of the faunal isolation of Avalonia (Cocks and Fortey, 1982). The timing of the docking of Avalonia with Baltica is controversial, and took place either during late Ordovician (Hutton and Murphy, 1987) or Silurian (Soper and Woodcock, 1990) times.

North-westward subduction of the Iapetus Ocean beneath Laurentia continued during Llandovery and Wenlock times (Leggett et al., 1979). By late Wenlock times, turbidite sandstones of northern England are petrographically, chemically and isotopically indistinguishable from contemporary strata in the Southern Uplands (McCaffrey, 1991), across the Iapetus Suture. Sediment from Laurentia was fed across to Avalonia (Murphy and Hutton, 1986; Kemp, 1987) and the Iapetus Collision Zone was buried beneath a developing foreland basin (Kneller, 1991). The prograding thrust front of this basin migrated southwards through late Silurian times (Barnes et al., 1989; Kneller et al., 1993), with final movement in the Acadian phase (Hughes et al., 1993).

The Acadian deformation phase, climaxing in Emsian times (Soper et al., 1987), resulted from northward impingement of Armorica against the southern edge of Avalonia, as a result of an early phase of closure of the Rheic Ocean basin (Soper, 1986a; McKerrow, personal communication, 1993). As a result of this jostling of continental masses, the south-west-trending Iapetus collision zone of western Britain was reactivated, generating sinistral transpression along major crustal lineaments such as the Menai Straits, Bala Fault and Welsh Borderland Fault System, and the clockwise transection of cleavage recognised in early Palaeozoic slate belts in Wales, the Lake District and Southern Uplands (Soper et al., 1987).

On the eastern side of Britain, and in the southern North Sea, concealed Caledonide basement structures are inferred to have a north-west or west-north-west (Tornquist) trend (Pharaoh et al., 1987). This is based on evidence of inherited Carboniferous cover structures (Turner, 1949; Smith, 1985; Soper et al., 1987), Caledonide metamorphic zonation (Pharaoh et al., 1987; Merriman et al., 1993) and the trend of gravity and magnetic anomalies and lineaments (Lee et al., 1990; 1993). Some north-west-trending structures may have been initiated in late Ordovician times, associated with collision of Avalonia and Baltica (Pharaoh et al., 1995). The Acadian phase resulted in reactivation of earlier structures as well as the development of new dextral transpressional structures.

STRUCTURE OF THE CALEDONIDE BASEMENT

The regional structural trend of the Caledonide basement of northern England is arcuate (Figures 4, 6) as described by Turner (1949), Wills (1951), Mitchell (1956; 1967), Moseley (1972) and Soper et al. (1987). It trends north-eastwards in the southern Lake District, veering east to west near Kendal and turning east-south-east in the northern Howgill Fells adjacent to the Dent Fault near Kirby Lonsdale and in the Craven inliers (Figure 7). Mitchell (1967) recognised a north-west-trending zone of structural divergence extending roughly through Kendal, reflected in the reversal in plunge of the Acadian folds. Soper et al. (1987) pointed out that the Acadian 'slate belts' of western Britain, from Wales to the Southern Uplands, are characterised by clockwise transection, compatible with the evidence for sinistral transpression described by Soper and Hutton (1984). This regime is true also of most of the Lake District, positive values on Figure 4 (after Soper et al., 1987) indicating clockwise cleavage transection of folds. However, the angle of transection decreases to zero (orthogonal strain) along a line trending north-north-west through Kendal, and attains negative values (anticlockwise transection) to the east of this line (negative values on Figure 4), for example in the Craven inliers. Soper et al. (1987) inferred that the Acadian strain regime affecting the concealed Caledonides of eastern England was dominated by dextral transpression, and that the structural arc seen in northern England resulted from indentation into the northern England Caledonides by the relatively rigid Midlands Microcraton. They attributed the northward motion of the indenter to collision of Armorica with the trailing edge of Avalonia, in Early Devonian (Emsian) times. Pharaoh et al. (1987) presented further metamorphic and structural evidence in favour of the 'rigid indenter' hypothesis. An important conclusion from this work is that the structural arc in northern England is a primary, Acadian structural feature, and not simply a consequence of refolding, as implied by some earlier studies (for example Mitchell, 1967).

An alternative hypothesis for the formation of the structural arc, has been proposed by Arthurton et al. (1988). This hypothesis envisages Acadian deformation taking place against a rigid bulwark of already deformed Ingleton Group metasedimentary rocks, forming part of the so-called Furness–Ingleborough–Norfolk Ridge (Wills, 1978); that is the controlling element of the arc is not the microcraton on the concave side of the arc, but the 'basement ridge' on its convex side. Evidence for the nature of the Furness–Ingleborough–Norfolk Magnetic Anomaly/Ridge, and its possible involvement in Acadian deformation, will be presented later. Obviously both hypotheses are complementary, and may have played a role in the development of the Acadian structural arc. Soper et al. (1987) acknowledge the possible buttressing effect of the Lake District composite batholith during Acadian deformation.

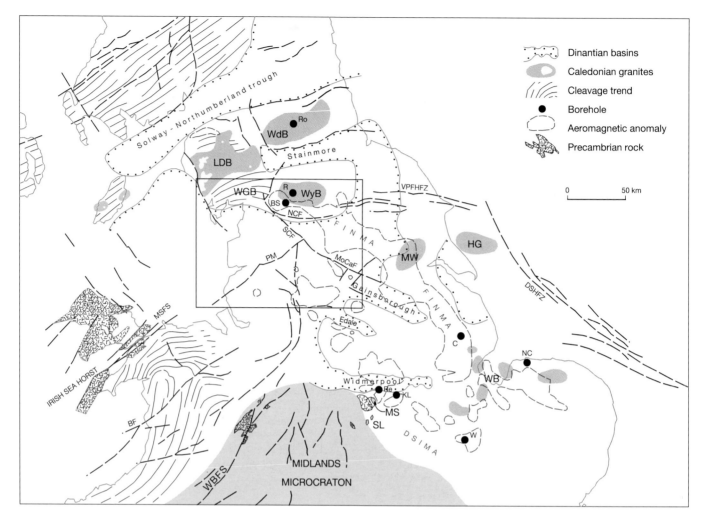

Figure 6 Generalised structural map of northern England to show location of major Caledonide fault zones, granitic intrusions and basement magnetic anomaly zones described in the text, together with principal Dinantian basin elements. Modified from Soper et al. (1987). Inferred granites after Allsop (1987) and Donato and Megson (1990).

Key to structural elements: BF Bala Fault Zone, DSHFZ Dowsing–South Hewett Fault Zone, MoCaF Morley–Campsall Fault, MSFS Menai Straits Fault System, NCF North Craven Fault, SCF South Craven Fault, VPFHFZ Vale of Pickering–Flamborough Head Fault Zone, WBFS Welsh Borderland Fault System, WGB Windermere Group Basin.

Key to igneous complexes: HG Hornsea Granite (inferred), LDB Lake District Batholith, MW Market Weighton Granite (inferred), WB Wash Batholith (inferred), WdB Weardale Batholith, WyB Wensleydale Batholith.

Key to magnetic anomalies: DSIMA Derby–St Ives Magnetic Anomaly, FINMA Furness–Ingleborough–Norfolk Magnetic Anomaly.

Key to onshore boreholes: BS Beckermonds Scar, C Claxby, KL Kirby Lane, NC North Creake, R Raydale, Re Rempstone, Ro Rookhope, W Warboys.

North-eastern basement domain

This domain is defined on the basis of a regional magnetic anomaly known as the Furness–Ingleborough–Norfolk Magnetic Anomaly (Bott, 1967; Wills, 1978; Allsop, 1987; Cornwell and Walker, 1989; Lee et al., 1990; 1991) or Magnetic Ridge (Wills, 1978). This anomaly is mapped at the 50 nT value in Figure 4 and is delimited on its southern side by the South Craven Fault. Farther to the south-

east, the Morley–Campsall Fault, the inferred continuation of the South Craven Fault, defines the boundary between the magnetic basement of the Askern–Spittal High and the Gainsborough Trough (Figure 6).

Wills (1978) believed that this domain comprised magnetic metamorphic rocks at relatively shallow depth. The IGS borehole at Beckermonds Scar (Berridge, 1982), located on one of the 100 nT anomaly peaks flanking the Wensleydale Granite (Figure 4), proved 260 m of steeply dipping magnetite-bearing siltstones and greywacke sandstones of Arenig age; these are correlated with the Ingleton Group (Arthurton et al., 1988) beneath Dinantian strata (Wilson and Cornwell, 1982). From their magnetic susceptibility it is estimated that these metasedimentary rocks contain up to 3 per cent magnetite by volume (Wilson and Cornwell, 1982); sufficient to account for the observed magnetic anomaly. The magnetite is almost pure and has been suggested to be of both primary (Berridge, 1982) and secondary hydrothermal (Cann, 1982) origin. However, this anomaly may be a local feature associated with the Wensleydale Granite and it is not clear whether these lithologies are typical of the domain as a whole. Busby et al. (1993) modelled the regional magnetic anomaly as being due to the presence of a substantial (up to 50 km wide, and 10 km deep) body of magnetic metasedimentary or igneous rock in the mid crust.

The regional magnetic anomaly belt is associated with a number of gravity lows on its north-eastern side, including that associated with the Wensleydale Granite. Outwith the region the presence of other granites at Market Weighton (Bott et al., 1978) and in the vicinity of the Wash (Chroston et al., 1987) has been inferred but not yet proved.

The age and origin of the Furness–Ingleborough–Norfolk Anomaly are matters of considerable speculation. Previous workers (for example Allsop, 1987) have favoured an early Devonian age for the anomaly belt, based on the inference that it was largely a metamorphic artefact, and also on the interpretation of the Rb-Sr age of the Wensleydale Granite as an emplacement date. Pharaoh et al. (1995) have speculated that the magnetic anomaly belt may mark the presence of a concealed mid to late Ordovician volcanic arc complex, forming the link between Ordovician arc volcanic rocks in the Lake District and in East Anglia (Pharaoh et al., 1993; Noble et al., 1993). This concept is compatible with the tectonic model proposed by Arthurton et al. (1988), invoking Acadian deformation against a rigid bulwark formed by the Furness–Ingleborough–Norfolk Ridge. The age of the granites associated with the ridge is a critical test of this hypothesis. Emplacement of the sodic Moorby Microgranite intrusion proved by Claxby 1 Borehole (Figure 6), chemically similar to the Wensleydale Granite (see above), has been reliably dated at 457 ± 20 Ma by the U-Pb zircon method (Noble et al., 1993). This suggests that at least some of these inferred granites were emplaced contemporaneously with Ordovician arc magmatism (Pharaoh et al., 1993), as in the Lake District (Cooper et al., 1993). If the Wensleydale Granite, like the Claxby Microgranite, was actually emplaced in Ordovician times, rather than in the early Devonian as suggested by its Rb-Sr age, then the formation of the magnetic anomaly belt may considerably predate the Acadian deformation phase. Confirmation of the age of emplacement of the intrusions described above using the U-Pb technique on zircon grains may prove an important test of these various hypotheses for the origin of the magnetic anomaly belt.

The presence of a calc-alkaline microdiorite minor intrusion in the Beckermonds Scar Borehole (see p.19) showing affinities to andesites of the Borrowdale Volcanic Group, and which probably predates the granite (see

above), suggests the presence of more mafic magmatic contributions to the crust of the anomaly belt. It follows that the Furness–Ingleborough–North Norfolk Anomaly belt may have originated during the arc magmatic phase in late Ordovician times. Elsewhere in Eastern England, calc-alkaline, arc-related magmatic rocks of Ordovician age are inferred to be the cause of the Hathern–Peterborough or Derby–St Ives Magnetic Anomaly (Allsop et al., 1987; Pharaoh et al., 1993). A contribution from such a source to the Furness–Ingleborough–Norfolk Magnetic Anomaly (in addition to that from the magnetic metasedimentary rocks proved by Beckermonds Scar Borehole) cannot be ruled out, particularly in view of the modelled depth of the magnetic body (Busby et al., 1993).

A description of the lithologies proved in this domain is given below, together with a deformational history.

Ingleton Group

The Ingleton Group comprises more than 800 m of turbiditic greywacke sandstones, siltstones and conglomerates, best displayed in the Chapel le Dale (Ingleton) Inlier (Figures 7 and 8). The base of the group is not seen, and the upper erosional limit is formed by unconformable strata of late Ordovician and Carboniferous age. A smaller outcrop occurs within the Ribblesdale Inlier at Horton. Strata penetrated by the Beckermonds Scar Borehole yielded probable Arenig acritarchs (Wilson and Cornwell, 1982). Radiometric dating by O'Nions et al. (1973) also suggested an early Ordovician age. Rastall (1906) recognised the presence of Precambrian igneous and metamorphic clasts, which Wills (1978) inferred were derived from the Midlands Microcraton. Study of slump-folds within the group by Leedal and Walker (1950) confirmed a southerly source, compatible with such an interpretation.

Further inferences on the origin and thickness of the Ingleton Group may be made from the correlative Skiddaw Group (Tremadoc–Llanvirn) of the Lake District. The Skiddaw Group is more completely exposed with a minimum stratigraphical thickness of about 5000 m (Cooper et al., 1993) and comprises southerly derived turbidites, mostly rather mud- and silt-dominated. The Watch Hill and Loweswater formations are coarser grained, more comparable to the Ingleton Group. The 1500 m thick Buttermere Formation (Webb and Cooper, 1988) of the Central Fells Belt (Figure 8) contains reworked Tremadoc and Arenig strata, slumped and redeposited to north-west of their original site of deposition.

The evidence reviewed above is compatible with the deposition of the Ingleton and Skiddaw groups on the tectonically unstable, active, northern margin of Avalonia in early Ordovician times.

Windermere Supergroup

Strata of the late Ordovician to Silurian Windermere Supergroup (Table 1) rest unconformably upon the Ingleton Group in the Craven inliers (Figure 7). In the Lake District, the Borrowdale Volcanic Supergroup (Llandeilo–Caradoc) underlies the Windermere Supergroup, except in the Furness inliers of the Southern Lake District (Figure 8). The structural position of the Askrigg

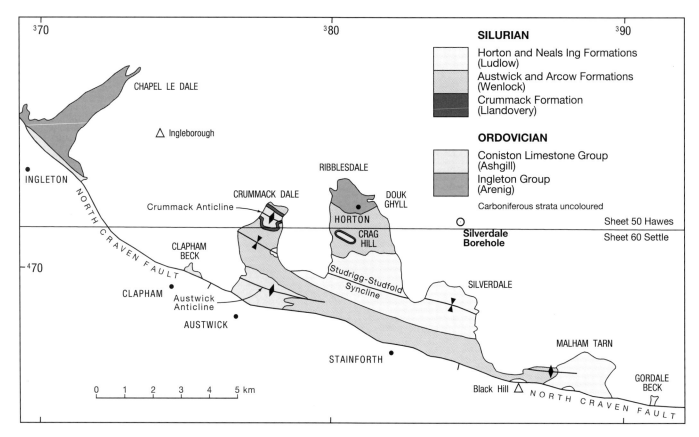

Figure 7   Detailed structural map of the Craven inliers (from Arthurton et al., 1988).

Block appears analogous to that of the Southern Lake District; if representatives of the Borrowdale Volcanic Group were originally present they were eroded prior to deposition of the Windermere Supergroup.

The thin Ashgill succession of the Dent Group (Kneller et al., 1994), formerly referred to as the Coniston Limestone Group (King and Wilcockson, 1934), consists mainly of calcareous siltstone and impure limestone with interbedded sandstone and conglomerate, with a number of non-sequences, recording a transition from shore-face through storm-dominated, mixed carbonate and clastic shelf to deeper shelf deposits (Kneller, 1991). The Middle Ashgill, Damhouse Bridge Tuff (Rawtheyan) represents a minor phase of felsic volcanism (Table 1).

Silurian strata represent deeper water environments; black graptolitic mudstones and barren green siltstones of the Crummack Formation (Llandovery), are succeeded by up to 1000 m of laminated hemipelagic siltstones with interbedded turbiditic sandstones of the Austwick Formation (Wenlock).

After a regression associated with a sea-level low-stand in late Wenlock times, subsidence accelerated in mid-Ludlow times and up to 7000 m of sand, silt and mud turbidites accumulated in the Southern Lake District (Soper and Woodcock, 1990). These deep-water strata reflect the encroachment of a foreland basin (Barnes et al., 1989) migrating from the north-west across the site of the former Iapetus Suture between northern England and the Southern Uplands of Scotland. In the Craven inliers, the Horton and Neals Ing formations (Arthurton et al., 1988) approach 1000 m in thickness (Table 1). Arrival of coarse-grained, thick, proximal turbidite sand from the north-west was later than in the Lake District (Arthurton et al., 1988). Laminated siltstones, penetrated by the Silverdale and Chapel House boreholes drilled through the Carboniferous Limestone are considered to belong to the Horton Formation (Arthurton et al., 1988), and demonstrate its extent eastward towards Wharfedale. The Neals Ing Formation represents the youngest Silurian strata exposed in the Craven inliers, and is unconformably overlain by Carboniferous Limestone. In the Southern Lake District, sedimentation continued at least into Přídolí times, the uppermost 1100 m of the Windermere Supergroup comprising siltstones, mudstones and sandstones reflect a return to shallow-water deposition (Cooper et al., 1993).

Caledonian deformation and metamorphism

Strata of the Ingleton Group are deformed by tight to isoclinal folds, on north-west-trending axes (Leedal and Walker, 1950), with axial planes dipping steeply towards the south-west, whereas strata of the Windermere Supergroup are affected by more open folds (Arthurton et al., 1988). This observation, together with the evidence, from mapping, for a major sub-Windermere Supergroup unconformity, led Arthurton et al. (1988) to propose the existence of a pre-Ashgill orogenic event. The younger Ordovician and Silurian strata of the inliers are deformed by close to open folds of end-Silurian or early Devonian

Figure 8 Correlation of Ordovician strata in northern England (from Cooper et al., 1993).

Approximate thickness in metres. Abreviations:

FM   formation,
SG   Supergroup;
CONG   conglomerate,
LST   limestone,
MUDST   mudstone,
RHY   rhyolite,
SH   shale,
VOLC   volcanic,
PUS   Pusgillian,
CAU   Cautleyan,
RAW   Rawtheyan,
HIR   Hirnantian,
LLY   Llandovery,
RHU   Rhuddanian.

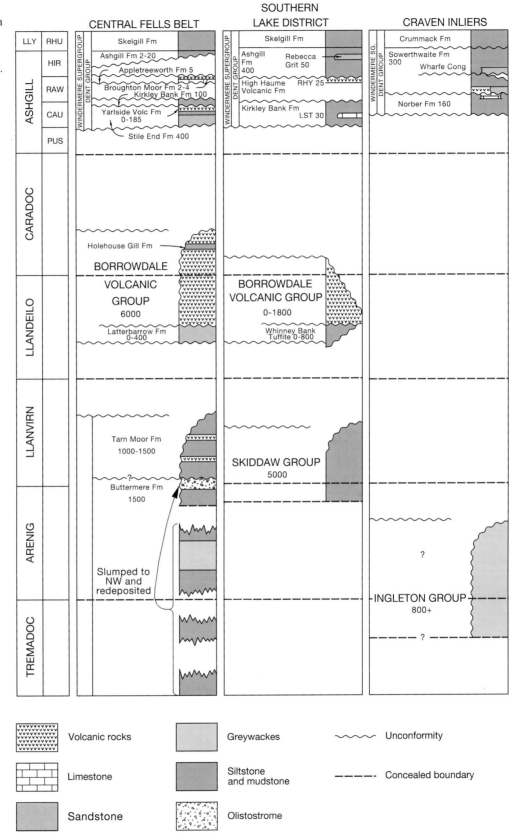

Group	Lake District		Craven Inliers		Graptolite Zone	Stage		Series	System
	Formation	Member	Formation	Member					
WINDERMERE SUPERGROUP	Scout Hill							PŘÍDOLÍ	SILURIAN
	Kirkby Moor				S. leintwardinensis	Ludfordian		LUDLOW	
	Underbarrow								
	Bannisdale	Tottlebank			S. incipiens				
	Yewbank		Neals Ing		L. scanicus	Gorstian			
	Moorhowe		Horton	Studfold Sst					
	Poolscar								
	Latrigg								
	Gawthwaite				N. nilssoni				
	Wray Castle		Arcow		M. ludensis	Homerian		WENLOCK	
	Coldwell	High Cross			G. nassa				
		Randy Pike			C. lundgreni				
	Birk Riggs		Austwick		C. ellesi	Sheinwoodian			
	Brathay				C. linnarssoni				
					C. rigidus				
					M. antennularius				
					M. riccartonensis				
					C. murchisoni				
		Dixon Ground			C. centrifugus				
Stockdale Subgroup	Browgill	Far House	Crummack	Capel Bank	M. crenulata	Telychian		LLANDOVERY	
					M. griestoniensis				
					M. crispus				
					M. turriculatus				
	Skelgill			Hunterstye	M. sedgwickii	Aeronian			
					M. convolutus				
					M. argenteus				
					D. magnus				
					M. triangulatus				
					C. cyphus	Rhuddanian			
					L. acinaces				
					A. atavus				
		Spengill			P. acuminatus				
	Red Gill	Church Beck	Sowerthwaite	Wharfe Cong	G. persculptus	Hirnantian	8	ASHGILL (part)	ORDOVICIAN
		Trout Beck	Jop Ridding Sst & Damhouse Bridge Tuff		C. extraordinarius				
Dent Subgroup	Appletreeworth Fm					Rawtheyan	7		
	Broughton Moor Fm		Norber Fm (part)				6		
							5		
			Norber		D. anceps		4		
	Kirkley Bank	Torver					3		
		Applethwaite				Cautleyan			
		Kentmere					2		
		basal clastics							
	Whirl Howe	Yarlside Volcanic Fm							
		Stile End							
		Longsleddale					1		

Table 1 Correlation of Windermere Supergroup strata in northern England.

age, associated with the Acadian orogenic phase (Soper et al., 1987). Three major eastward plunging fold axes are mapped in the inliers; the Studrigg–Studfold Syncline and flanking Crummack and Austwick anticlines (Figure 7). A west-north-west-trending, near-vertical axial planar cleavage is associated with the Acadian deformation. According to Arthurton et al. (1988) the intensity of this folding (as measured by amplitude and wavelength of minor-scale folding) decreases northward through the inliers; this observation is used as supporting evidence for their inference of end-Silurian deformation occurring against a resistant ridge of previously deformed Ingleton Group strata.

The evidence for pre-Acadian deformation in northern England is still controversial. An early orogeny, predating the Borrowdale Volcanic Group, was proposed by Simpson (1967) and Helm (1970) to explain certain structures in the Skiddaw Group, but these are now attributed either to soft sediment deformation (Banham et al., 1981; Cooper et al., 1993) associated with syndepositional slumping (see Ingleton Group) or to pre-volcanic uplift (Branney and Soper, 1988) resulting in 2500–5000 m of uplift and erosion (Hughes et al., 1993). Neither of these events generated folds associated with penetrative fabrics (Hughes et al., 1993). The Borrowdale Volcanic Group is affected by gentle folds such as the Ulpha Syncline (Soper and Numan, 1974; Soper et al., 1987) which predate the unconformity at the base of the Windermere Supergroup. A volcanotectonic origin, associated with caldera-collapse, has been proposed for these folds (Branney and Soper, 1988). According to Hughes et al. (1993), there is no evidence for compressional deformation prior to the deposition of the Windermere Supergroup, and late Ordovician deformation is restricted to uplift and erosion, perhaps following emplacement of Ordovician components of the Lake District Batholith (Firman and Lee, 1986).

Deformation of late Ordovician age is documented outside the region in the Welsh Borders, manifested in uplift along the Tywi Anticline and dextral displacement on the Pontesford–Linley Fault System (Lynas, 1988; Woodcock and Gibbons, 1988). This deformation is attributed to the Shelvian Orogenic Phase (Toghill, 1992). Evidence for late Ordovician deformation in the Midlands Microcraton has been presented by Carney et al. (1992). Pharaoh et al. (1995) have suggested that this pre-Acadian orogenic phase also affects the basement of the southern North Sea region, and may record the docking of the Avalonia Microcontinent with Baltica in the late Ordovician, as postulated by Hutton and Murphy (1987).

Evidence for the metamorphic grade of the Caledonide basement is provided by studies of white mica crystallinity within mudrocks, neomorphic metamorphic minerals in igneous rocks and organic maturation indices (Figure 9). The study by Thomas (1986) using the Hb_{rel} index, indicated the presence of widespread anchizonal conditions in the Skiddaw Group, and studies of conodont colour index and igneous alteration mineralogy appeared to confirm these results (Fettes et al., 1985a). The map of Fettes et al. (1985b), summarising these results, indicates little spatial variation in metamorphic grade. Subsequently more detailed studies have demonstrated zones

of epizonal (greenschist facies) conditions, particularly associated with the contact aureoles surrounding the Skiddaw, Shap and Ennerdale intrusions, and at Crummock Water, as well as local areas of diagenetic zone conditions, including parts of the Skiddaw Group (Fortey et al., 1993). Most of the Windermere Supergroup (including correlatives in the Craven inliers) is metamorphosed in low anchizone conditions.

Samples of pelitic rocks from basement provings in the region were analysed by X-ray diffraction (XRD) to provide crystallinity data which may be compared to the published data. The analytical conditions are described by Merriman et al. (1993). The new data are listed in Table 2. Silurian mudrocks from the Silverdale and Chapel House boreholes on the Askrigg Block yield low anchizonal values, comparable to those of the exposed Windermere Supergroup (Ashgill–Přídolí). Data for one sample of mudrock associated with greywacke of the Ingleton Group (Tremadoc–Arenig) from Beckermonds Scar Borehole, lies just inside the epizone. This result could indicate that the Ingleton Group has a higher metamorphic grade (and hence greater depth of burial) than the Windermere Supergroup, but such a conclusion cannot be firmly reached on the basis of one analysis. Beckermonds Scar Borehole is located within the thermal aureole of the Wensleydale Granite (Berridge, 1982) and the elevated metamorphic grade may simply reflect the heat of intrusion, as observed in parts of the Skiddaw Group (Fortey et al., 1993).

Wensleydale Granite

The Caledonide basement of northern England is intruded by numerous batholithic complexes of predominantly granitic composition (Figure 6), now exposed in the Lake District and concealed under the Alston and Askrigg blocks (for example Bott, 1967; Dunham, 1974). The concealed Wensleydale Granite was proved by the Raydale Borehole (Dunham, 1974) following studies of the negative gravity anomaly over the Askrigg Block (Whetton et al., 1956; Bott, 1961, 1967; Myers and Wardell, 1967).

The Wensleydale Granite is pink, medium grained and non-porphyritic; it lacks a magmatic foliation and resembles more closely the Ennerdale Intrusion of the Lake District than the granites of Skiddaw, Shap and Eskdale (Dunham and Wilson, 1985). It is also distinct from the Weardale Granite, which is coarser grained and contains an igneous foliation (Dunham et al., 1965). The mineralogy of the Wensleydale Granite comprises K-feldspar (salmon pink microperthite), greenish cream albitic plagioclase, quartz and chlorite, the latter pseudomorphing magmatic biotite (Dunham, 1974; Webb and Brown, 1989). Quartz and feldspar may form graphic intergrowths, indicating rapid cooling or volatile loss. Common accessory minerals include apatite and zircon. Post-magmatic alteration includes chloritisation (of biotite), variable sericitisation, particularly of K-feldspar, and introduction of dolomite into veins and cavities, the latter accompanied by sulphide mineralisation in places.

The granite is strongly affected by near-vertical fracturing accompanied by steep veins of quartz and carbonate at some levels. Dunham (1974) noted hematisation along

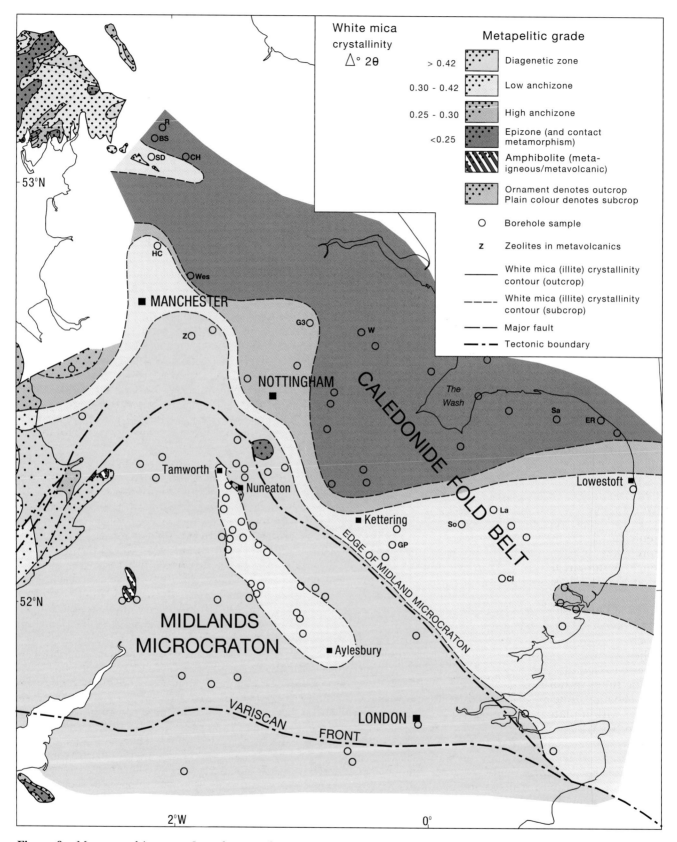

Figure 9   Metamorphic map of northern and eastern England showing white mica crystallinity (Kubler indices) of pre-Carboniferous mudrocks encountered by boreholes. Modified from Merriman et al. (1993).

Key to boreholes: BS Beckermonds Scar, CH Chapel House, G3 Grove 3, HC Holme Chapel 1, R Raydale, SD Silverdale, W Welton 1, Wes Wessenden 1.

Table 2 White mica-crystallinity (Kubler index) data for pre-Carboniferous mudrocks proved by boreholes in northern England.

Borehole	Depth (m)	Kubler ($\Delta°2\theta$)	Stratigraphical age
Beckermonds	295.5	0.24	Arenig
Chapel House	94.5	0.29	Ludlow
Chapel House	106.0	0.23	Ludlow
Holme Chapel	1975.1	0.32	Unknown
Holme Chapel	1981.5	0.41	Unknown
Silverdale	193.5	0.37	Ludlow
Silverdale	200.7	0.37	Ludlow
Wessenden 1	1124.7	0.21	Unknown
Wessenden 1	1125.5	0.19	Unknown
Wessenden 1	1127.0	0.19	Unknown

joints. In thin-section, an anastomosing, near-vertical, fracture-pressure-solution cleavage is recognised, with discrete fractures/lamellae typically spaced at intervals of 0.2–1 mm. Where these fractures cut across crystals of quartz and feldspar they take the form of deformation bands, locally associated with sub-grain development. Where the fractures coincide with igneous grain boundaries, the latter are strongly affected by pressure-solution, and development of stylolitic fractures. Some of the fractures pass longitudinally into thin quartz veins, which show pressure shadowing. Thicker quartz veins, injected parallel to cleavage, are also affected by deformation bands, pressure-solution and pressure shadowing.

The presence of a tectonic deformation fabric within the Wensleydale Granite has not been described previously. Brown et al. (1987) regard the granite as a post-orogenic intrusion, like the Weardale Batholith. This interpretation must be revised in the light of the above evidence. A similar, non-penetrative fracture/pressure solution cleavage has been recognised in the Moorby Microgranite, intruded into the concealed Caledonide basement of Lincolnshire, and is believed to be of Acadian age (Pharaoh et al., 1990; 1997).

Geochemical data for the Wensleydale Granite were published by Webb and Brown (1989) and are depicted together with comparative data from Caledonian felsic magmatic suites in northern England in Figures 10, 11. The geochemical patterns of the Wensleydale Granite are typical of within-plate granites, sloping progressively downward from Ta to Sm and Yb, and closest to those of the Moorby Microgranite from the concealed Caledonides of Lincolnshire (Figure 10a). The absence of significant Nb-depletion and Ce-enrichment suggests that neither granite has a significant arc-magmatic component in its patterns. Such a component is readily apparent in the geochemical patterns of felsic Borrowdale Volcanic Group rocks (Figure 10b), and the Threlkeld and Ennerdale intrusions (Figure 10c) which are considered comagmatic with the felsic volcanic rocks (Cooper et al., 1993). The early Devonian Skiddaw and Shap granites exhibit strong depletion of Y and heavy rare earth elements (HREE), in addition to their characteristic enrichment in Rb.

On Figure 11a, the Wensleydale Granite and Moorby Microgranite plot together with felsic Borrowdale Volcanic Group rocks in the within-plate field. The Ennerdale Granophyre is compositionally similar, but the data overlap into the volcanic arc + syncollision granite field of Figure 11a and b. Data for HHP granites, such as Skiddaw, Shap and Weardale, occupy a cluster distinct from the foregoing magmas. The Rb-Y/Nb diagram (Figure 11) confirms the syncollision affinities of the HHP granites, notwithstanding the lower reliability of interpretation of this particular diagram because of the potential mobility of Rb.

The lower content of Y and HREE, for example Yb in the HHP granites, probably reflects retention of these elements in residual phases such as amphibole or garnet. Increasing fractionation of REE patterns with time is believed to favour the role of garnet as such a residual phase (O'Brien et al., 1985).

The Wensleydale Granite has yielded a Rb-Sr whole-rock isochron age of 400 ± 10 Ma (Sr initial ratio = 0.721 ± 0.0044) and a K-Ar feldspar separate age of about 300 Ma (Dunham, 1974). The Rb-Sr age is thus comparable to that obtained for Caledonian granites elsewhere in northern England, for example the Shap Granite (Wadge et al., 1978). The Moorby Microgranite of Lincolnshire is geochemically very similar to the Wensleydale Granite (see above), and has yielded a Rb-Sr isochron age of 400 ± 9 Ma (Pharaoh et al., 1990), identical within the errors to the Rb-Sr age for the Wensleydale Granite. However, a study of U-Pb isotope systematics of zircon grains from the same intrusion demonstrated that the intrusion was actually emplaced in Ordovician (Caradoc) times, and that the Sr isotope system was disturbed by later events, most probably the Acadian deformation phase in early to mid-Devonian times (Noble et al., 1993). It is therefore possible that the Sr isotopic system of the Wensleydale Granite has also been reset, particularly in view of the cleavage development described earlier.

Use of discrimination diagrams to evaluate the tectonic setting of granites has been criticised on a number of grounds, for example it has been demonstrated that the diagram may reflect more accurately the tectonic environment of the source protolith from which the granite was melted, rather than the actual tectonic environment of emplacement (Arculus, 1987; Twist and Harmer, 1987). Nevertheless it is clear that individual granite complexes in northern England plot in a consistent and coherent way on such diagrams, which suggests that the latter do highlight significant differences in petrogenesis between the earlier, Ordovician synvolcanic plutons (for example Ennerdale, Moorby and possibly Wensleydale), and the early Devonian HHP granites (for example Weardale, Shap and Skiddaw). The contrasts indicate differences in pre-emplacement fractionation history, in the degree of fractionation, and possibly in primary magma compositions, between these two major groups of intrusions (Brown et al., 1987). The presence of granite in the Caledonian basement has strongly influenced subsequent Carboniferous basin evolution, in particular the location and behaviour of the Alston and Askrigg blocks (Bott, 1967). Likely effects of Caledonian granitic intrusions include:

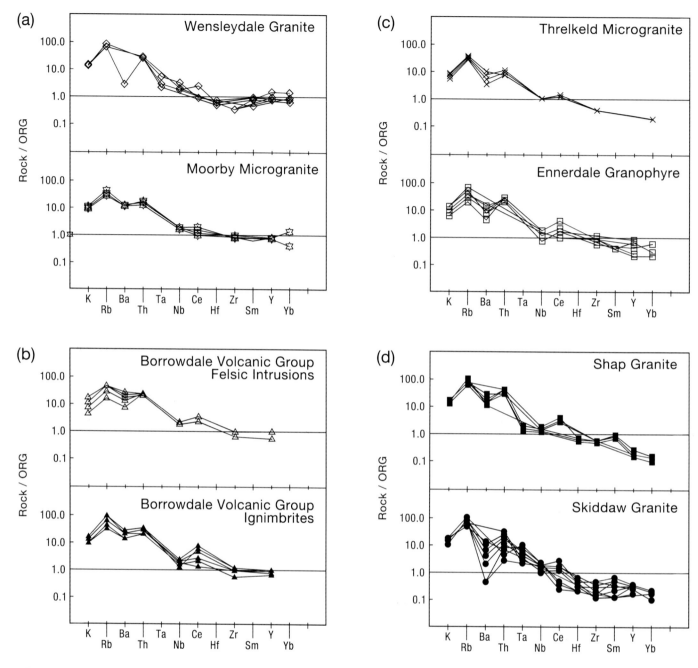

Figure 10   ORG-normalised geochemical patterns for representative samples of granite and felsic components of the Borrowdale Volcanic Group from northern and eastern England. Geochemical data from Webb and Brown (1984), O'Brien et al. (1985), Branney et al. (1992) and Beddoe-Stephens and Mason (1991). ORG normalising values from Pearce et al. (1984).

a. 'Buoyancy' effect — deficiency in mass of the granitic batholith, reflected in a Bouguer gravity anomaly low, may result in local isostatic disequilibrium (Bott, 1967).

b. 'Annealing' effect — emplacement of the granitic batholith heals faults and fractures in a region of crust converting it into a rigid block.

c. 'Thermal chimney' effect — high heat flow through the granite subsequent to emplacement, particularly if it

is of the high heat production (HHP) variety (Plant et al., 1985), may be reflected in the development of convective hydrothermal systems in the country rocks, as well as thermal maturation (Creaney, 1980) and mineralisation (Plant and Jones, 1989) of the Carboniferous cover strata.

The relative importance of these effects varies from one granitic complex to another, depending on chemical composition and other factors.

Minor intrusions

The Beckermonds Scar Borehole encountered a quartz-microdiorite intrusion emplaced into Ingleton Group strata between 328.72 and 344.37 m depth (Berridge, 1982). Both upper and lower contacts show chilling. Thin-sections of these chill zones contain a spaced, anastomosing, tectonic cleavage, marked by discrete zones of phyllosilicate development; they are cut by two generations of veins bearing magnetite, chlorite and calcite, and carbonate and pyrite. The interior of the intrusion is unaffected by cleavage, and consists of randomly intergrown 'stumpy' prisms of plagioclase and prismatic hornblende, severely altered to mosaics of white mica and calcite, and chlorite respectively. The groundmass is less coarse and consists of plagioclase, hornblende, quartz and accessory oxide (now leucoxene).

Berridge (1982) did not recognise the presence within the microdiorite of magnetite-bearing veins, associated with early hydrothermal alteration during emplacement of the Wensleydale Granite, and cited this as evidence for a post-granite age for the microdiorite. The recognition of the early generation of veining necessitates re-evaluation of this interpretation. The intense alteration of the microdiorite described above is more compatible with a pre-granite age. Isotopic data for the age of emplacement are not available.

MORB-normalised geochemical patterns for the microdiorite are presented in Figure 12, together with comparative data for andesite lavas of the Borrowdale Volcanic Group. The microdiorite patterns are typical of those of mafic and intermediate igneous rocks associated with calc-alkaline magmatic arcs, that is relative enrichment of Th, Ce with respect to Nb (Pearce, 1982). The similarity of the patterns of the microdiorite and Borrowdale Volcanic Group andesites suggests that the two suites formed in similar tectonic environments, and may be comagmatically related.

Limited magnetic susceptibility data for the microdiorite were published by Wilson and Cornwell (1982). One sample, at about 340 m depth in the Beckermonds Scar Borehole, has a susceptibility of about 12.4×10^{-3} SI units, rather less than the highly magnetic Ingleton Group country rocks.

South-western basement domain

The structural geometry of the concealed Caledonide basement of the major part of the region lying south of the South Craven Fault is not directly observable, although it is possible to infer the overall basement structural trend from the orientation of inherited structures which con-

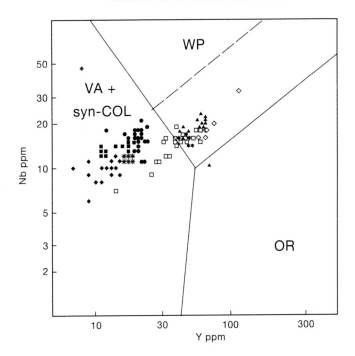

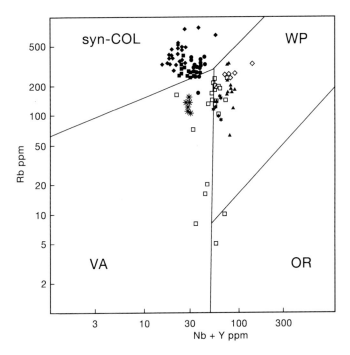

* Moorby Microgranite
▲ Borrowdale Volcanic Group Ignimbrite
△ Borrowdale Volcanic Group Felsic intrusion
◇ Wensleydale Granite
□ Ennerdale Granophyre
✳ Threlkeld Microgranite
● Skiddaw Granite
■ Shap Granite
◆ Weardale Granite

Figure 11 Geochemical discrimination diagrams for granite tectonic environments. VA, volcanic arc; syn-COL, syn-collision; WP, within-plate; OR, ocean-ridge. Data sources as Figure 10. Fields after Pearce et al. (1984)

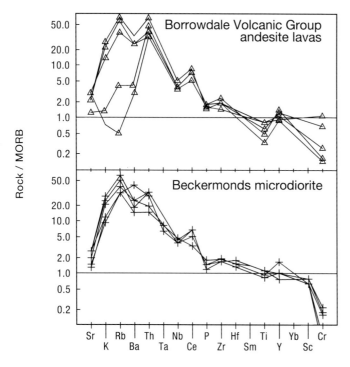

Figure 12 MORB-normalised geochemical patterns for the Beckermonds microdiorite. MORB-normalised values from Pearce (1982). Geochemical data from Webb and Brown (1989) and O'Brien et al. (1985)

trolled the Carboniferous evolution of the region, as noted by Turner (1949) and Soper et al. (1987). The arcuate structural trend in the Caledonide basement is mirrored in the arcuate trend of major faults which controlled the subsequent Dinantian evolution of the region (Figure 4). The Caledonian basement is only sampled by two deep boreholes and the nature of the structures shown is largely inferred from subsequent Carboniferous basin development. On basement highs, it is more likely that pre-Carboniferous erosion removed some or all of Windermere Supergroup equivalents. Beneath the basins, Silurian cover may be preserved, although neither of the deep boreholes has confirmed this hypothesis. For convenience, these structures will be described in two areas, east and west of the north–south-trending Pennine Line.

Western area

Purple slates (undated) proved by the Holme Chapel 1 Borehole yield low anchizonal crystallinity values (Table 2). Without biostratigraphical data it is not possible to determine the affinity of these samples, although there is little lithological resemblance to the exposed early Palaeozoic strata of the Craven inliers.

Major Carboniferous structures in the western area, for example the Pendle Fault/Monocline System and the Bowland Line (Chapter Three), have a south-west–north-east trend, typical of Caledonide structures in western Britain. Both of the above fault systems are major Dinantian syndepositional structures with normal throws of

the order of several thousands of metres, and controlled Dinantian basin development. Subsequent Variscan reversal of these structures, for example to form the Pendle Monocline and subsidiary folds, indicates the reactivation of long lasting zones of weakness within the pre-Carboniferous basement; and major south-west–north-east-trending Caledonian thrust or transcurrent fault zones represent the most likely heterogeneities.

It is conceivable that the Pendle Fault System represents the reactivation of a concealed north-east extension of the Menai Strait Fault System (Gibbons, 1987) of North Wales. This comprises a complex set of lineaments active since Neoproterozoic (and/or early Cambrian) times, when it formed a transcurrent shear zone along which the Monian Terranes of Anglesey and Avalon composite terrane of southern Britain were brought into juxtaposition (Gibbons, 1987). Subsequent reactivation during early Ordovician, Devonian and Carboniferous times was dominantly dip-slip in nature (Gibbons, 1987). The Menai Straits lineament is imaged as a set of inclined reflectors on deep seismic reflection profile WINCH4, dipping north-west beneath the crust of the south Irish Sea (Klemperer and Hobbs, 1992). The Pendle Fault System, with northward Dinantian downthrow, is apparently terminated against the north-west-trending South Craven Fault, which partitions the Harrogate Basin from the remainder of the region. The Skipton Fault, with which the Pendle Fault is virtually colinear, shows an opposing direction of downthrow. The main controlling fault of the Harrogate Basin is the North Craven Fault, with southward Dinantian downthrow, and in this area no clear reactivation of a putative Menai–Pendle Lineament took place. The north-east continuity of such a lineament beyond the South Craven Fault is therefore suspect.

At the far western extremity of the area, bordering the East Irish Sea Basin, numerous north–south and north-north-west-trending faults are associated with development of minor basins of Permo-Triassic age, for example the Woodeford, Humphrey Head, Croxteth and Brookhouse faults. Such faults cut the Carboniferous structures at high oblique angles and it is unclear if they represent 'clean-breaks' initiated in post-Carboniferous times, orthogonal to the established Variscan structures, or a reactivation of a much older, possibly even Neoproterozoic structural grain such as the Malvernoid trend.

Eastern area

Cleaved green siltstones proved by Wessenden 1 Borehole yield epizonal crystallinities (Table 2). Attempts at biostratigraphical dating proved unsuccessful, three samples being barren (information from Dr S G Molyneux). Merriman et al. (1993) speculated that this basement proving represented a possible extension towards the north-west of the belt of possible Precambrian to Cambrian green phyllites and quartzites proved by boreholes in the East Midlands, for example Welton 1 and Grove 3 (Pharaoh et al., 1987; Lee et al., 1991). Certainly, there are geochemical similarities between samples from these boreholes and the Wessenden 1 Borehole (Figure

13, Table 3). Unfortunately the borehole control is too sparse to indicate whether the belt of epizonal grade metapelites extends north-west to join Silurian epizonal rocks in the southern Lake District, or is a feature of a sub-Windermere Supergroup metamorphic basement.

Samples of red dolomitic mudrocks from the base of Boulsworth Borehole yield low diagenetic zone values ($> 0.79 \, \Delta^{\circ}2\theta$) compatible with values expected for rocks of late Devonian age, and a structural position above the Acadian unconformity.

The north-west-trending South Craven Fault partitions the Harrogate Basin from the Bowland Basin (Chapter Three). The fault appears to continue south-east into the Morley–Campsall Fault Zone (Figure 4), the two fault systems together bounding the south-west edge of the block of crust associated with the Furness– Ingleborough– Norfolk Anomaly. It is therefore inferred that the South Craven–Morley Campsall Lineament represents a fundamental line of partition within the region, and almost certainly reflects a change in the nature of the pre-Carboniferous basement.

The Middle Craven Fault has a present-day downthrow to the south of up to 500 m at the base of the Dinantian, and terminates against the South Craven Fault. The North Craven Fault has less substantial Dinantian downthrow, and parallels the trend of Acadian folding in the Craven inliers. Both the Middle and North Craven faults cut obliquely across the north-west-trending Furness–

Table 3 Geochemical data for pre-Carboniferous basement proved by Wessenden 1 Borehole, together with comparative data for similar rocks proved in Welton 1 and Grove 3 boreholes.

Sample number	Wes3691	Wes3699	Gr2930.4	Gr2930.8	Gr2931.0	Gr2931.1	WE1
Borehole	Wessenden	Wessenden	Grove 3	Grove 3	Grove 3	Grove 3	Welton 1
Lithology	Siltstone	Siltstone	Phyllite	Phyllite	Phyllite	Phyllite	Phyllite
Depth (m)	1125.02	1127.46	2930.4	2930.8	2931.0	2931.1	2560.0
Other data	XN	XN	XN	XN+PE	XN	XN	XN
SiO$_2$	61.20	61.70	74.27	73.32	67.95	71.29	58.58
TiO$_2$	.82	.68	.53	.56	.56	.49	1.15
Al$_2$O$_3$	16.76	15.90	13.90	15.89	15.21	14.32	22.29
Fe$_2$O$_3$	8.03	6.80	3.61	3.78	5.55	1.77	9.11
MnO	.13	.12	.09	.10	.72	.09	.10
MgO	2.89	2.86	1.26	1.33	2.10	.94	2.30
CaO	.69	2.07	1.78	.30	3.40	6.67	56
Na$_2$O	1.59	.15	2.23	1.50	1.04	1.29	2.82
K$_2$O	3.88	4.81	2.44	3.41	3.32	3.31	2.82
P$_2$O$_5$	.11	.12	.06	.02	.07	.16	.10
LOI	3.61	4.90	—	—	—	—	.18
Rest	.17	.19	.12	.13	.16	.11	.18
Total	99.88	199.30	100.29	100.34	100.08	100.44	100.01

Trace elements in parts per million

Ba	49	492	293	350	349	295	479
CeX	43	97	68	61	79	32	61
Co	17	17	20	22	16	18	23
Cr	41	84	31	24	22	31	55
Cu	6	17	15	10	61	21	28
Nb	18	16	9	12	11	10	13
Ni	20	26	15	14	21	8	26
Pb	8	10	15	9	31	13	13
Rb	130	153	80	117	110	100	83
Sr	47	33	52	32	143	87	144
Th	15	15	—	4	—	—	—
V	118	95	52	70	79	64	135
Y	18	30	36	33	52	35	39
Zn	115.	97	57	52	94	27	89
Zr	168	166	153	157	169	146	217
La	32	68	—	28.73	—	—	—
Ce	43	97	68	52.88	79	32	61
Nd	20	50	—	21.33	—	—	—
Yb	—	—	—	3.01	—	—	—

Boreholes (data from Webb and Brown, 1989). Major elements and most trace elements determined by X-ray Fluorescence (XRF) Spectrometry at Nottingham University (XN). PE denotes traces by Inductively Coupled Plasma Emmission Spectrometry at Egham. LOI, loss on ignition; CeX, Ce by XRF; Rest, traces as major elements.

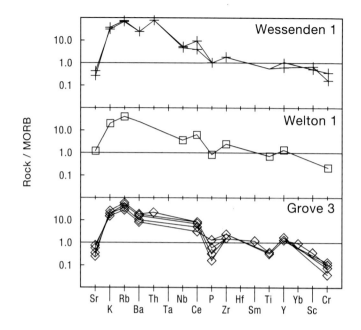

Ingleborough–Norfolk Magnetic Anomaly. They are interpreted here as relatively young structures initiated in Dinantian times to accommodate the rigid, granite-cored Askrigg Block, along lines of weakness inherited from the Acadian phase of deformation.

The Morley–Campsall Fault and Alport Fault have a north-west–south-east trend, and significant Dinantian downthrow, like many Dinantian structures in the Carboniferous basin east of the Pennine axis (Fraser et al., 1990; Ebdon et al., 1990). It is likely that many of these structures represent reactivation of major thrust faults or other structures within the concealed Caledonide basement of eastern England (Soper et al., 1987; Lee et al., 1991; 1993; Pharaoh et al., 1994).

Figure 13   MORB-normalised geochemical patterns for metasedimentary rocks from Wessenden 1 Borehole and comparative data from other provings of the 'green phyllite association'.

THREE
Carboniferous structure and structural evolution

A complex system of basins and blocks, demarcated by major faults, forms the structural framework of the region. This chapter describes the progressive development of these structural features, augmenting and complementing the detailed structural information given in the depth and thickness maps (Maps 1–9) and the Regional Cross-sections.

CARBONIFEROUS BASIN DEVELOPMENT

The plate-tectonic process which most strongly influenced Carboniferous structural development of the region was the formation, several hundred kilometres to the south, in mainland Europe, of a collision-type orogenic belt in the Iberian–Armorican–Massif Central region of the Hercynides (Leeder, 1982). Northwards subduction of the Rheic Ocean resulted in regional back-arc extension to the north of this orogenic belt.

Carboniferous basin development in the region can be split broadly into two main phases. In early Carboniferous times, rapidly subsiding, fault-controlled, extensional basins developed between structurally elevated emergent blocks. This was succeeded, later in Carboniferous times, by more regional subsidence, which was characterised by a lack of major fault-control, and led to submergence and depositional onlap of the earlier structural highs.

This type of two-stage subsidence history, with a rapid synextensional 'rift' phase, followed by a more gradual postextensional 'sag' phase, is common to many sedimentary basins and can be attributed to the process of lithospheric extension. Where lithospheric extension is uniform (McKenzie, 1978), extensional thinning of the crust leads to isostatic subsidence and the development of fault-bounded basins (the synextensional phase of basin evolution). Simultaneously, extension and thinning of the underlying lithosphere gives rise to a positive thermal anomaly. Subsequently, this gradually decays, giving a further, time-dependent thermal relaxation subsidence (the postextensional phase of basin evolution). The postextensional subsidence is of a regional nature, whose associated, largely unfaulted, sedimentary sequences overlie the earlier faulted basins, overlapping their margins onto the previously emergent intervening blocks.

The Carboniferous basin–block system

The early Carboniferous basin–block system (Figure 4) developed during regional lithospheric extension, and formed the basic structural template which governed the subsequent structural evolution of the region. Later tectonic episodes, notably late Carboniferous regional subsidence, end-Carboniferous (Variscan) basin inversion, Mesozoic extension-related basin subsidence and Cenozoic (Alpine) regional uplift, reactivated many of the principal fault-lines and progressively modified the original early Carboniferous extensional basin–block system, but its overall form persists to the present day (Map 1).

The principal early Carboniferous extensional structures of the region are illustrated in Figure 14 and discussed more fully below. They formed by north–south, (Leeder, 1982) or north-north-west–south-south-east (Lee, 1988) directed tension acting upon the structurally heterogeneous Caledonian basement (Chapter Two). The structural trends of the principal faults were strongly influenced by the structural grain of the underlying basement, and fall into four domains, in contrast to the three domains defined by Gawthorpe et al. (1989).

Domain 1

Domain 1 lies in the north of the region, north of the Craven Fault System, and has a relatively low fault density with dominantly east–west-trending structures. This domain comprises the Lake District and Askrigg blocks, underlain by the Lake District Batholith and the Wensleydale Granite respectively, together with the Stainmore Trough.

Domain 2

Domain 2 comprises the south-western part of the region, south of the Craven Fault System and west of the Pennine Line, comprising the Bowland and Rossendale basins and intervening highs. It is dominated by north-east-trending structures with subordinate north-west–south-east faults. This is thought to indicate that the Dinantian faults were strongly influenced by the reactivation of underlying basement structures, the dominant north-east–south-west orientation being parallel to the principal Caledonian faults in the Lake District, and North Wales (Woodcock and Gibbons, 1988).

Domain 3

Domain 3 lies in the south and central parts of the region, south of the Craven Fault System and east of the Pennine Line. It is dominated by well-spaced east–west-trending faults, which demarcate its major structures; the Harrogate Basin, the Holme High and the Alport Basin.

Domain 4

Domain 4 is situated in the far south-east of the region, comprising essentially the north-western part of the Gainsborough Trough and the Askern-Spittal High. It is dominated by north-west-trending faults with subordinate

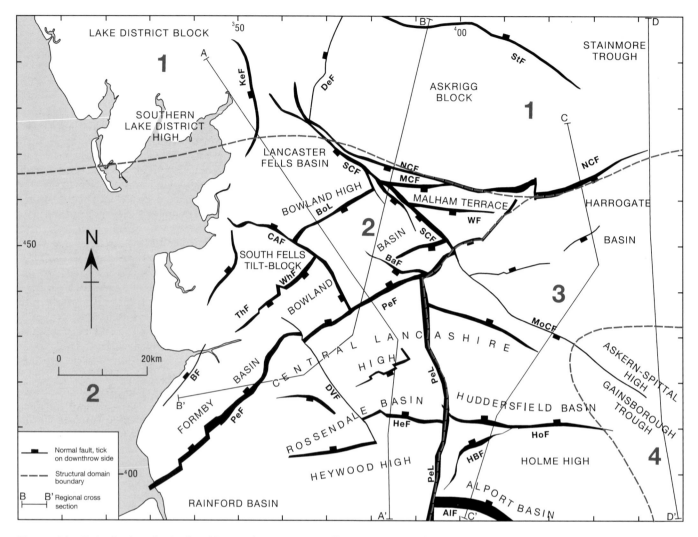

Figure 14 Principal early Carboniferous (synextensional) structures of the region.

AlF Alport Fault; Baf Barnoldswick Fault; BF Banks Fault; BoL Bowland Line; CAF Clitheroe-Abbeystead Fault System; DeF Dent Fault; DVF Darwen Valley Fault; HBF Herridge-Bradshaw Fault; HeF Heywood Fault; HoF Holme Fault; KeF Kendal Fault; MCF Middle Craven Fault; MoCF Morley–Campsall Fault; NCF North Craven Fault; PeF Pendle Fault System; PeL Pennine Line; SCF South Craven Fault; StF Stockdale Fault; ThF Thornley Fault; WhF Whitewell Fault; WF Winterburn Fault.

1–4 structural domains
Lines A–A′, B–B′, C–C′ refer to regional cross-sections accompanying structural maps at back of book.

east to west and north-south–trending faults. Again this is likely to reflect the orientation of underlying basement structures which hereabouts is thought to be dominantly north-west–south-east (Chapter Two).

The general east–west trend of faults in domains 1 and 3 may reflect a transitional position in the structural arc between the north-east trend of Welsh and north-west English Caledonides, and the north-west trend of the eastern English Caledonides (Chapter Two).

By the beginning of late Carboniferous times, extension had mostly ceased and the marked structural differentiation between blocks and basins, characteristic of the early Carboniferous, was much diminished. Fraser and Gawthorpe (1990) have defined an early Carboniferous

synextensional phase of basin development as lasting from the Courceyan to the early Brigantian and a later Carboniferous postextensional phase as lasting from the mid-Brigantian to the Westphalian. Associated synextensional 'syn-rift' (Map 4) and postextensional 'post-rift' (Maps 6 and 8) megasequences were deposited (Fraser and Gawthorpe, 1990). For convenience of description, the same convention is adopted here, but it is stressed that the transition from synextensional to postextensional basin development is by no means clear-cut in the region (see below). Several periods of postextensional subsidence occurred within the synextensional phase, and minor episodes of extension may have continued into the postextensional phase.

Synextensional phase of basin development (Courceyan to early Brigantian)

The nature and timing of early Carboniferous extension has been the subject of much recent debate (Table 4). Regional studies of northern England (for example Gawthorpe et al., 1989; Fraser and Gawthorpe, 1990) have identified several extensional episodes from four main lines of evidence: thickness variations associated with syndepositional normal faulting, sequence boundaries (including unconformities), facies changes and event deposits. Gawthorpe et al. (1989), using these criteria, recognised four episodes of Dinantian extension in northern England, separated by intervals of more regional subsidence characteristic of relative tectonic quiescence. The first extensional episode (latest Devonian–Courceyan) was considered by these authors to be the most important. Fraser and Gawthorpe (1990) identified three episodes of Dinantian extension, but argued that the most important (corresponding to their sequence EC3) was in Arundian to early Holkerian times. This conclusion was based principally upon their interpretation of a very thick EC3 sequence in the Stainmore Trough and particularly well-developed stratigraphical wedging and onlap of interpreted EC3 in the Gainsborough Trough (to the south-east of the region). We believe however that these authors overestimated the thickness of EC3 both in the Stainmore Trough, (Collier, 1991; Chadwick et al., 1995), and possibly also in the Gainsborough Trough, where it is poorly stratigraphically constrained. More local studies have enabled other workers tentatively to identify specific extensional episodes (for example Adams et al., 1990; Riley, 1990).

In the region, there appears to have been a prolonged phase of rapid crustal extension early in the Dinantian. From the initiation of sedimentation until deposition of the Chatburn Limestone in early Chadian times, deposition was largely restricted to rapidly subsiding, fault-bounded basins (Map 2). Sedimentation appears in general terms to have kept pace with subsidence. Strata which were deposited outside these basins are much thinner and of marginal facies. We therefore conclude that this episode of extension constitutes the principal extensional event in this region, as it was in the region to the north (Chadwick et al., 1995), a view also held by Gawthorpe et al., (1989). It was at this time that the overall form of the early Carboniferous basin-block system was established, with the formation of major asymmetrical basins and their basin-controlling normal faults (Table 4). The north or north-north-west-directed extension produced large, dominantly dip-slip displacements on those structures which were roughly east–west trending, such as the Craven, Pendle, Holme and Alport faults (and the Butterknowle Fault to the north of the region). In addition to these main faults, synthetic and antithetic normal faults form small intrabasin fault blocks. Other structures such as the Dent, South Craven and Pennine faults developed at a high angle to the main basin-margin normal faults. These probably suffered strongly oblique-slip or transcurrent displacements and perhaps acted as transfer-zones (Gibbs, 1984), linking displacements on adjacent, but offset, normal fault segments.

Following deposition of the Chatburn Limestone, a general rise in relative sea-level in the region led to the progressive inundation of previously emergent areas. The Holme and Central Lancashire highs were submerged in Chadian times and the Askrigg Block was finally completely submerged in Holkerian times. This increasing component of regional subsidence in mid to late Dinantian times is thought to be similar in nature to the succeeding Namurian and Westphalian subsidence, being of an essentially postextensional character. However, the presence of occasional deep-water conglomeratic and turbiditic deposits, and facies changes across faults, points to continued pulses of episodic extension. Moreover, the Dinantian sequence overlying the Chatburn Limestone thickens considerably and changes facies over the same faults which were active in the main, early Dinantian extensional phase. This period may be regarded therefore as one of episodic extension and fault reactivation, not significantly altering the existing basin architecture, and transitional between early Dinantian synextensional and post-Dinantian thermal relaxation subsidence (Table 4).

Principal Dinantian depocentres of the region are the Stainmore Trough with up to 4500 m of Dinantian strata, the Bowland and Harrogate basins with more than 4000 m and more than 3000 m of preserved strata respectively and the poorly understood Rainford and Formby basins in the west and south-west of the region (Figure 14, Map 4).

In latest Dinantian times, sequence EC6 of Fraser and Gawthorpe (1990), may be taken, somewhat arbitrarily, as marking the end of the synextensional megasequence. This sequence is associated with probable minor early Brigantian basin inversion in northern England. Evidence of this in the region comes mostly from the Bowland and Formby basins. The southern margin of the Formby Basin was apparently weakly inverted at about this time (Figure 43), as the hangingwall-block of the Pendle Fault was uplifted (see p.42), Namurian strata onlapping onto the resulting fold. Near to the northern margin of the Bowland Basin, minor reversal (down-north displacement) of the Middle Craven Fault is documented by Arthurton et al. (1988). Possible local fault reversal at about this time has also been described from the South Lake District High (Adams et al., 1990). These minor inversions were apparently contemporaneous with thrust and nappe emplacement in south-west England (Sellwood and Thomas, 1986), and formed precursors to the main Variscan basin inversion at the end of the Carboniferous.

Postextensional phase of basin development (late Brigantian to Westphalian)

The postextensional phase of basin evolution in the region is here taken as commencing in late Brigantian times (Table 4), with deposition of the Bowland Shales (Chapter Four). The postextensional megasequence corresponds roughly, therefore, to the Silesian (Namurian and Westphalian) succession, which, because of later

Table 4   The nature and timing of Carboniferous extension and subsidence.

Shaded areas represent periods of rifting.

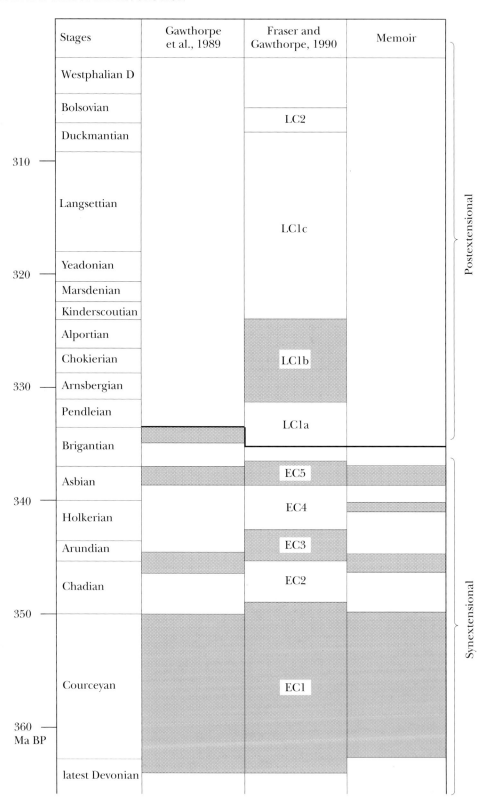

erosion is, at best, partially preserved over only part of the region (Maps 6 and 8).

Postextensional subsidence resulting from thermal relaxation effects following extensional thinning of the lithosphere (McKenzie, 1978), is of a regional nature and is associated with largley unfaulted postextensional sequences which blanket the earlier extensional basins. Postextensional depocentres would, theoretically, be expected to overlie the region of maximum lithospheric thinning. Three additional factors, however, led to more complex patterns of postextensional deposition in the region, affecting particularly the Namurian sequence. Specifically, they all resulted in preferentially thick sequences being laid down over the earlier extensional basins:

i) It is likely that at the end of Dinantian times there was still a substantial topographical relief, inherited from the Dinantian basin–block system, and accentuated by platform carbonate build-ups. This led to substantial water depths in the sediment-starved grabens. It is likely that lower Namurian strata filled up this residual relief, consequently thickening markedly into the earlier basins.

ii) The effects of differential compaction meant that for a given amount of subsidence (or a given water depth), thicker strata were deposited over basinal areas, due to compaction of underlying strata than over adjacent blocks, or highs. The effects of differential compaction at basin margins are commonly manifest as down-to-the-basin normal faults which propagate upwards, from the earlier extensional basin-margin faults, through the post-extensional sequence.

iii) Minor episodes of extension may well have continued into Silesian times, with renewed normal displacements on basin-controlling normal faults. It is very difficult to distinguish between these and the effects of differential compaction.

Namurian subsidence patterns differed markedly from those of the Dinantian, conforming broadly to theoretical postextensional behaviour in that the strong structural contrasts of the early Carboniferous basin-block system were much subdued. This is exemplified by preserved Namurian thicknesses (Map 6). Although a complete Namurian sequence is only preserved in the east and south of the region, the main depositional patterns may be surmised. Firstly, the lack of major syndepositional structural control above the basins and highs in the southern part of the region is readily apparent. Thickness trends hereabouts are regional in nature and, to a large degree, independent of the underlying mosaic of extensional features. The thinnest part of the (fully preserved) Namurian sequence lies in the south-eastern part of the region, where it is typically less than 1000 m and locally less than 800 m thick. From here the general trend is for the sequence to thicken north-westwards towards the Bowland and Harrogate basins. This thickening trend is particularly well developed farther west, where the sequence is 1200 m thick at the southern edge of the region, but thickens northwards across the underlying Heywood High, Rossendale Basin and Central Lancashire High, to about 2000 m in the Pendle Monocline (Earp et al., 1961) at the southern margin of the Bowland Basin. Namurian strata are now absent from the much of the Bowland Basin itself, but it seems probable that in excess of 2000 m of strata were deposited there. Relatively thick Namurian strata were probably deposited also in the Harrogate Basin, the two basins defining a broad east-north-east-trending zone of relatively rapid Namurian subsidence. This was undoubtedly partly due to the inherited effects of the underlying extensional basins, but may also indicate a zone of enhanced lithospheric thinning during the Dinantian. The fact that the

zone was later to become the locus of Variscan crustal shortening, manifest as the Ribblesdale Foldbelt (see p.46), lends further support to the possibility of a fundamental line of crustal, or even lithospheric weakness hereabouts. To the north of the Bowland and Harrogate basins, Silesian strata are very poorly preserved, but the overall trend seems to be one of gradual northwards thinning. For example, the complete Namurian sequence in the Stainmore Trough, some 25 km to the north of the region, is locally less than 800 m thick (Chadwick et al., 1995). An even thinner sequence would be expected on the Askrigg and Lake District blocks, bearing in mind the lack of underlying basins, and the likelihood of less lithospheric extension. This is to some extent borne out by a thin (typically less than 600 m thick) Namurian sequence on the northern margin of the Lake District Block (Chadwick et al., 1995) and a succession only 50 m thick in west Cumbria.

The Westphalian sequence was deposited in a regime of postextensional regional subsidence but detailed patterns of deposition are poorly constrained, because a complete sequence is nowhere preserved in the region. Maximum preserved thicknesses occur in the south where there are locally more than 1500 m of Westphalian strata. A clue to regional depositional trends is afforded by the work of Calver (1968) who mapped the Langsettian and Duckmantian strata. He postulated a depocentre close to the southern edge of the region beneath the northern margin of the Cheshire Basin (Figure 46), with thicknesses in excess of 1500 m. Strata thin westwards and eastwards, and to a lesser degree northwards, from the depocentre.

Minor thickness variations may be related to the compactability of the underlying Dinantian and Namurian successions. For example there is some evidence of thinner Lower Coal Measures on the central part of the Central Lancashire High, where they are underlain by Dinantian platform carbonates, than to the north or to the south.

The thickness of Westphalian strata deposited in the Bowland Basin is a matter for conjecture. Local northwards thickening towards the basin is observed between the Bacup area and the Burnley Coalfield (Wright et al., 1927; Earp et al., 1961), but whether this is just a local perturbation on a regional northwards thinning trend, or of more widespread significance is uncertain. To the north of the Bowland Basin, the Ingleton Coalfield crops out, lying above the eastern corner of the Lancaster Fells Basin. Strata here are thinner than equivalent strata to the south-east of the Bowland Basin (Arthurton et al., 1988). This is consistent with, but does not prove, regional northwards thinning. It is certainly conceivable that a very thick Westphalian sequence was deposited within the Bowland Basin, coincident with the Namurian depocentre.

As intimated above, smaller-scale structures may well have locally influenced patterns of postextensional subsidence. Minor normal faulting may have continued into Silesian times, particularly along basin margins. More significantly, minor episodes of basin inversion may have affected the region from time to time. Angular discordances within the Namurian sequences inferred in several of the folds of the Ribblesdale Foldbelt (notably the Skipton and Catlow anticlines) have been taken to indicate syndepositional Namurian folding (see pp.47, 50). The Ingleton Coalfield lies in the hangingwall-block of the Hollintree Fault, which suffered significant Variscan reversal (Ford, 1954); major unconformities in its Westphalian sequence may attest to episodes of minor basin inversion

To conclude, postextensional subsidence in the region is, in detail, rather poorly understood, because of incomplete preservation of Silesian strata. The locus of maximum Namurian subsidence lay above the Bowland Basin whereas the Westphalian depocentre appears to have been situated considerably farther south. This is difficult to explain. Differential compaction effects may have played a part in developing a relatively thicker Namurian sequence above the Bowland Basin. Another possibility is that the completely eroded Westphalian sequence of the Bowland Basin was much thicker than present preservation suggests. Certainly, the idea of a simple, saucer-shaped Silesian basin centred close to the southern margin of the region for example, Fraser and Gawthorpe, 1990) requires careful review.

Principal structural features

The principal features of the Carboniferous basin–block system were, to all intents and purposes, fully formed by the end of the synextensional phase of basin development (Figure 14). They fall into three basic categories defined below.

A **basin** is an area characterised by thick, relatively complete, synextensional sedimentary sequences. The synextensional basins of the region are largely fault bounded, being in general controlled by syndepositional normal displacements on major basin-margin faults, several tens of kilometres in length. Faults on opposed basin margins are usually not of equal magnitude, giving the basins markedly asymmetrical profiles. A **block** comprises an area, partially or wholly fault-bounded, characterised by thin, incomplete, synextensional sedimentary sequences. Blocks are underpinned by rigid, buoyant, basement granites. It is likely that blocks were topographically elevated during all extensional episodes in the post-Acadian structural history of the region. A **high** may be partially fault-bounded, and is characterised by thin, incomplete, synextensional sedimentary sequences. Unlike blocks, highs are not necessarily underlain by basement granites. Their topographical elevation results from the basin-controlling regional fault pattern. Because of this, any change in the distribution of displacements within the fault network can render them short-lived.

Lake District Block

The region impinges upon the southern part of the Lake District Block which forms an important structural high, underpinned by the Lake District granitic batholith (Chapter Two). The limits of the block, in Dinantian

times, were rather poorly defined. It passes westwards into the Manx–Cumbria Ridge, southwards into the Southern Lake District High and south-eastwards into the Lancaster Fells Basin (Regional Cross-section 1, Section A–A'). Within the region, Lower Palaeozoic basement rocks crop out on the block, cover rocks being absent (Map 1). Preserved Carboniferous strata from the northern part of the block (Chadwick et al., 1995) and from the South Lake District High (see below) indicate that it was probably covered by a very thin, incomplete, Dinantian succession. The block probably remained emergent through early Dinantian times, southward tilting of its upper surface gradually allowing northward onlap of Arundian and younger strata (Adams et al., 1990). It is likely that latest Dinantian, Namurian and Westphalian strata were deposited over most if not all of the block.

Southern Lake District High

The Southern Lake District High is essentially the south-dipping flank of the Lake District Block. The Dinantian succession on the high is thin, being stratigraphically thickest and most complete in the south and onlaps northwards across the south-dipping basement surface (Adams et al., 1990). The high is cut by several roughly north-trending normal faults (Map 1). The most easterly of these, the Kendal Fault, is a down-to-the-west normal fault juxtaposing Dinantian strata in its hangingwall-block and basement rocks in the footwall-block (Moseley, 1972). Seismic reflection data across the southerly continuation of the Kendal Fault, near Priest-Hutton, and within the Quernmore structure (p.58) suggest that early Dinantian strata thicken eastwards into the structure, indicating an easterly deepening Dinantian half-graben controlled to the east by a normal fault which downthrows to the west. Other faults to the west also show evidence of limited early Carboniferous movement (Adams et al., 1990), but are predominantly post-Dinantian in age. These observations are consistent with the South Lake District High being dissected, in Dinantian times, by a series of small north–south-trending half-grabens. The orientation of these structures, subparallel to the presumed extension direction, may well have been inherited from pre-existing basement structures. The half-grabens were subsequently inverted during Variscan times (see p.44).

Askrigg Block

Forming the southern half of the 'Rigid Block of North-West Yorkshire' (Marr, 1921), the Askrigg Block (Regional Cross-section B–B') comprises an important structural high, underpinned by the Wensleydale Granite (Chapter Two). The block has the form of a northerly dipping tilt-block (Map 1), bounded to the south by the Craven Fault System and to the west by the Dent Fault. The nature of the northern and eastern flanks of the block is uncertain. They may dip steadily north-east towards the Stainmore Trough, with the progressive incoming, by regional onlap, of a thicker, more complete Dinantian succession (see Chapter Four). On the other hand, seismic data in the south-western part of the Stainmore Trough show only slight southwards and westward shallowing of the

Caledonian basement, insufficient when projected southwards and westwards to give the observed basement elevation beneath the block. The northern margin of the block, therefore, is inferred to coincide with the Stockdale Faults which downthrow to the north. The eastern flank of the block, at least in part, is also probably marked by down-to-the-east faulting, the location of which has not yet been identified.

Compared with the basins to the south, the Dinantian rocks on the block are relatively undeformed, forming a broad dome open towards the Craven Faults and plunging gently to the north. The southern and central parts of the Askrigg Block are almost devoid of faults, but faulting increases northwards towards the Stockdale Disturbance (Dunham and Wilson, 1985).

The Carboniferous succession on the Askrigg Block is thin and incomplete, particularly so close to its southern margin, on the footwall of the North Craven Fault. Here, Arundian and locally Holkerian strata rest unconformably on the Lower Palaeozoic basement, which locally comes to crop. The Carboniferous succession thickens steadily northwards and eastwards into the Stainmore Trough, thickening occurring both stratigraphically and by the addition of progressively older Dinantian strata (see p.66). Where overlain by Namurian strata on the eastern flank of the block the Dinantian succession is in places thought to be less than 500 m thick (Map 4). Doubtless it was even thinner on the crestal parts of the block. Subsequent submergence was interrupted in Pendleian times by uplift and tilting towards the north-west, which gave rise to an unconformity beneath the Grassington Grit (Dunham and Wilson, 1985).

Malham Terrace

Also termed the Transition-zone (Arthurton et al., 1988), the Malham Terrace is bounded to the north by the North Craven Fault and to the south by the Winterburn Fault (Figure 14). The terrace has a complex structure, being cut by several east–south-east-trending faults, including the Middle Craven Fault. Because of the difficulty in apportioning throws to these faults, the depth of basement hereabouts is poorly constrained, but it is believed that the terrace forms an area of basement depths intermediate between the Askrigg Block to the north and the Bowland Basin to the south (Map 1). Dinantian thicknesses are likewise poorly constrained, but are thought to be in the range 1000 to 2000 m (Map 4).

Lancaster Fells Basin

The Lancaster Fells Basin (Gawthorpe et al. 1989; Horbury 1989) is a small structure in the northern part of the main Craven Basin (Figure 14, Regional Cross-section A–A'). It forms the northerly down-dip continuation of the tilted Bowland High, lying south-west of the Craven Fault System and south of the Lake District Block, from which it is probably separated by large faults. There is a moderate thickening of the Dinantian succession into the basin where it is typically some 1600 m thick (Map 4). The youngest Carboniferous strata preserved being the Bolsovian (Westphalian C) red measures which unconformably overlie Langsettian and Duckmantian (West-

phalian A and B) grey measures in the Ingleton Coalfield (Ford, 1954).

South Fells Tilt Block

The South Fells Tilt Block (Lawrence et al., 1987) lies to the south-west of the Clitheroe–Abbeystead Fault System (Figure 14). The structure of the tilt-block, poorly understood due to the paucity of seismic reflection data, is largely defined from gravity interpretations (Lawrence et al., 1988), and it is believed to dip generally to the north-west (Map 1). Its south-eastern margin is marked by two Variscan folds, the Whitewell and Thornley anticlines (Aitkenhead et al., 1992), which lie above the Whitewell and Thornley faults. These faults are Dinantian down-to-the-south normal faults marking the northern margin of the Bowland Basin hereabouts. The southern and western margins are poorly constrained, probably being faulted. Dinantian strata are typically some 2000 m thick on the block and thicken stratigraphically westwards.

Bowland High

The Bowland High (termed the Bowland Block by Arthurton et al., 1988), is an important intra-basinal structure lying to the north-west of the Bowland Basin (Figure 14). Its south-eastern margin corresponds to a geophysical feature termed the Bowland Line, interpreted either as a southerly slope in the basement surface (Arthurton et al., 1988), or as preferred here, a down-to-the-south Dinantian syndepositional normal fault (Regional Cross-section A–A'), above which lie two Variscan structures, the Sykes and Catlow anticlines (p.50). The north-eastern limit of the high is marked by the South Craven Fault System which separates it from the Malham Terrace, with which it has many structural affinities (Arthurton et al., 1988). The south-western limit of the high is marked by the north-west-trending, Clitheroe–Abbeystead Fault System. The Bowland High forms a north-west-dipping tilt block which passes into the Lancaster Fells Basin (Gawthorpe et al., 1989; Horbury, 1989). Dinantian strata are less than 800 m thick on its crest (Map 4), thickening east, west and northwards, the high being onlapped at various times during the Dinantian.

Bowland Basin

The Bowland Basin (Lawrence et al., 1987; Gawthorpe et al. 1989), also termed the Craven Basin (Arthurton et al., 1988) is one of the main depocentres of the region, forming a north-east-trending asymmetrical graben, bounded to the south by the Pendle Fault System (and the overlying Pendle Monocline) and to the north by the Bowland Line and the Whitewell and Thornley faults (Figure 14, Regional Cross-sections A–A' and B–B'). Seismic reflection data indicate that the basin passes south-westwards, into the Formby Basin, which is concealed beneath the Permo-Triassic cover of the West Lancashire Basin. The basin contains a very thick Dinantian fill with preserved thicknesses in excess of 4000 m (Map 4), close to the Pendle Fault (Figure 15). Even greater thicknesses may have been deposited in the central parts of the basin, where the upper Dinantian sequence has since been eroded. Within the basin, a borehole located in the core of

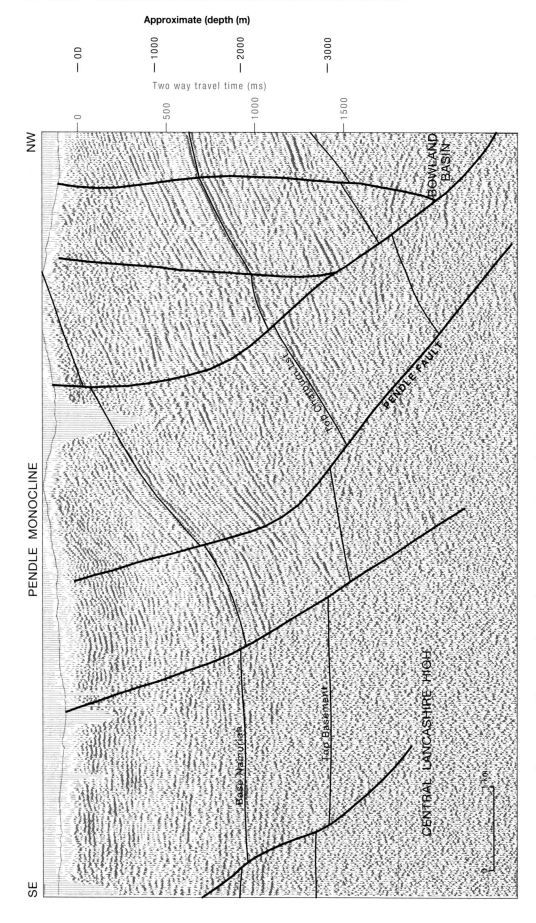

Figure 15   Seismic reflection profile across the southern margin of the Bowland Basin. Note thickening of Dinantian sequence across Pendle Fault.

the Swinden Anticline, proved some 683 m of unbottomed Courceyan strata (Charsley, 1984). Seismic reflection data reveal at least a further 1600 to 1700 m of strata beneath the terminal depth of the borehole (Map 2), being of presumed Courceyan age and possibly older (Devonian). Dinantian basin development was controlled by large, syndepositional normal displacements on the Pendle Fault System and the Bowland Line. In addition to the dominant east-north-east-trending normal faults, the basin is crossed by several north-west-trending transverse faults, for example the Clitheroe–Abbeystead Fault System, the Barnoldswick Fault and the South Craven Fault System. These faults presumably experienced strongly oblique displacements, possibly acting in a transfer role during both extensional basin development and subsequent basin inversion. West of the Clitheroe–Abbeystead Fault, Courceyan strata are believed to be thickest in the hangingwall-block of the Bowland Line (Map 2), which appears to have been the major basin-controlling fault in the earliest stages of basin development. Later in Dinantian times, the structural polarity of the basin changed as the major displacements switched to the Pendle Fault System, the Clitheroe–Abbeystead Fault acting in a transfer role, with possible 'scissors' type displacements. The South Craven Fault System which transects the north-eastern part of the basin appears to offset the Pendle Fault and, more significantly, it offsets the main Dinantian basin depocentre from the Harrogate Basin to the east (Maps 2 and 4). The eastern extremity of the Bowland Basin comprises a triangular area, bounded by the Winterburn Fault to the north and the postulated Pendle–Bolton Abbey faults to the south-east. The Dinantian sequence hereabouts is exposed in the Skipton Anticline where Hudson and Mitchell (1937) estimated up to 1800 m of Dinantian strata, of basinal facies. The depth of basement hereabouts is uncertain. The Embsay Borehole was initially believed to have reached Devonian strata (Hudson, 1938b), but this is not now thought to be the case (N J Riley, personal communication).

The Bowland Basin suffered considerable Variscan inversion and consequent erosion. Thus, younger parts of the Carboniferous sequence are now absent in many parts of the basin, with strata of Courceyan to early Namurian age either cropping out or being unconformably overlain by Permo-Triassic rocks. Of the major basins in the region, the Bowland Basin has the lowest proportion of its original sedimentary fill still preserved. On the Central Lancashire High, to the south of the Pendle Monocline and the (concealed) underlying Pendle Fault, Coal Measures of Bolsovian age are present in the asymmetrical Blackburn–Burnley Syncline (Wright et al., 1927). These were presumably also deposited within the Bowland Basin prior to basin inversion.

The majority of north-east-trending structures of the Ribblesdale Foldbelt, which constitute the most obvious expression of Variscan movements in the region (see p.44), are associated with the reactivation of faults in the Bowland Basin. In particular the Pendle Monocline, the Lothersdale Anticline and the Skipton Anticline are major inversion structures associated with reversal of the southern bounding faults of the basin.

Harrogate Basin

This broad basinal area lies to the east of the Bowland Basin, offset *en échelon* from it by the South Craven–Morley Campsall Fault System. It forms a roughly triangular area bounded by the Pendle and North Craven faults to the north-west, the South Craven and Morley–Campsall faults to the south-east, and the eastern boundary of the region to the east. The basin has the rough form of a south-west-shallowing asymmetrical graben, but it is not as sharply fault-defined as the Bowland Basin (Regional Cross-sections C–C′ and D–D′). Sparse seismic data coverage renders the south-west part of the basin, in the vicinity of the Morley–Campsall faults, very poorly understood. Basement depths are greatest in the north-east, locally in excess of 4000 m, where the basin passes northwards into the Stainmore Trough. Elsewhere basement depths are generally in excess of 3000 m (Map 1). However, it is stressed that the base of the Carboniferous succession in the basin is nowhere proved by boreholes and is consequently poorly constrained. Interpreted depths correspond to the base of coherent seismic reflections, and may be significantly shallower than true basement depths. A moderately thick Dinantian succession, typically in excess of 3000 m thick (Map 4) is overlain by Namurian strata, up to 1200 m thick where fully preserved (Map 6). Westphalian rocks (Map 8) are preserved in the east and thicken eastwards beneath the Permo-Triassic cover. The basin is cut by several predominantly east-north-east-trending normal faults, parallel and forming a continuation of the Pendle Fault trend. Because of the difficulty in identifying deep structures on the seismic data, the throws on these faults at the top of Lower Palaeozoic basement, may be much larger than shown. Many of these faults appear to be locally offset by north-west-trending transfer faults, which, particularly in the Bradford and Skipton district, form the dominant surface fault trend. In the northern part of the basin many of these normal faults suffered subsequent Variscan reversal to form inversion structures such as the Harrogate and Ellenthorpe anticlines (p.56). The North Craven Fault, was also subsequently reversed, forming several inversion structures at the basin's northern margin (see p.39).

Stainmore Trough

The region encompasses only the southern part of this very deep basin; its faulted northern margin, the Closehouse–Lunedale–Butterknowle fault system lying some 25 km to the north (Collier 1991; Chadwick et al., 1995). This broad region of thick Carboniferous strata corresponds to the 'basinal area of Cleveland' (Kent, 1980). The base of the Carboniferous succession, nowhere penetrated by boreholes, is taken at the base of a thick sequence of well-developed, subhorizontal, seismic reflections (Figure 16). Devonian strata may also be present at the base of this seismic sequence, but for the purposes of this account they are assumed to be absent. The top of Caledonian basement is therefore taken as synonymous with the base of the Carboniferous which locally may lie at depths greater than 6000 m (Map 1).

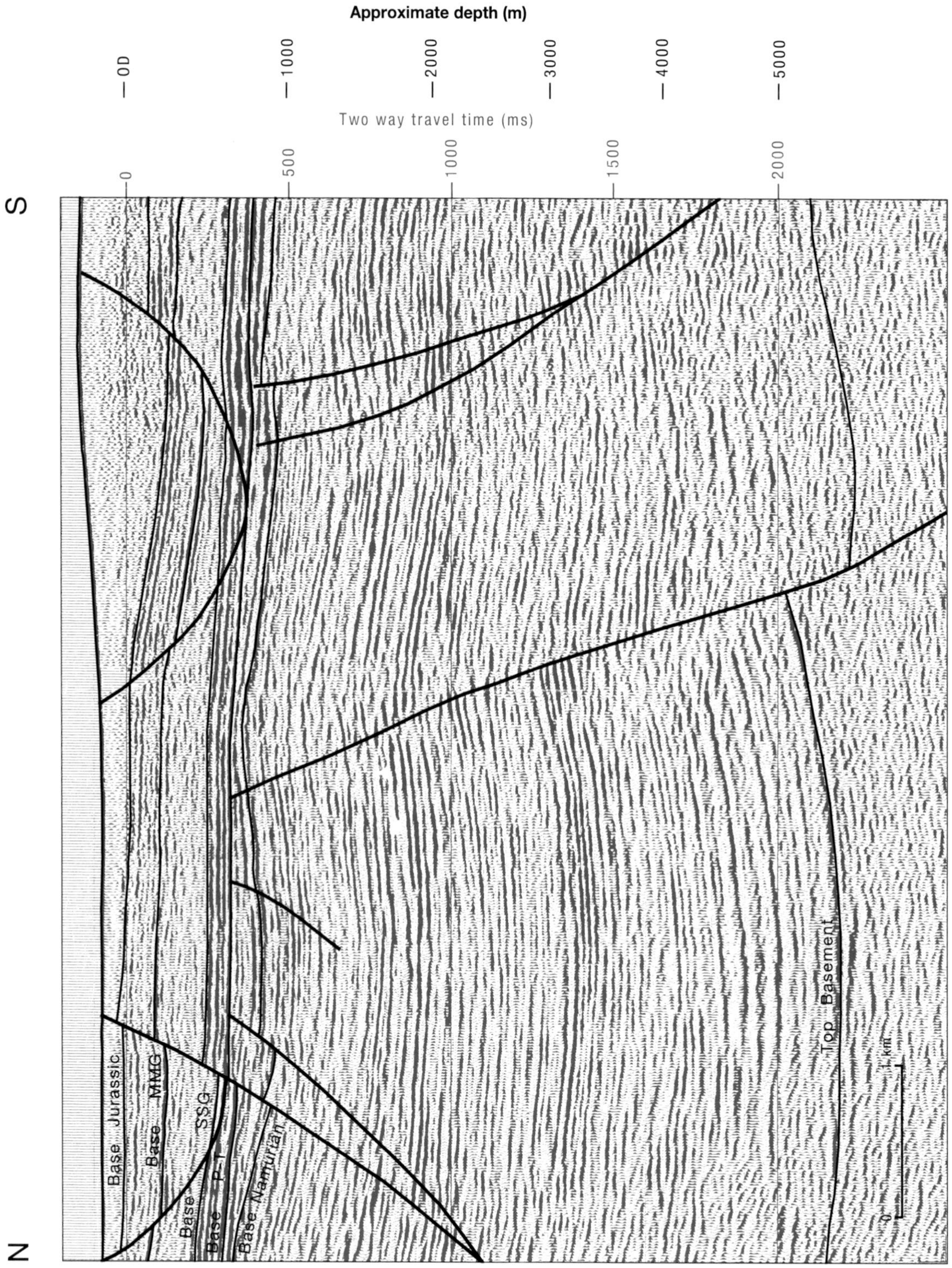

Figure 16 Seismic reflection profile in the southern part of the Stainmore Trough, showing a very thick Dinantian sequence overlain by thin Namurian strata. Permo-Triassic strata unconformably overlie the Carboniferous succession.

The thickness of the Dinantian succession of the Stainmore Trough is interpreted to increase northwards from about 3000 m at the south end of the basin to more than 4500 m at the north edge of the region (Map 4). North of the region, the Dinantian thickens still further to about 5000 m on the hangingwall-block of the Closehouse–Lunedale-Butterknowle fault system. The Dinantian succession also thins markedly south-westwards onto the Askrigg Block (Map 4), basal beds onlapping southwards onto the Lower Palaeozoic basement surface and probably thinning substantially across the Stockdale Faults, as envisaged by Collier (1991).

A seismic sequence boundary can be observed locally, separating an underlying extensional tilt-block sequence with minor stratigraphical thickening towards small normal faults from an overlying more uniformly deposited sequence. This sequence boundary may correspond to the end of the main Courceyan–early Chadian extensional phase.

The thickness of the Namurian succession (Stainmore Group) in the southern part of the Stainmore Trough varies considerably, depending upon how much of the unit is preserved beneath the angular unconformity at the base of the Permo-Triassic succession (Map 6). In much of the area only the lower part of the unit is preserved (Figure 16) and it may be absent locally. Progressively younger Namurian strata come to subcrop eastwards, beneath the Permo-Triassic cover. Thickness changes are therefore principally a preservation effect; the seismic data indicate that stratigraphical (that is depositional) thickness variations in the Stainmore Group hereabouts are minimal.

Coal Measures are nowhere preserved in the southern part of the Stainmore Trough, having been removed by Variscan erosion.

The Carboniferous rocks of the southern part of the Stainmore Trough are cut by only rather small faults which for the most part do not penetrate the base Permo-Triassic unconformity (Figure 16); their displacements therefore predate deposition of the basal Permian deposits. The faults in general trend roughly east to west, are subplanar with moderate to steep dips and have normal, dominantly down-to-the-south, displacements. On most of the faults the throw decreases upwards through the Carboniferous sequence, signifying syndepositional (early Carboniferous) movement as well as post-Namurian displacement.

Locally, the base of the Stainmore Group is cut by minor reverse faulting (Figure 16). These small reverse faults appear to pass downwards into normal displacements in the Dinantian succession, indicative of minor reversal of an earlier, syndepositional normal fault. These reverse faults do not penetrate the basal Permian unconformity and presumably occurred in Variscan (end-Carboniferous) times. Minor folding associated with Variscan events is also locally present.

Central Lancashire High

The Central Lancashire High forms an important area of relatively shallow basement between the Bowland Basin to the north and the Rossendale Basin to the south (Figure 14). It is a north-easterly trending structural feature, whose northern limit is marked by the Pendle Monocline and the underlying Pendle Fault Regional Cross-sections A–A' and B–B', Figure 15). The western margin of the high is poorly constrained but it appears to extend south-westwards as the footwall-block of the Pendle Fault. The eastern margin of the high is poorly defined but it can certainly be traced well to the east of the Pennine Line. The high culminates some 10 km to the south of the Pendle Fault where it forms a ridge running roughly from the Roddlesworth Borehole, through Holme Chapel Borehole (basement 1696 m below OD) and on through Boulsworth Borehole to the east (Map 1). From this ridge the basement surface generally dips away southwards, across minor southerly throwing normal faults, into the Rossendale Basin. The Dinantian sequence on the high is thin, in many places less than 1000 m (Map 4). Boreholes on the high and also on the Heywood High, prove Dinantian platform carbonates (Chapter Four) whilst Fletcherbank Borehole within the intervening Rossendale Basin, proved uppermost Dinantian carbonates of basinal character. The high shows a carbonate build-up gradually drowned during the Dinantian, as basinal sequences onlapped the structure from both the north and the south. By Namurian times, the structure was all but submerged and strata of Pendleian age and younger pass, unaffected, across the site of the former high (Maps 6 and 8).

Rossendale Basin

The Rossendale Basin forms a narrow east-north-east-trending basinal area to the south of the Central Lancashire High (Regional Cross-section A–A') and has only one deep borehole (Fletcherbank) proving strata of Namurian and Dinantian age, the latter of basinal type. No borehole has reached basement within the basin. It is bounded by the Central Lancashire High to the north and the Heywood High to the south. The basin is separated from the Huddersfield Basin to the east by the north–south-trending Pennine Line (Figure 14), however this structure is of uncertain displacement and the two basins may be effectively contiguous. To the west, the basin is poorly imaged on seismic reflection data, but data in the east reveal a well-developed south-deepening half-graben structure within which the Dinantian sequence may attain a thickness of more than 1600 m (Map 4). Within the basin a continuous Carboniferous succession is present, through to strata of early Duckmantian age at crop.

The southern limit of the basin is poorly defined, being best constrained in the east, where the northerly throwing Heywood Fault separates the basin from the Heywood High to the south (Regional Cross-section A–A'). Faulting in the basin is dominated by north-west–south-east fault-sets which show a tendency to concentrate into zones, two of which are the Darwen Valley and Todmorden 'smash belts' (Wright et al., 1927). The zones may be up to 5 km in width and break up the Rossendale Anticline (see p.61). Wright et al. (1927) suggested that the absence of faulting between these zones may be related to thickened grits in the area. Another explanation may lie in the underlying Dinantian geology. The Darwen Valley Fault passes between the main Asbian–Brigantian carbonate build-ups (Chapter Four) and the curiously curved down-to-the-west Brinscall Fault appears to lie just to the west of the inferred curved western limit of the main Asbian–Brigantian mound (Figure 42). It may be, therefore, that these massive and resistant Dinantian platform deposits, (possibly themselves controlled by faults during deposition), influenced the course of the main faults in the overlying Silesian cover sequences, by channelling strain around their margins.

Compared to the Ribblesdale Foldbelt there is little evidence of major basin inversion hereabouts (Figure 24).

Heywood High

The Heywood High lies to the south of the Rossendale Basin (Figure 14) and is partially concealed by Permo-Triassic strata of the northern Cheshire Basin. The northern margin of the high, most clearly defined in the east, is marked by the down-to-the-north Heywood Fault (Regional Cross-Section A–A′) which appears to be sinistrally offset by the north-west-trending Darwen Valley Fault. The westerly extension of the high is poorly understood, being concealed beneath Permo-Triassic cover rocks. It may coalesce with the westerly extension of the Central Lancashire High in the vicinity of the Upholland boreholes, before dipping westwards into a more basinal area. The southerly extent of the high is not clear. Seismic reflection data show a thick Carboniferous sequence dipping southwards beneath the Permo-Triassic cover of the Cheshire Basin (37). The eastern flank of the high appears to dip eastwards towards the Pennine Line. The Dinantian sequence on the high is poorly constrained, but probably is less than 1500 m thick in many parts (Map 4). The high marked an area of shallow marine platform carbonate sedimentation during the Dinantian (Strank, 1982; 1990). The Heywood Borehole and outcrop information prove a Dinantian through to Westphalian succession, albeit incomplete.

Huddersfield Basin

Identified initially on the basis of gravity interpretation (Lee, 1988), this poorly understood structural feature lies to the north of the Holme High (Figure 14, Regional Cross-section C–C′), separated from it by the east-trending Holme Fault (Figure 17). Dinantian strata in the basin are thought to be typically about 2000 m thick (Map 4), thickening eastwards into the Gainsborough Trough. The basin has roughly the form of an east–west-trending half-graben, shallowing northwards on to the Central Lancashire High. It appears to be separated from the Rossendale Basin to the west by the Pennine Line. However, the nature of this structure is uncertain hereabouts and the two basins may be contiguous.

Holme High

The east to west-trending Holme High (Figure 14, Regional Cross-section C–C′), also known as the Holme Platform (Gutteridge, 1991), is an important structurally elevated area. Its highest point is close to the Wessenden Borehole, which penetrated possible Lower Palaeozoic slates at 606 m below OD (Figure 17). The northern margin of the high is defined by the Holme Fault. Its western margin, is marked by the north-north-east-trending Herridge–Bradshaw Fault which separates the high from the Goyt Trough. On its south side, the Holme High dips southwards, into the Alport Basin. To the east it dips steadily towards the Gainsborough Trough. The Holme High is cut only by small faults, whose trend is only poorly defined by the sparse seismic grid which covers the area.

The Dinantian succession at Wessenden is only 614 m thick, severely condensed compared to an interpreted thickness of some 2000 m just north of the Holme Fault in the Huddersfield Basin and over 3000 m in the Alport Basin to the south (Map 4). This marked thinning onto the high is accompanied by marked onlap of the Dinantian succession (Figure 17).

Sedimentological descriptions of cores and cuttings from the Wessenden Borehole suggest that the Holme High had a topographical expression throughout Dinantian times. Shallow marine conditions dominated near the crest of the high, whereas deeper marine conditions were dominant in the Alport Basin. At Wessenden most of the Dinantian succession consists of platform carbonates deposited in shallow marine environments. The rest of the succession consists of shales. This contrasts with the Alport Borehole in the Alport Basin to the south, where, in Arundian to early Asbian times, deposition is interpreted to have taken place on the middle part of a carbonate ramp.

In the Wessenden Borehole there is an unconformity between the youngest Dinantian strata, of probable early Asbian age, and the oldest Namurian strata, thin Edale Shales (probably Kinderscoutian). This unconformity is illustrated vividly by seismic reflection data which show significant onlap onto the Asbian unconformity surface (Figure 17).

Alport Basin

The Alport Basin is a new term, describing a half-graben lying to the north of the newly interpreted Alport Fault (Regional Cross-section C–C′). The existence of a basinal area hereabouts was initially inferred from gravity and sedimentological studies (Lee, 1988; Gutteridge, 1991), but the precise location of its southern bounding fault was not well constrained. The Edale Borehole (some 5 km to the south of the region) penetrated into late Asbian or early Brigantian strata, interpreted to represent bioclastic turbidites derived from the Derbyshire Carbonate Platform (Gutteridge, 1991), and thus indicates a basinal setting at least during late Dinantian times. The southern bounding fault of the basin was therefore assumed to lie south of the Edale Borehole, the whole basinal area to the north of the Derbyshire Carbonate Platform being referred to as the Edale Basin (for example Lee, 1988; Gutteridge, 1991). However the seismic reflection data indicate the presence of a large, down-to-the north, normal fault (Figure 18), here termed the Alport Fault, which lies to the north of the Edale Borehole and divides the Edale Basin into two, the northern part being termed the Alport

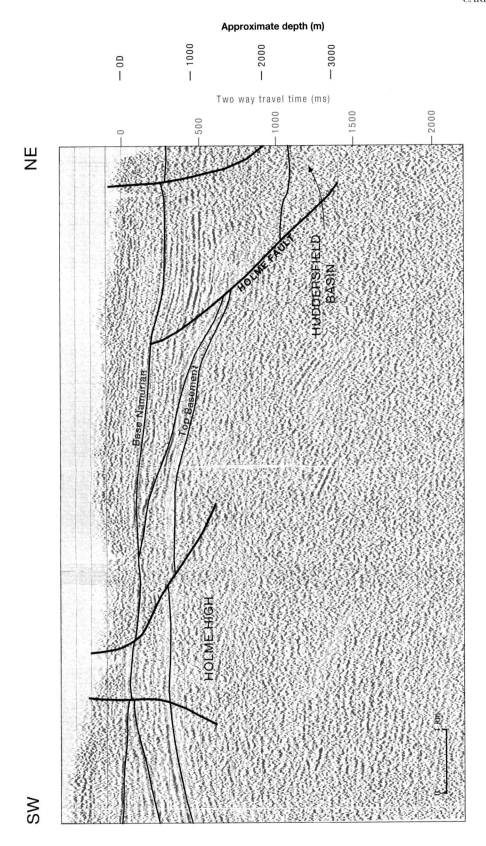

Figure 17 Seismic reflection profile across the Holme High. Note Dinantian platform carbonate build-up.

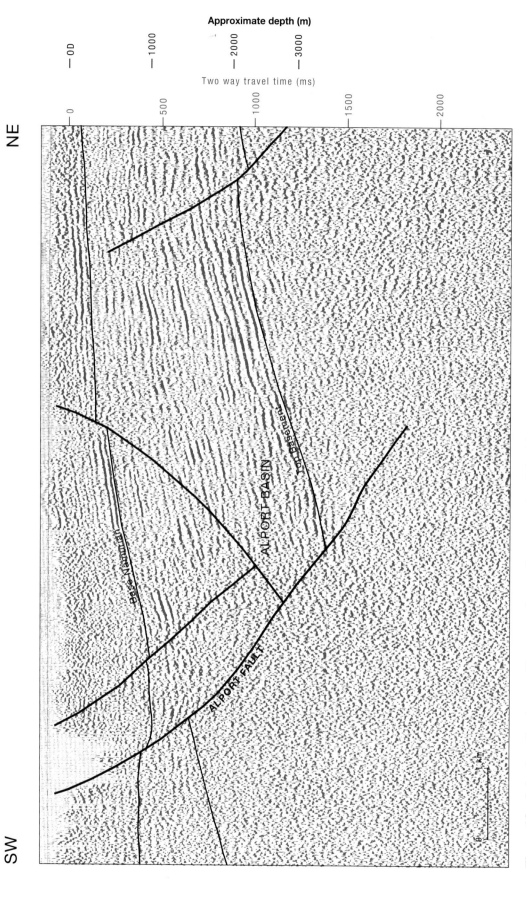

Figure 18   Seismic reflection profile across the southern margin of the Alport Basin and the Alport Fault.

Basin. The basin may pass eastwards into the Gainsborough Trough.

The basin is interpreted to contain more than 3000 m of Dinantian strata, thickest close to the Alport Fault (Map 4). The Alport Borehole bottomed in strata of Arundian age at a depth of 778.8 m. Thus the bulk of the basin-fill must be Arundian or older. Gutteridge (1991) suggests that parts of the Dinantian basin-fill were derived from the contemporaneous carbonate platform on the Holme High to the north.

Gainsborough Trough

The westernmost part of this major Dinantian basin impinges upon the south-eastern corner of the region (Figure 14, Regional Cross-section D–D′). The basin has the overall form of north-west-trending, north-east-deepening asymmetrical graben, bounded to the north-east by the Morley–Campsall Fault. In the region, Dinantian thicknesses in the trough barely exceed 2500 m (Map 4), but to the south-east more than 4000 m of Dinantian strata are likely to be present (Fraser and Gawthorpe, 1990).

Askern–Spittal High

This feature (Figure 14) forms the uplifted footwall-block of the Morley–Campsall Fault, lying to the north of the Gainsborough Trough. It is not well developed within the region, culminating farther east.

Cheshire Basin

In the extreme south of the region the Carboniferous basin configuration is poorly understood but it seems likely that a Dinantian basinal area lies to the south of the Heywood High, beneath the Permo-Triassic Cheshire Basin (Regional Cross-section A–A′). Hereabouts, a thick, largely complete Carboniferous sequence underlies Permo-Triassic strata (Figure 19), the base of the Dinantian lying at considerable depth (over 5000 m in places).

Formby Basin

The north-east-trending Formby Basin forms the south-westerly continuation of the Bowland Basin, beneath Permo-Triassic cover (Regional Cross-section B–B′). The basin is demarcated to the south-east by the Pendle Fault System. The base of the Carboniferous succession is poorly constrained, but may lie at considerable depth, locally in excess of 6000 m (Map 1). Dinantian thicknesses, also poorly constrained, may be comparable to the Bowland Basin to the north-east (Map 4). Like the Bowland Basin, the Formby Basin suffered strong Variscan inversion, Dinantian strata coming to subcrop beneath the Permo-Triassic cover (Map 5).

Rainford Basin

This poorly understood basin lies in the extreme south-west of the region (Figure 14). The base of the Carboniferous succession may lie at depths greater than 4000 m, but this is very poorly constrained. The basin may be contiguous with the thick Carboniferous deposits beneath the northern part of the Cheshire Basin.

Major faults

Kendal Fault

This north–south-trending, down-to-the-west, normal fault marks the eastern margin of the South Lake District High, faulting Dinantian strata against Lower Palaeozoic basement rocks (Figure 2, Figure 14, Map 1). Its displacement history is uncertain, but it is likely to have controlled Dinantian sedimentation to some extent. It passes southwards into the Hutton Monocline (p.58) which downthrows to the east, suggesting a significant component of Variscan reversal; lying roughly parallel to the nearby Dent Fault System, it may well have a similar structural history.

Dent Fault System

The north-north-west-trending Dent Fault System marks the western margin of the Askrigg Block, separating it from the Lower Palaeozoic basement rocks of the Lake District Block (Figure 2, Figure 14). In the region, the fault is composed of a number of vertical to steeply westwards-dipping planes; at the surface it is a reverse fault and downthrows to the east. As preserved, the fault is thus predominantly a Variscan feature and is described more fully on p.57. The early Carboniferous (extensional) history of the fault cannot be fully assessed, because of the lack of a complete section of preserved Carboniferous strata on its hanging-wall block. However the presence of possibly Chadian, alluvial fan deposits (the Sedburgh Conglomerate; Underhill et al., 1988), on its hanging-wall block, suggest that at least the southern part of the fault system was active, with a westerly downthrow, in early Carboniferous times. North–south or north-north-west–south-south-east extension acting on the fault system would have produced either highly oblique dextral transtension or strike-slip displacements. Thus the fault system may have played a significant transfer role during basin development, possibly helping to link extension in the Stainmore Trough with that in the Bowland Basin.

Stockdale Fault

Close to the northern limit of the region, the Stockdale Fault (Figure 14) forms, at the surface, a roughly east-trending system of minor faults and folds, with an overall downthrow generally to the north known as the Stockdale Disturbance (Dunham and Wilson, 1985). The nature of the structure at depth is unknown, but it has been proposed as marking the northern margin of the Askrigg Block on the basis of gravity data (Bott, 1967). Certainly, the northern margin of the Askrigg Block is likely to be faulted (Collier, 1991), because northward extrapolation of sedimentary dips on the block cannot account for the great thicknesses of strata preserved in the Stainmore Trough, a short distance to the north (Chadwick et al., 1995). Collier (1991) introduced the term Stockdale Fault for the structure and estimated a northerly downthrow of some 3000 m the base of the Carboniferous. Here we consider displacements up to 1000 m across the Stockdale Fault to be more likely, although other associated faults with northerly downthrows are probably also present in the subsurface.

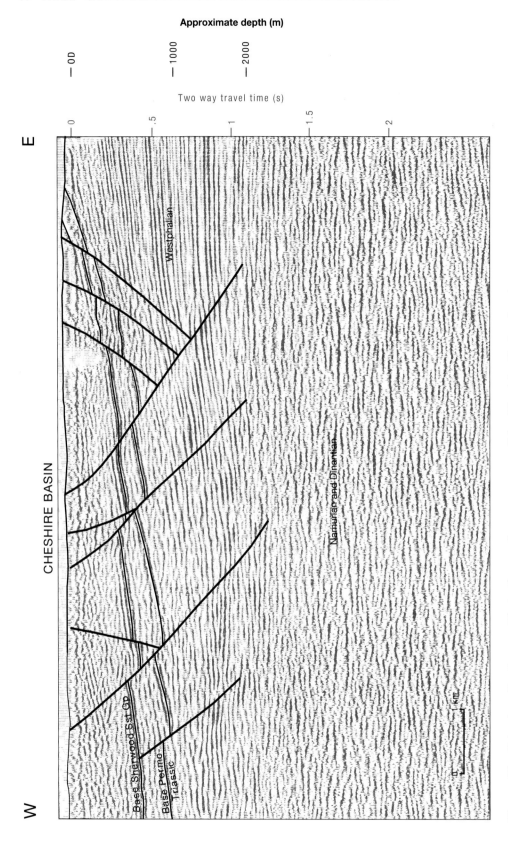

Figure 19   Seismic reflection profile in the northernmost part of the Cheshire Basin, showing Permo-Triassic strata unconformably overlying a thick Carboniferous sequence (strongly layered reflections correspond to Westphalian strata).

North–Middle Craven Fault System

The North–Middle Craven Fault System, forming the southern margin of the Askrigg Block, is one of the longest structures in the region, stretching some 70 km from the Dent Fault System in the west to the Stainmore Trough in the east (Figure 2, Figure 14, Regional Cross-sections B–B′ and C–C′). Our understanding of the fault system is based on detailed surface mapping (for example Arthurton et al., 1988), and seismic reflection data.

The fault system is best exposed in the Settle district where lower Palaeozoic basement rocks locally form its footwall outcrop (Figure 2, Map 1). Here the North Craven Fault forms a complex of subparallel fractures, which probably dip steeply to the south. The fault throws the Malham Formation (late Holkerian–Asbian) down to the south by as much as 160 m (Arthurton et al., 1988). Displacement of the fault at depth hereabouts is uncertain, but is likely to be much greater than that at outcrop. The Middle Craven Fault in the Settle district is rather better understood. The fault has a steep to moderate (locally down to 45°) southerly dip. It throws the Malham Formation down to the south by some 300 m, and the top of the Chapel House Limestone about 400 m, indicative of pre-Brigantian syndepositional normal displacements. Arundian to Holkerian normal displacement is inferred from the abrupt southward thickening of the Kilnsey Formation. Minor reversal in early Brigantian times is indicated by northwards thickening of the Lower Hawes Limestone. Renewed normal displacement took place in late Brigantian times, with Bowland Shales lapping against a contemporaneous south-facing fault scarp. There is also evidence for intra-Pendleian and post-Pendleian movements on the fault.

To the east of the Settle district, the North and Middle Craven faults coalesce to form a single large fault. In the Pateley Bridge district, the fault has not been mapped in detail at the surface, but it is well illustrated by seismic reflection data (Figure 20). It is a subplanar normal fault dipping to the south at about 50°. The throw on the fault hereabouts is somewhat uncertain because of difficulty in identifying the base Carboniferous seismic reflector, but is estimated at about 1800 m (Map 1). The thickness of the Dinantian succession increases threefold southwards across the fault, from about 800 m on the Askrigg Block to more than 2200 m in the Harrogate Basin (Map 4), indicative of large Dinantian syndepositional displacements. It is likely that much of this thickening took place in early Dinantian times (before and during the deposition of Chatburn Limestone), but this cannot be proved due to the poorly constrained Dinantian stratigraphy. The fault is offset dextrally, by about 3 km, by a steep north-trending transcurrent fault (Figure 20) which may have acted as a transfer fault during basin development. Towards the east of the Pateley Bridge district the fault system splits into a complex of faults commonly *en échelon*. The main fault dips south, throwing the basement some 1000 m down to the south (Figure 21). Here the Dinantian succession also thickens southwards across the fault, though not so markedly as farther west, from about

1400 m on the Askrigg Block to about 2200 m in the Harrogate Basin (Map 4). Eastwards, the throw on the fault gradually diminishes further, to die out in the Harrogate district. The fault also shows much evidence hereabouts of later, presumably Variscan, reversal, Namurian strata showing a present net reverse displacement (Figure 21).

South Craven Fault System

The South Craven Fault System (termed the Gargrave Fault in the Settle district), is a complex, south-westerly throwing structure, which splays south-eastwards from the Middle Craven Fault (Figure 14). Where the fault traverses the north-east part of the Bowland Basin it appears to have played an important transfer role by offsetting the Dinantian depocentres of the Bowland and Harrogate basins (Maps 2 and 4). It also appeared to compartmentalise subsequent Variscan basin inversion, by offsetting the adjacent Lothersdale and Skipton anticlines (see p.47). It should be noted that these large offsets, perhaps a 15 km dextral shift of the Bowland and Harrogate basin depocentres, do not indicate a comparable amount of transcurrent motion on the fault. The offsets were present at the onset of basin formation and have probably been only slightly changed since.

A series of east–west-trending structures, such as the Middle Craven and Winterburn faults, splay eastwards from the South Craven fault, to define the Malham Terrace. Basinwards, to the south-west, a number of similarly throwing faults, including the Lawkland and Gargrave faults (Arthurton et al., 1988), lie roughly parallel to the South Craven Fault System, producing a stepped basin margin between the Bowland Basin and the Malham Terrace. Seismic reflection data acquired across the fault system (Wadge et al., 1983) confirm complex faulting and folding.

Interpretation of the seismic reflection data is difficult within the fault system because of structural complexity and the variable nature of the reflections as basinal stratigraphical units pass northwards into platform facies. Nevertheless, within the Pendleside Limestone, a down-to-the-south-west throw of some 200 m is estimated across the South Craven Fault (Wadge, et al., 1983). It is likely that the throw at the base of the Carboniferous succession is much greater, perhaps being in excess of 1000 m (Map 1). Considerable Dinantian syndepositional movement is thus indicated. Its orientation relative to the presumed extensional stress field suggests that the fault system suffered strongly oblique displacements during basin development, perhaps forming a transfer margin to the Bowland Basin. A hanging-wall anticline to the Gargrave Fault, affecting the Grassington Grit attests to post-Namurian, probably Variscan, fault reversal (Arthurton et al., 1988).

Clitheroe–Abbeystead Fault System

The north-west-trending Clitheroe–Abbeystead Fault System (Brandon et al., 1998) marks the south-western limit of the Bowland High, before passing south-eastwards into the Bowland Basin (Figure 14). The fault system appears to have a long history of movement,

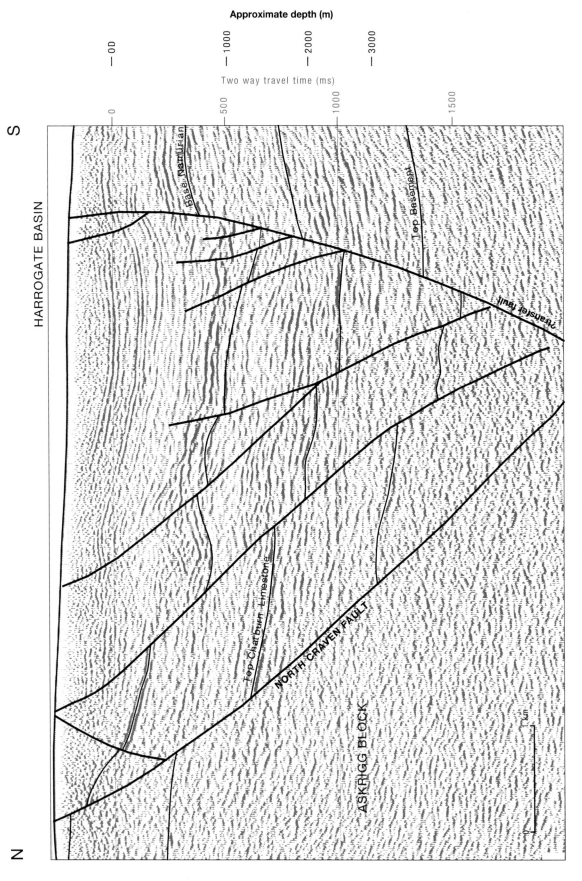

Figure 20   Seismic reflection profile across the North Craven Fault and associated steep transfer fault. Note thickening of Dinantian sequence across fault. Note also minor Variscan reverse fault splaying off the major fault.

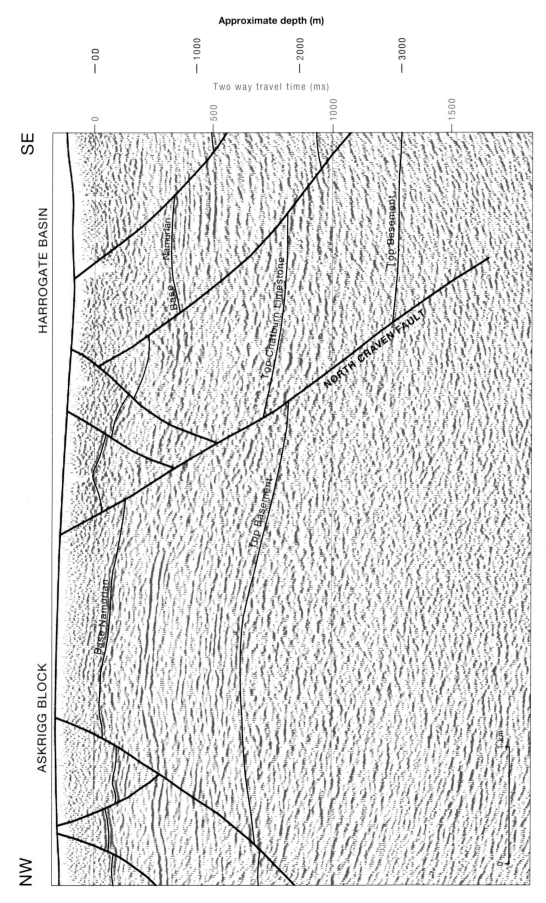

Figure 21 Seismic reflection profile across the North Craven Fault. Note reverse displacement at level of base Namurian, due to Variscan reversal.

clearly affecting Dinantian thicknesses. It has the appearance of a flower-structure on seismic reflection data, which, together with a variable sense of throw along its length, suggest a degree of oblique or transcurrent motion. It appears to sinistrally offset major syndepositional normal faults marking the northern margin of the Bowland Basin. We interpret this offset as indicating that the fault acted in transfer mode during Dinantian basin development, compartmentalising subsidence in the Bowland Basin. The fault also truncates several large inversion anticlines, and clearly acted as a transfer fault during Variscan basin inversion (see p.50).

Barnoldswick Fault

This large intrabasin normal fault (Figure 14) trends west-north-west, and has a large down-to-the-south displacement (Maps 1 and 3) at its eastern end forming an antithetic fault to the Pendle Fault. Its trend is subparallel to the Clitheroe–Abbeystead and South Craven fault systems and it is likely to have suffered strongly oblique displacements during basin development, possibly acting in a transfer role; in places the fault has the appearance on seismic reflection data of a positive flower-structure (Figure 22). The fault truncates the dextrally offset Thornton and Middop anticlines. Earp et al. (1961) took this to indicate 1 km of dextral displacement on the fault, but this is not necessary if the fault acted in a transfer role during basin inversion.

Pendle Fault

The Pendle Fault System (Fraser and Gawthorpe 1990) is a major, concealed, east-north-east-trending, normal fault, probably more than 60 km and perhaps more than 100 km long, which forms the southern margin of the Bowland and Formby basins (Figure 14, Regional Cross- sections A–A′ and B–B′). Seismic reflection data (Figure 15) indicate that the fault system has a large, down-to-the-north throw at the base of the Carboniferous which decreases markedly upwards, indicating syndepositional normal displacement during Dinantian times. In later Carboniferous times the fault experienced only minor normal displacements, but suffered major end-Carboniferous reversal (see p.47). At the margin of the Bowland Basin, present-day displacements at basement level are up to 1200 m (Map 1), but allowing for subsequent Variscan reversal, the original northerly downthrow on the fault system may locally have approached 3000 m. A large component of this occurred in the Dinantian, the Dinantian sequence thickening from about 2000 m on the northern edge of the Central Lancashire High to over 4000 m in the Bowland Basin (Map 4). Where the fault swings south, to mark the south-east margin of the Formby Basin, it may have acted as a major oblique-slip, transfer fault. Here, displacements at basement level are probably considerably in excess of 2000 m down-to-the-north-west (Map 1), though this is due, at least in part, to Permian and younger normal faulting.

Heywood Fault

There is little or no evidence of this fault at surface. Seismic reflection data indicate a roughly east-trending normal fault, separating the Rossendale Basin and the Heywood High (Regional Cross-section A–A′). Displacements at basement level locally reach about 1000 m (Map 1), with a northwards thickening of some 400 m in the Dinantian succession across the fault (Map 4). Normal movements diminished during the Dinantian, after which it was largely inactive prior to Variscan reverse reactivation (see p.61).

Holme Fault

The Holme Fault marks the northern margin of the Holme High (Regional Cross-section C–C′, Figure 17). It is a down-to-the-north normal fault with a maximum throw of around 1100 m at the base of the Dinantian (Map 1). It was active principally in Dinantian times, Dinantian strata thickening northwards across the fault by about 1000 m into the Huddersfield Basin (Map 4). The trend of the fault is poorly constrained, but it is here assumed to correspond to a prominent east–west-trending gravity anomaly.

The Herridge–Bradshaw Fault

The Herridge–Bradshaw Fault is poorly resolved by the existing seismic data but is interpreted as a north-north-east–north-east-trending normal fault, downthrowing to the west and forming the western margin of the Holme High (Figure 14). At surface it has only a small displacement, being mapped as the Herridge–Bradshaw fractures (Bromehead et al., 1933), but at depth it is a much larger structure, with a throw of about 1500 m at the base of the Dinantian (Map 1), and with a corresponding thickening of the Dinantian sequence (Map 4). The Herridge–Bradshaw Fault, together with two smaller subparallel faults, and a regional westerly dip, are interpreted to displace the base of the Dinantian from about 600 m below OD on the Holme High to about 3800 m depth less than 10 km to the south-west (Map 1).

The Morley–Campsall Fault

The Morley–Campsall Fault lies in a poorly understood area separating the Harrogate Basin from the Huddersfield Basin to the south (Figure 14). The fault corresponds to significant gravity and magnetic anomalies, but in the region there is evidence of only a rather small throw, less than 200 m down-to-the-south, at the top of the Dinantian (Map 5). The throw of the fault at the base of the Carboniferous is not known, it is here portrayed as similar to that at the top of the Dinantian (Regional Cross-section C–C′), but, bearing in mind that many major Dinantian synsedimentary faults have much reduced throw at higher levels, it may be much larger than this. There appears to be little significant Silesian synsedimentary movement on the fault in the region.

The Morley–Campsall Fault becomes a demonstrably larger structure to the south-east, where it forms the northern margin of the Gainsborough Trough, separating it from the Askern–Spittal High. The fault is believed to pass north-westwards into the South Craven Fault System, the two faults together forming an important regional transfer structure.

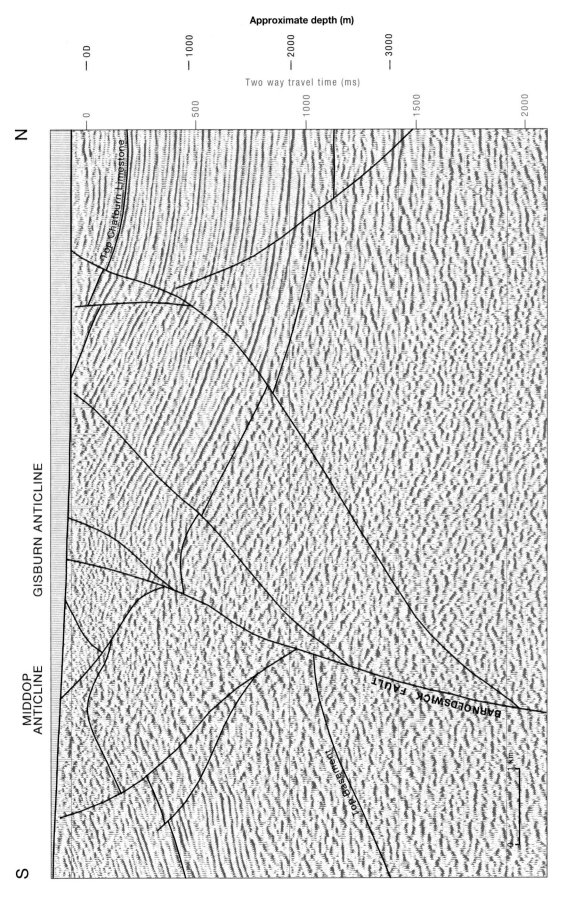

Figure 22 Seismic reflection profile across the Barnoldswick Fault. Note that the fault has the appearance of a positive flower-structure, with Middop and Gisburn anticlines lying between the faults.

Pennine Line

This linear structural feature extends for some 50 km, from the southern margin of the Bowland Basin, to the southern edge of the region (Figure 14). It is poorly understood, being only locally crossed by seismic reflection data, and its influence on Dinantian basin development is uncertain — it may, wholly or in part, be a Variscan structure (see p.60 — Pennine Monocline). In the north, close to the Boulsworth Borehole on the Central Lancashire High, the north–south-trending, westwards verging, Pennine Monocline is underlain by an easterly dipping fault with a reverse, down-to-the-west displacement at the base of the Carboniferous (see p.60). The monocline can be traced southwards at surface (presumably with its underlying fault) as the Todmorden Smash Belt (Wright et al., 1927). Whether the subsurface fault maintains its reverse displacement or whether it passes southwards into a down-to-the-east normal fault is uncertain. Consequently, the role of the Pennine Line during Dinantian basin development is unknown; it may have separated the Rossendale Basin from the Huddersfield Basin to the east. Conversely, the fault and monocline may be wholly Variscan structures, with no earlier history of movement. The Pennine Line passes southwards into the Tame Fault, which downthrows to the west, but the transition is not understood due to the lack of seismic reflection data. Farther south, some authors (for example Lee, 1988; Gawthorpe et al., 1989) recognise a large down-to-the-east normal fault, along the continuation of the Pennine Line, termed the Lask Edge Fault. This putative structure is extrapolated northwards from the Staffordshire area (some 30 km south of the region) on the basis of gravity interpretation and its existence must be regarded as wholly conjectural.

Alport Fault

This newly recognised structure is interpreted as a large, east to east-south-east-trending, down-to-the-north, Dinantian, normal fault forming the southern margin of the Alport Basin (Regional Cross-section C–C′, Figure 18). Its position is well constrained by seismic data; at the base of the Dinantian it is interpreted to lie some 2 km south of the Alport Borehole and 4 km north of the Edale Borehole. At the top of the Dinantian it lies south of the region, some 3 km south of the Alport Borehole and 3 km north of the Edale Borehole. The fault appears to have little significant expression at the surface but has a throw of some 3000 m at the base of the Dinantian (Map 1), almost all of which can be attributed to thickening of the Dinantian succession (Map 4).

VARISCAN BASIN INVERSION

In latest Carboniferous times final closure of the Rheic Ocean culminated in the Variscan Orogeny, which resulted in large-scale thrust and nappe emplacement in northern France, Belgium, southern England, south Wales and southern Ireland, with associated regional crustal shortening. A zone of northerly directed thrusts, known as the Variscan Front, is thought to mark the northern limit of regional Variscan compressional deformation in southern England. Central and northern England lie to the north of the Variscan Front, on the Variscan Foreland, where Variscan deformation was much less pervasive, being largely restricted to the reversal of pre-existing Dinantian normal faults and associated basin inversion (Figure 23). The main Variscan movements in the region postdate the preserved Westphalian rocks and predate deposition of the Permian strata which rest unconformably on the Carboniferous beds. Dating the precise onset of the main Variscan movements is difficult, evidence from central England (Glover et al., 1993) suggests that inversion may have commenced as early as Bolsovian times. Moreover, as discussed above, it is likely that even earlier, minor episodes of compression influenced patterns of Silesian sedimentation.

Principal inversion structures

The Variscan origin of many of the structures described below cannot strictly be proved, except where these structures are overlain by undeformed Permo-Triassic strata. It is possible that some structures formed much later, during Cenozoic (Alpine) compression; it is certainly likely that many of the Variscan structures were to some degree modified by an Alpine overprint.

Variscan deformation in the region is most evident in the Ribblesdale Foldbelt, which lies between the Askrigg Block to the north and the Central Lancashire High to the south, deforming the sedimentary-fills of the Bowland Basin and, to a lesser degree, the northern part of the Harrogate Basin. The Ribblesdale Foldbelt extends east-north-east–west-south-west for at least 80 m and is up to 25 km wide (Figure 23). It may well mark a fundamental line of basement weakness, coinciding with the possible locus of maximum lithospheric thinning in the Dinantian (see above). The foldbelt comprises an *en échelon* set of north-east-trending anticlines with broad intervening synclines. The anticlines are mostly between 5 and 10 km long and most are asymmetrical. This characteristic asymmetry, together with seismic reflection evidence, indicates that the anticlines formed by (oblique) reversal of earlier (Dinantian) normal faults. Large structures, such as the Pendle Monocline, formed by reversal of major basin-controlling normal faults, smaller structures formed by reversal of less important intra-basin faults. Horizontal shortening across the foldbelt was estimated to be about 10 per cent by Arthurton (1984).

Arthurton (1984) identified unconformities in the cores of many of these folds in the Bowland area. He argued that this demonstrated syndepositional folding and concluded that the structures were established principally in late Chadian to Pendleian times. The seismic data show however, that any syndepositional development of the anticlines was insignificant compared to subsequent Variscan deformation.

A distinction can perhaps be drawn between the style of deformation in the Ribblesdale Foldbelt and elsewhere in the region. Away from the foldbelt, Variscan shortening is manifest by reverse, or oblique-reverse dis-

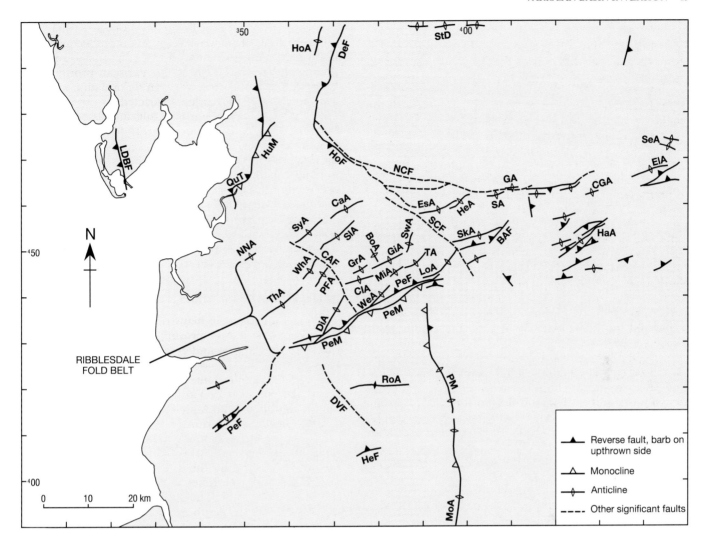

Figure 23 Principal Variscan (end-Carboniferous) structures of the region.

BAF Bolton Abbey Fault; BoA Bolton Anticline; CaA Catlow Anticline; CAF Clitheroe–Abbeystead Fault; CGA Cayton Gill Anticline; ClA Clitheroe Anticline; DeF Dent Fault; DiA Dinkley Anticline; DVF Darwen Valley Fault; ElA Ellenthorpe Anticline; EsA Eshton Anticline; GiA Gisburn Anticline; GA Grindleton Anticline; GA Greenhow Anticline; HaA Harrogate Anticline; HeA Hetton Anticline; HeF Heywood Fault; HoA Howgills Anticline; HoF Hollintree Fault; HuM Hutton Monocline; LDBF Lake District Boundary Fault System; LoA Lothersdale Anticline; MiA Middop Anticline; MoA Mossley Anticline NCF Nicky Nook Anticline; PeF Pendle Fault System; PeM Pennine Monocline; PM Pendle Monocline; PFA Plantation Farm Anticline; QuT Quernmore Thrust; RoA Rossendale Anticline; SA Skyrholme Anticline; SCF South Craven Fault; SeA Sessay Anticline; SkA Skipton Anticline; SlA Slaidburn Anticline; StD Stockdale Disturbance; SwA Swinden Anticline; SyA Sykes Anticline; TA Thornton Anticline; ThA Thornley Anticline; WeA Wheatley Anticline; WhA Whitewell Anticline.

placements along reactivated lines of earlier faulting. The obliquity of displacement on any particular reactivated fault, would have depended on the orientation of the fault relative to the shortening direction. Thus, reverse displacements, particularly pronounced on north–south-trending features such as the Dent Line and the Pennine Monocline (see below), indicate a component of regional east–west shortening. This is consistent with the prevailing geometry of inversion structures to the north of the region (Chadwick et al., 1995). A more detailed study of faults and joints in the Lancaster

district (Brandon et al., 1998), advocated east-south-east–west-north-west regional Variscan shortening. On the basis of fold distribution, Arthurton (1988) argued that the Ribblesdale Foldbelt developed principally in response to dextral shear, rather than regional shortening. Certainly, transpressive structures are locally well developed in the foldbelt (for example the Lothersdale Anticline p.47). It may well be the case that regional shortening resulted in relative movements of the Askrigg Block and the central Lancashire High. As a consequence, the Bowland and, to a lesser extent, the Harrogate basins, sandwiched between these two relatively rigid blocks may well have suffered quite severe local shear stresses, which led to the development of the Ribblesdale Foldbelt.

The amount of erosion in the region attributable to Variscan uplift was considerable (Figure 24). Erosion was least severe (typically less than 1000 m of removed strata) in the south-east and southern parts of the region, where thick Westphalian successions are still preserved beneath Permo-Triassic cover. The Askrigg and Lake District blocks did not suffer basin inversion, but rather experienced regional peneplanation prior to the onset of Permo-Triassic deposition. Elsewhere, typically more than 1500 m of strata were removed. Erosion was most severe in the Ribblesdale Foldbelt, which was associated with strong inversion of the Bowland Basin and, to a lesser degree, parts of the Harrogate Basin. Here, locally up to 4000 m of strata may have been removed in anticlinal cores. These large amounts of uplift, again point to regional crustal shortening as the overall Variscan tectonic regime.

INVERSION STRUCTURES OF THE RIBBLESDALE FOLDBELT

Three major structures of the Ribblesdale Foldbelt are associated with inversion of the southern margin of the Bowland Basin and are described below:

Pendle Monocline

This major, east-north-east-trending feature, traceable for some 40 km along the southern margin of the Bowland Basin (Figure 23), is the largest inversion structure in the region (Regional Cross-sections A–A' and B–B', Figure 15). At its south-western end the monocline gradually dies out in a zone of complex faulting associated with the edge of the Permo-Triassic West Lancashire Basin. At its eastern end, the monocline passes into the southern limb of the Lothersdale Anticline (Figure 23) which takes over as the principal inversion structure on the southern edge of the Bowland Basin. The Pendle Monocline faces south, folding late Dinantian, Namurian and Westphalian strata (Wright et al., 1927; Arthurton, 1984; Fraser and Gawthorpe, 1990). In the Clitheroe district, nearly 3000 m

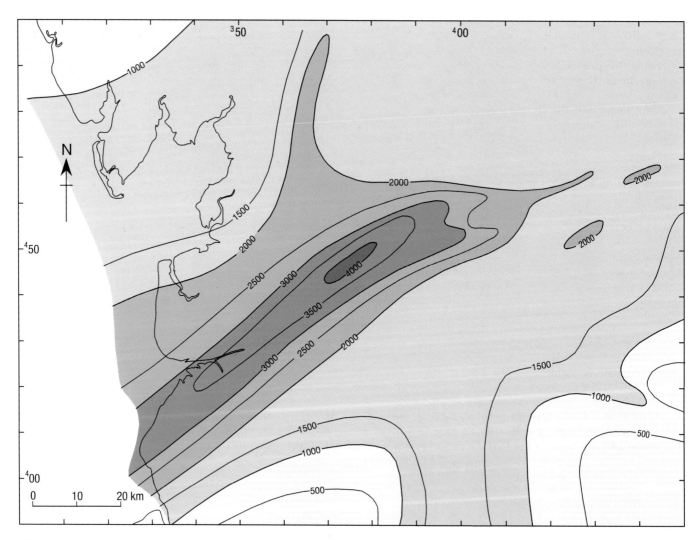

Figure 24   Estimated thickness of strata (metres) removed by erosion following Variscan uplift (modified after Fraser and Gawthorpe, 1990).

of Dinantian to Westphalian strata, dipping at 50–70°, crop out in a distance of less than 5 km. The fold amplitude is more than 1000 m along much of its length and locally up to 2000 m, displacing strata down-to-the-south. The monocline formed by Variscan reversal of the down-to-the-north Pendle Fault System which it overlies (Figure 15). The subsurface structure of the monocline is quite complex and varies along its length (Figure 25). The southern limb is commonly cut by down-to-the-north reverse faults which propagate upwards from the Pendle Fault at depth (Figures 15 and 25). In places it has a well-developed axial crest with a significant northern limb, forming the Dinkley Anticline (Figure 25). Farther south, in the Formby Basin, the Pendle Fault shows signs of minor reversal during Brigantian times with the development of syndepositional folds (Figure 43).

Lothersdale Anticline

This large structure (Figure 23) crops out in the Clitheroe district (Earp et al., 1961) and is mapped with a roughly north-east axial trend, its southern limb passing south-westwards into the Pendle Monocline. It is partially truncated at its western end by the Barnoldswick Fault, and truncated at its eastern end by the South Craven Fault, which offsets it from the Skipton Anticline to the north-east. Outcrop evidence of the structure is rather poor, but indicates the presence of a large, north-east-trending down-to-the-north-west reverse fault cutting the north-west limb of the fold. Seismic reflection data reveal that the anticline lies above the north-east-dipping Pendle Fault (Figure 26) which forms the southern margin of the Bowland Basin. In detail however, the subsurface structure of the anticline is complex and not fully understood. In its central part, the Lothersdale Anticline comprises a tight, roughly symmetrical fold cut by reverse faults on both limbs, and in its axial core (Figure 26a). To the west the anticline becomes broader and less symmetrical, its south-east limb being steeper and larger than the north-east limb (Figure 26b). Maximum fold amplitude of the structure approaches 1500m. Overall, the Lothersdale Anticline has the appearance of a positive flower-structure, indicative of transpressional deformation. It lies in the hanging-wall block of the normal, down-to-the-north Pendle Fault, and presumably resulted from oblique-reversal of that fault.

Skipton Anticline

North-east of the South Craven Fault System the easternmost part of the Bowland Basin has been strongly inverted, the Skipton Anticline forming the major inversion structure at the southern margin (Figure 23). This complex but poorly understood structure is of considerable importance because the rocks exposed in its core provide insights into the nature and thickness of the Dinantian succession hereabouts. There are no seismic data in the vicinity and knowledge of the anticline is based exclusively on outcrop information (Hudson and Mitchell, 1937; Arthurton, 1983). The anticline trends east-north-east for some 11 km, bounded to the west by the South Craven Fault System, with the Bolton Abbey Fault at its eastern end. The structure is roughly symmetrical, the northern limb showing a steady moderate to steep dip, but the southern limb is

more complex with subsidiary folding. The axial trace of the anticline is roughly co-incident with the Skipton Rock Fault, a steep north-north-west-dipping reverse fault, which probably formed contemporaneously with the main folding episode. Judging from the cross-section in Hudson and Mitchell (1937, fig. 9), the amplitude of the main fold is probably in excess of 1500 m. The subsurface structure of the anticline is a matter for conjecture. The nature of the north-east-trending Bolton Abbey Fault, which marks the eastern end of the anticline, may be of some importance. The fault has a large, down-to-the-south-east throw at surface, but its subsurface nature is poorly understood. Hudson and Mitchell (1937) indicate a lack of evidence that it is anything other than a simple tensional fault, but it is considered here that the steep south-eastwards dips, immediately to the north-west of the fault are characteristic of transpressional hanging-wall deformation. This, and the fact that it cuts Namurian strata, suggest that the Bolton Abbey Fault may be a reverse fault of Variscan age, dipping to the north-west. Thus, the Skipton Anticline may be interpreted as similar to the Lothersdale Anticline to the south-west, lying in the hanging-wall block of a partially concealed, north-west-dipping, reversed, normal fault (Map 5). This fault would be interpreted as forming the easterly continuation of the Pendle Fault, with the Skipton Anticline being viewed as the strongly inverted eastern extremity of the Bowland Basin. The extent to which the top Lower Palaeozoic basement surface was folded is uncertain here (Map 1) it is portrayed as being quite sharply flexured, in rough concordance with overlying strata, but it may be the case, as with inversion structures elsewhere in the region, that folding was restricted to the shallower parts of the succession.

Evidence of structural discordance between the small-scale folds on the southern limb of the anticline, and the broader folding of Namurian strata around the edge of the structure led Hudson and Mitchell (1937) to propose that the main structural development of the anticline took place in Brigantian times. This was broadly supported by Arthurton (1983) who considered it to be broadly contemporaneous with Dinantian unconformities developed in other folds of the Ribblesdale Foldbelt. Moseley (1962) challenged this view, he considered that the small- and large-scale folding was contemporaneous (any discordance being due to disharmonic folding), and, by implication, Variscan (end-Carboniferous) in age. Moseley's interpretation is favoured here. Seismic profiles through similar structures elsewhere in the Ribblesdale Foldbelt, suggest that whilst some earlier Carboniferous folding may have occurred, particularly in Brigantian times (for example reversal of the Middle Craven Fault), this was of minor importance compared to end-Carboniferous (Variscan) deformation.

Inversion structures associated with inversion at the northern margin of the Bowland Basin are described below:

Whitewell Anticline

The north-east-trending Whitewell Anticline (Figure 23) lies to the north-east of the Thornley Anticline in an *en échelon* relationship. It has a highly irregular periclinal

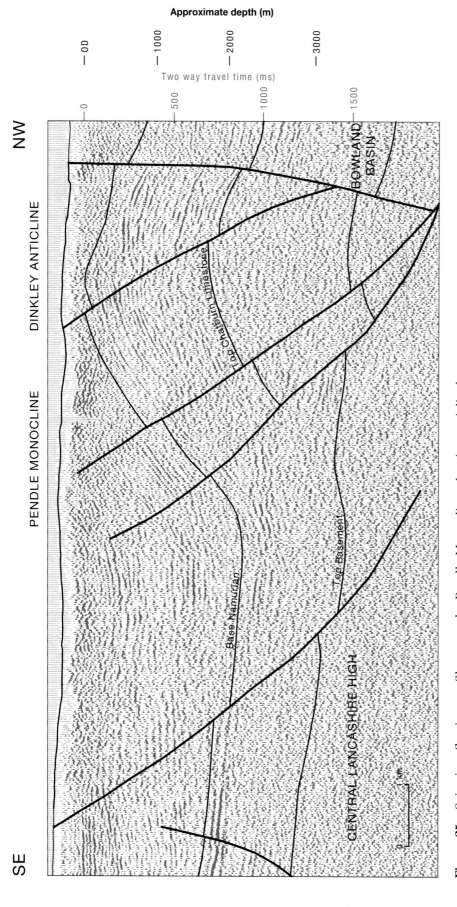

Figure 25   Seismic reflection profile across the Pendle Monocline, showing anticlinal culmination as the Dinkley Anticline.

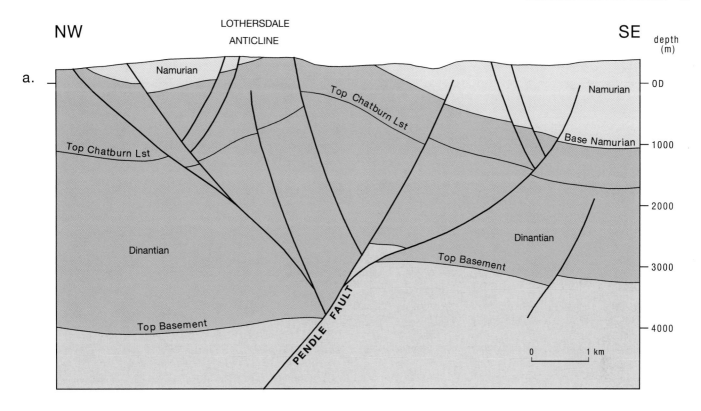

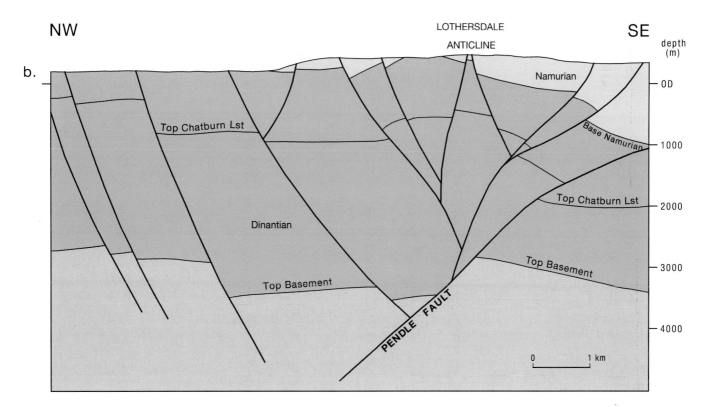

Figure 26   Cross-sections through the Lothersdale Anticline, based on seismic reflection data
a. central part b. western end.

form, comprising three sub-ordinate *en échelon* anticlines (Aitkenhead et al., 1992). It lies in the hanging-wall block of the postulated Whitewell Fault, a large down-to-the-south-east normal fault, which forms the northern margin of the Bowland Basin hereabouts, and presumably formed by reversal of this structure during Variscan basin inversion (Figure 27a).

Thornley Anticline

The Thornley Anticline (Figure 23) trends north-east, is at least 11 km long, and may extend farther to the south-west beneath Permo-Triassic cover. At its eastern end the anticline passes *en échelon* into the Whitewell and Plantation Farm anticlines. Surface exposures are sparse but indicate small west-verging folds superimposed upon the main fold (Aitkenhead et al., 1992). In the subsurface, the anticline forms a slightly asymmetrical north-west-verging structure whose amplitude may locally exceed 1000 m (Figure 27b). It lies in the hanging-wall block of the postulated Thornley Fault, a large normal fault, downthrowing to the south-east which forms the northern margin of the Bowland Basin hereabouts, and presumably formed by reversal of this structure during Variscan basin inversion.

Plantation Farm Anticline

The Plantation Farm Anticline (Figure 23) is parallel to the Whitewell Anticline, lying to its south-east. The structure is developed in an argillaceous, fissile part of the Dinantian sequence, and is correspondingly tight and narrow with a north-west-vergence and a steep, locally cleaved, north-west limb (Aitkenhead et al., 1992). In the subsurface, the anticline lies in the hanging-wall block of the down-to-the-north Doeford Reverse Fault. Both structures presumably developed by reversal of the easterly continuation of the subsurface Thornley Fault during Variscan basin inversion (Figure 27b).

The Whitewell and Plantation Farm anticlines may be truncated to the north-east by the transverse Clitheroe–Abbeysteads Fault Zone, which offsets sinistrally the northern margin of the Bowland Basin several kilometres to the north-west. North-east of this, the basin margin is marked in the subsurface by the Bowland Line, which is associated with two large inversion structures.

Sykes Anticline

The Sykes Anticline trends north-east for some 8 km (Figure 23). It is terminated to the south-west by the Clitheroe–Abbeysteads Fault System (known locally as the Mellor Knoll Fault, Aitkenhead et al., 1992) and may pass north-eastwards into the Catlow Anticline. The internal structure of the anticline is complex with a disharmonic relationship between the upper part of the fold, developed in Pendle Grit, and lower levels involving Dinantian strata, due to a structurally weak layer of Bowland Shales between (Moseley, 1962). Strong asymmetry and north-west-vergence is characteristic of the anticline at deeper levels. The anticline lies above the Bowland Line (Figure 27c), which corresponds to a postulated down-to-the-south-east normal fault forming the northern margin of the Bowland Basin hereabouts, and pre-

sumably developed by reversal of this structure during Variscan basin inversion.

Catlow Anticline

The Catlow Anticline is an north-east-trending structure, some 10 km long and lying roughly along strike from the Sykes Anticline to the south-west (Figure 23). It forms an asymmetrical pericline, with a steeper, locally vertical, north-west limb (Arthurton et al., 1988). Subsidiary folds are superimposed on the main structure. There is evidence of a north-east-trending down-to-the-north reverse fault cutting the north-west limb. The fault and fold presumably formed roughly synchronously, the fold developing in the hanging-wall of the fault during reverse displacement. The structure is also cut by north-west-trending cross-faults. It is believed that the anticline formed by reversal of the fault corresponding to the Bowland Line, in a manner similar to formation of the Sykes Anticline. Arthurton et al., (1988) cite evidence that the fold formed in Namurian times. Whilst folding of Namurian age cannot be ruled out, it is considered here that most of the folding was probably later than this, of end-Carboniferous (Variscan) age.

Within the Bowland Basin itself there are several important inversion structures, formed by the reversal of intrabasin normal faults.

Dinkley Anticline

The Dinkley Anticline, some 15 km in length, lies near the southern margin of the Bowland Basin, close to the Pendle Monocline (Figure 23). In its western half, the anticline trends east-north-east and has the form of a faulted positive flower-structure (Figure 25), the Pendle Monocline forming its southern limb. Farther east the Dinkley Anticline diverges from the Pendle Monocline, trending north-east into the Bowland Basin to produce a large indentation in the base Namurian outcrop (Map 6).

Slaidburn Anticline

This large inversion structure (Figure 23) brings Dinantian strata to crop in its core. Seismic reflection data are limited to one or two lines, the quality of which are poor and the interpretation is equivocal (Regional Cross-section A–A', Figure 28). Two faults appear to underlie the anticline, throwing to the north-west and the south-east. The main fault is not clear but from the attitude of the anticline and the down-to-the-north thrust on the north-western limb, the south-easterly throwing fault on the northern side of the anticline may be assumed to have controlled the development of the structure during any compressive/transpressive phases.

Clitheroe Anticline

This major east-north-east-trending structure (Figure 23) is markedly asymmetrical with a steeper, locally overturned, northern limb. The anticline lies in the hanging-wall block of a large, east-north-east-trending, low-angle, down-to-the-north, reverse fault; the Horrocksford Hall Thrust (Figure 29). The fault and fold presumably formed roughly synchronously, the fold developing in the hanging-wall of the fault during reverse displacement. The throw on the

Figure 27 Cross-sections through inversion structures at the northern margin of the Bowland Basin
a. Whitewell and Plantation Farm anticlines (adapted from Aitkenhead et al., 1992)
b. Thornley Anticline (adapted from Aitkenhead et al., 1992)
c. Sykes Anticline (adapted from Moseley, 1962).

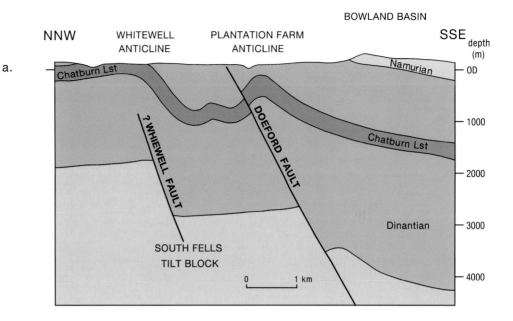

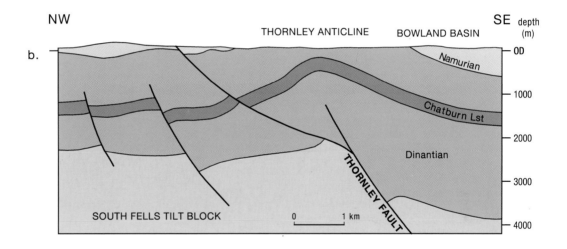

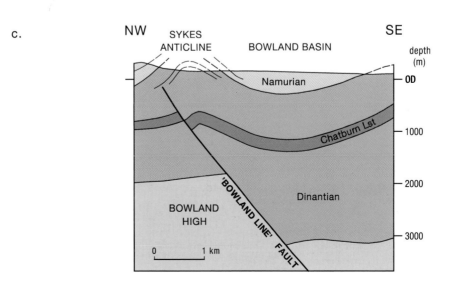

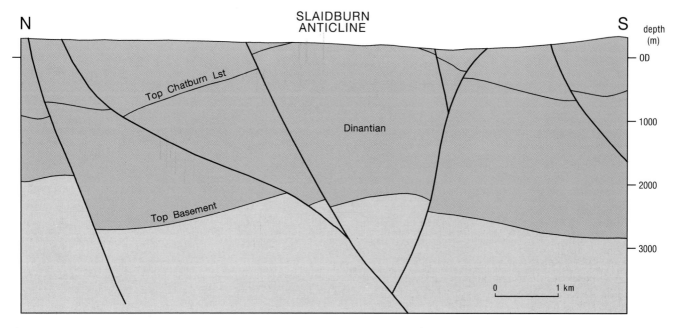

Figure 28   Cross-section through the Slaidburn Anticline.

Horrocksford Hall Thrust is estimated to be at least 450 m along much of its outcrop and locally more than 650 m (Earp et al., 1961). In some parts the reversal of this fault may have been sufficient to cause significant reverse displacement at the base of the Carboniferous (Figure 29). The amount of north-north-west-directed shortening associated with this structure was therefore considerable. Viewed on a larger scale, the south-east-dipping Horrocksford Hall Thrust may intersect the Pendle Fault at depth, in an antithetic manner (Regional Cross-section A–A′). The Clitheroe Anticline can therefore be viewed as the northern limb of a large asymmetrical 'pop-up' structure (Figure 30) which formed in the hanging-wall block of the Pendle Fault, the Pendle Monocline forming the (larger) southern limb. On seismic reflection data, this pop-up structure has the form of a positive flower-structure, with a splay of several north-directed reverse faults, underlying the Horrocksford Hall Thrust and coming to outcrop farther north. One of these faults underlies and controlled development of the Grindleton Anticline.

Grindleton Anticline

This east-north-east-trending asymmetrical structure (Figure 23) has a steeper northern limb which is cut by reverse faults downthrowing to the north. Faulting and folding presumably developed roughly synchronously, the fold forming in the hanging-wall of the faults during reverse displacement. Seismic reflection data suggest that the reverse faults dip southwards to link at depth with the Pendle Fault and to form a large 'pop-up' structure in its hanging-wall block (Figure 30).

Wheatley Anticline

A major perturbation in the outcrop patterns occurs in the area between the Clitheroe Anticline and the Pendle Monocline. This previously unnamed structure, trending north-east, lies *en échelon* with the Dinkley and Lothersdale anticlines all of which are located immediately to the north of the Pendle Monocline (Figure 23). It is here termed the Wheatley Anticline, being a somewhat complex (possibly composite) structure with an essentially box-fold style (Figures 30 and 31), plunging to the east and south-south-west. It provides a structural window, bringing Dinantian strata to crop in its core, within an area of Namurian strata. The western limb of the southerly plunging component is associated with a high-angle fault, interpreted from the seismic reflection data as trending north-north-east. The structural style has characteristics of a positive flower structure (Figure 31), the implication being that the fold was generated in a zone of transpressive deformation.

Gisburn–Swinden Anticline

This composite structure, some 12 km in length, comprising the Swinden and Gisburn anticlines, lies *en échelon* with the Clitheroe Anticline (Figure 23). The two folds form a structure which trends east-north-east in the west, swinging round to the north-east, farther east. There is a variation in structural style and complexity along its length, but it essentially comprises an anticline developed in the hanging-wall of a reverse fault (Figure 32). To the north-east, the Swinden Anticline forms what appears to be a positive flower-structure which changes near to the Gargrave Fault into a form which more resembles a negative flower-structure.

To the south-west, the Gisburn Anticline is cut by the complex Barnoldswick Fault System. Notably, seismic reflection data hereabouts (Figure 22) show that the lower Dinantian sequence does not show pronounced stratigraphical thinning over the crest of the structure.

Figure 29 Seismic reflection profile across the Clitheroe Anticline and the Horrocksford Hall Thrust.

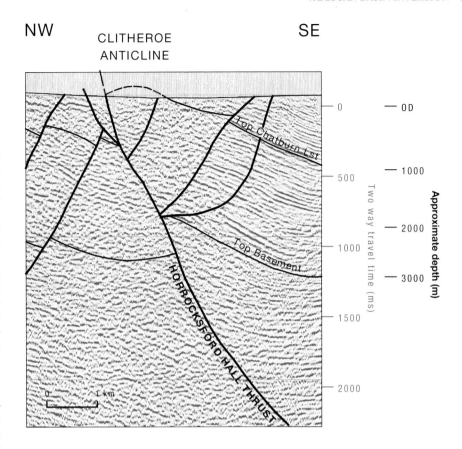

Middop Anticline

The Middop Anticline trends north-east (Figure 23), and is cut off to the south-west and north-east by the Middop and Barnoldswick faults respectively. The structure is poorly imaged on the seismic reflection data, presumably the result of its close proximity to the structurally complex fault zone. It is interpreted to lie between the Barnoldswick Fault and the Middop Fault (here interpreted to be a small north-west-trending, down-to-the-west reverse fault) with the structural characteristics of a positive flower structure (Figure 22).

Thornton Anticline

The Thornton Anticline is an north-east-trending structure parallel to and north-west of the Lothersdale Anticline (Figure 23). It is a tight asymmetrical fold, with a steeper south-east limb, vertical in places with superimposed subsidiary folds. The subsurface nature of the anticline is uncertain. It is unclear whether, like most of the folds hereabouts, it formed by reversal of an underlying fault, or whether it is associated with transcurrent movement on the nearby Barnoldswick Fault.

Bolton Anticline

This small, previously unnamed anticline, situated to the north of the Gisburn–Swinden Anticline, has not been recognised at outcrop, but is clearly seen on the seismic data (Figure 33) in the region of Bolton-by-Bowland. The trend of the fold is not well-constrained because the seismic data are sparse, but the fold appears to trend north-north-west. The anticline lies in the hanging-wall block of what is interpreted to be a northerly throwing normal fault which has suffered some subsequent reversal. This reversal of the fault was not sufficient to reverse the throw, either at the top of the Chatburn Limestone or at the top of the basement. The structure is particularly noteworthy in showing a lack of stratigraphical thinning of Dinantian strata over the crest of the structure, which demonstrates that the fold did not form in early Dinantian times.

Several small inversion structures lie close to, but beyond the Bowland Basin proper.

Nicky Nook Anticline

Situated in the northern part of the South Fells Tilt-block (Figure 23), the Nicky Nook Anticline is an asymmetric east-north-east-trending structure, verging to the south (Aitkenhead et al., 1992). The isolated position of this structure and the steepness of its limbs makes its continuation in the subsurface uncertain, but its development is presumably related to the reverse reactivation of underlying normal faults.

Eshton and Hetton anticlines

These structures form asymmetrical east-north-east-trending folds with steep northern limbs. The Eshton Anticline is truncated to the south-west by the South Craven Fault System (termed the Gargrave Fault hereabouts). The anticlines are cut by and oblique to the Winterburn Fault and pass across it on to the Malham Terrace. The mode of formation of these structures is uncertain, but is presumably related to transpressional reversal of the complex basin margin hereabouts.

The eastern part of the Ribblesdale Foldbelt comprises structures which developed by fault-reactivation during inversion of the Harrogate Basin. Particularly pronounced inversion of the basin took place at its northern margin marked by the North Craven Fault.

North Craven Fault

The North Craven Fault, marking the southern margin of the Askrigg Block (Regional Cross-section C–C′), was probably reversed to a greater or lesser degree along much of its length during Variscan basin inversion (Figure 23). The best evidence for this lies in the east, where seismic reflection data show several minor inversion structures

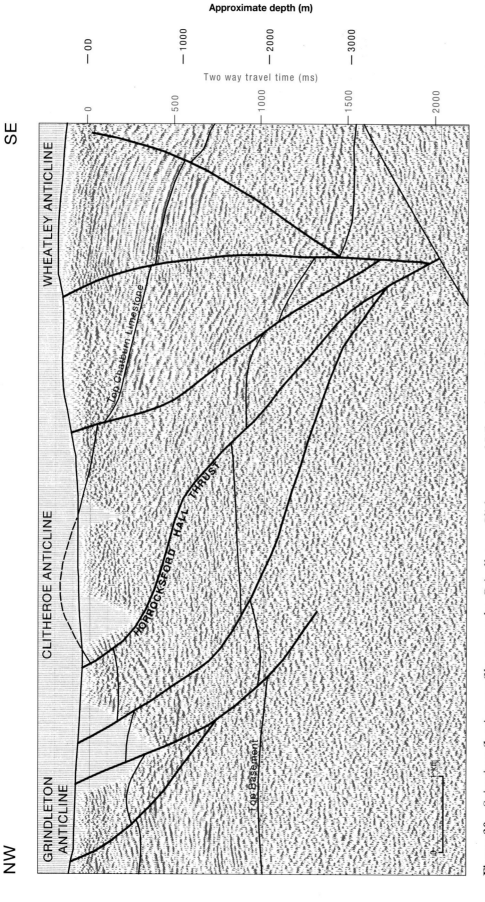

Figure 30   Seismic reflection profile across the Grindleton, Clitheroe and Wheatley anticlines, showing fault linkages at depth.

SW

NE

WHEATLEY ANTICLINE

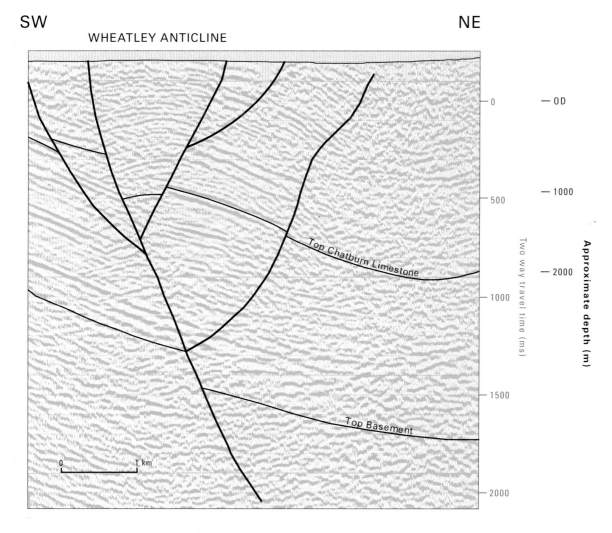

Figure 31   Seismic reflection profile across the Wheatley Anticline.

associated with the fault at the northern margin of the Harrogate Basin. Small anticlines lie in the hanging-wall block of the fault, and in places the throw has been reversed at shallow depths (Figure 21). Elsewhere reversal was less than the original normal displacement and the fault shows a normal sense of throw at all preserved levels (Figure 20). Transfer faults offsetting the fault undoubtedly compartmentalised compression and did themselves suffer oblique-reversal to form positive flower-structures (Figure 34).

Two inversion anticlines similar to those seen on the seismic data occur farther west, where the North Craven Fault separates the Askrigg Block and the Malham Terrace.

Skyrholme Anticline

The Skyrholme Anticline trends east-north-east and lies in the hanging-wall block of the North Craven Fault at the northern margin of the Malham Terrace. Judging from the cross-section in Dunham and Stubblefield (1944), the fold is asymmetrical with a steeper northern

limb, and has an amplitude locally of some 200 m (possibly more elsewhere).

Greenhow Anticline

The Greenhow Anticline lies to the north-east of the Skyrholme Anticline, but in the foot-wall block of the North Craven Fault, on the Askrigg Block. The fold trends roughly east-north-east, is asymmetrical with a steeper normal limb and has an amplitude of up to 300 m (Dunham and Stubblefield, 1944). Unlike the Skyrholme structure, the Greenhow Anticline cannot be ascribed to reversal of the North Craven Fault. It lies in the hanging-wall block of the Bycliffe Fault (which bifurcates from the North Craven Fault, penetrating west-north-west into the Askrigg Block) and may have formed by reversal of this structure.

Several inversion structures formed within the Harrogate Basin by the reversal of intra-basin normal faults. Unlike the inversion structures farther west, the Variscan (pre-Permo-Triassic) age of some of these features can be unequivocally demonstrated due to their relatively undeformed Permo-Triassic cover.

Figure 32 Seismic reflection profile across the Swinden Anticline.

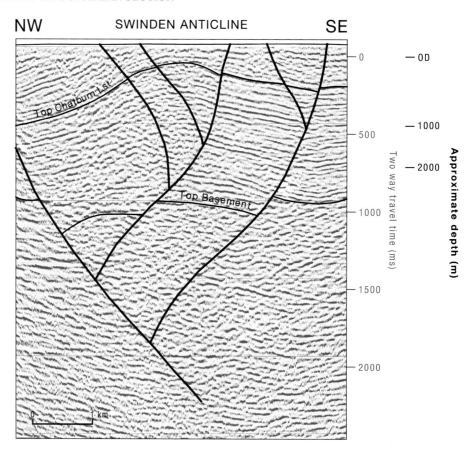

Harrogate Anticline

The Harrogate Anticline (Regional Cross-section C–C′) can be mapped at surface as an asymmetrical, periclinal fold, trending north-east through Harrogate, but with a more easterly trend farther south (Cooper and Burgess, 1993). The steep north-west limb dips locally at up to 80° and is cut by high-angle reverse faults. Its south-east limb is less steep with dips typically less than 45°. Minor folds, parallel to the main axial trend, are superimposed on the main fold near Beckwith. Seismic data elucidate the subsurface structure of the Harrogate Anticline (Figure 35a). It appears to have originated as a minor, Dinantian, syndepositional, down-to-the-south, normal fault which suffered subsequent Variscan reversal to form a reverse-faulted hanging-wall anticline. The overall form of the structure has many characteristics of a positive flower structure (as defined by Harding, 1985), indicative of oblique compression.

Cayton Gill Anticline

Some 10 km north of the Harrogate Anticline (Figure 23), the Cayton Gill Anticline is a symmetrical east–west-trending fold with a vertical axial plane, and associated with sinistral oblique-slip faulting (Cooper amd Burgess, 1993). This structure and similar features to the north may be associated with inversion near the southern margin of the Askrigg Block (compare with Figure 21)

Sessay Anticline

Concealed by Permo-Triassic cover rocks, the Sessay Anticline (Figure 23) is a composite term for a two gentle, asymmetrical anticlines developed within the Stainmore Group. The seismic data are of rather poor quality and the axial trend of the folds is uncertain. They appear to be situated in the hanging-wall blocks of north-dipping faults, which show small reverse (down-to-the-south) displacements of the base of the Stainmore Group, passing down into normal displacements within the Dinantian. The structures appear to have formed prior to deposition of the Permo-Triassic cover, and are interpreted to result from Variscan reversal of earlier normal faults.

Ellenthorpe Anticline

Concealed by Permo-Triassic cover rocks, the Ellenthorpe Anticline is an east–west-trending, asymmetrical faulted anticline which brings Dinantian strata to subcrop beneath the Permo-Triassic cover (Regional Cross-section D–D′). Its southern limb is cut by several north-dipping reverse faults which show significant down-to-the-south reverse displacements at the base of the Stainmore Group (Figures 35b and 48). The faults coalesce at depth onto a single fault, but poor seismic data quality precludes unequivocal assessment of displacement at depth. It is possible though, that the top of Caledonian basement is also reversely faulted.

The Ellenthorpe Anticline has suffered post-Variscan extensional collapse, by normal reactivation of its bounding reverse faults to form the Bilton–Scriven structure (see p.82).

Many other small inversion structures lie within the Ribblesdale Foldbelt and are described in the relevant BGS memoirs. In addition, it is likely that the foldbelt extends a considerable distance to the south-west, beneath the West Lancashire Basin. Many other structures may be present there, concealed beneath the Permo-Triassic cover and undetected because of poor quality seismic data. Two anticlines that can be seen on the seismic data hereabouts lie in the Formby Basin. One of the structures is associated with reversal of the Pendle Fault at the southern margin of the basin, the other is associated with inversion of the central parts of the basin (Figure 43).

OTHER INVERSION STRUCTURES

Lake District Boundary Fault System

In the region, the Lake District Boundary Fault System (Figure 23) in Permo-Triassic rocks is a down-to-the-west

SW

BOLTON ANTICLINE

NE

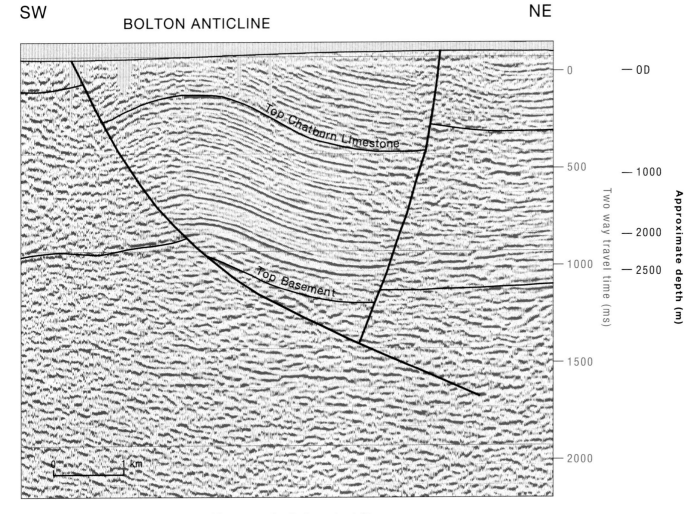

Top Chatburn Limestone

Top Basement

0

500

1000

1500

2000

0D

1000

2000

2500

Two way travel time (ms)

Approximate depth (m)

0   1 km

Figure 33 Seismic reflection profile across the Bolton Anticline.

system of normal faults (Chapter Seven), but because of this Permo-Triassic cover, its Carboniferous structural history is poorly understood. The magnitude of any early Carboniferous extensional displacement on the fault system is unknown. Seismic reflection data (Figure 50) indicate that the preserved Carboniferous succession is markedly different to the west of the faults. In particular, seismo-stratigraphically different rocks subcrop beneath the Permo-Triassic on either side of the fault. This is consistent with, but not uniquely diagnostic of, Variscan reverse displacements (with downthrows towards the east) along the fault system. The fact that similarly trending structures (for example the Dent Fault), suffered Variscan reversal, suggests that the Lake District Boundary Fault System is also likely to have done so.

Dent Fault System

The Dent Fault System (Figure 23) is unusual in the region in that it appears to show net reverse displacements at basement level, indicating that any Dinantian normal movements on the fault were outweighed by subsequent Variscan reversal. Although no seismic line crosses the fault, detailed mapping of the field relation-

ships render it relatively well understood (Underhill et al., 1988). The fault system comprises a series of vertical to steeply west-dipping fault planes. Maximum throw on the faults occurs in the south, in Dent Dale, where a large, down-to-the-east, reverse displacement is recognised (Dunham and Wilson, 1985). Here, Dinantian strata of the Askrigg Block form the foot-wall of the fault and are thrown against Lower Palaeozoic basement rocks of the Lake District Block in its hanging-wall, which are folded into the Howgills Anticline (Figure 23) (Edwards et al., 1954). The throw on the fault system decreases to about 800 m near Sedburgh, and diminishes still further to the north. An east-facing and slightly overturned monocline is dissected by the faults along the length of the fault system. This structural configuration was interpreted as indicative of east–west-directed Variscan shortening by Burgess and Holliday (1979). This is consistent with the assumed, dominant, east–west, Variscan, shortening direction seen farther north, in the Northumberland Trough (for example Chadwick et al., 1995). However recently, Underhill et al., (1988) have identified local development of features akin to a positive flowerstructure (as defined by Harding, 1985), indicative of

Figure 34 Transfer fault associated with the North Craven Fault System, having the form of a positive flower-structure, indicative of oblique-compression.

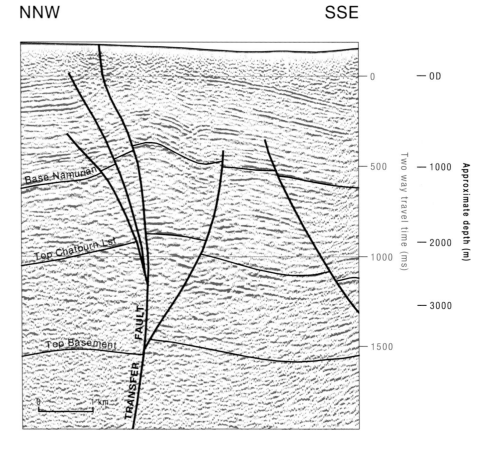

strike-slip displacements, and other kinematic indications of sinistral transpression. These are interpreted as occurring in response to north–south-directed Variscan shortening. However, the possibility of later structural overprints such as Permo-Mesozoic transtension and Cenozoic (Alpine) transpression complicate the picture still further and render unequivocal interpretations difficult.

South of the Dent Fault, the western end of the North Craven Fault System separates the Askrigg Block from the Lancaster Fells Basin, possibly forming a near-transfer basin margin. The Hollintree Fault forms a strand of the North Craven Fault System here-abouts.

Hollintree Fault

This Fault lies parallel to and just to the south-west of the North Craven Fault (Figure 23), cutting the Ingleton Coalfield. Downthrowing to the north-east, with a reverse displacement (possibly with a marked sinistral component) of more than 300 m (Ford, 1954) indicates Variscan inversion of the Lancaster Fells Basin.

Stockdale Disturbance

Interpreted here as marking the northern margin of the Askrigg Block (Figure 23), separating it from the Stainmore Trough to the north, the Stockdale Fault is believed to dip northwards, with a large normal down-to-the-north throw in the subsurface. At outcrop a series of *en échelon* monoclines and anticlines lie in the hanging-wall block of the fault, which, together with the fault, constitute the Stockdale Disturbance (Dunham and Wilson, 1985). The folds are typically a few kilometres in length with amplitudes approaching 100 m. They presumably formed by Variscan reversal of the subsurface fault, associated with inversion of the southern margin of the Stainmore Trough.

Hutton Monocline and the Quernmore Thrust

The Hutton Monocline (Figure 23) has a near vertical, east-facing limb represented by a belt of strata some 800 m wide, with the dip of the strata decreasing to horizontal over a distance of only 40 m. No faulting is observed at surface (Moseley, 1972; Brandon et al., 1998). Seismic reflection data across the Quernmore structure and near

Priest Hutton, though equivocal, suggest the presence of an underlying, normal fault, subsequently reversed. Displacements at the base of the Carboniferous are uncertain however, the seismic reflection data being poor. Both normal (down-to-the-west) and reverse (down-to-the-east) net displacements are possible, the latter indicated on Regional Cross-section A–A′.

Gravity data (Brandon et al., 1998), indicate that the Quernmore Fault continues northwards into the Hutton Monocline and thence northwards to Priest Hutton where the Urswick Limestone and Gleaston formations (Dinantian) and the Pendle Grit (Namurian) turn to vertical against an easterly throwing north–south fault (Turner, 1935). At this point, although the monocline dies out, a fault continues northwards into the Kendal Fault, but an east-facing faulted monocline extends north-east to Hutton Roof. The Kendal Fault is a down-to-the-west, normal fault, which was active in Dinantian times (see p.37). Other north to south-trending faults and monoclinal structures hereabouts, for example the Silverdale Anticline or Disturbance (Moseley, 1972; Underhill et al., 1988) form important inversion structures on the South Lake District High. It is likely that these were similar to the Kendal Fault, being active in Dinantian times as down-to-the-west normal faults, which were subsequently reversed during Variscan transpression or compression. In general terms the Variscan history of these faults is probably analogous to that of the Dent Fault.

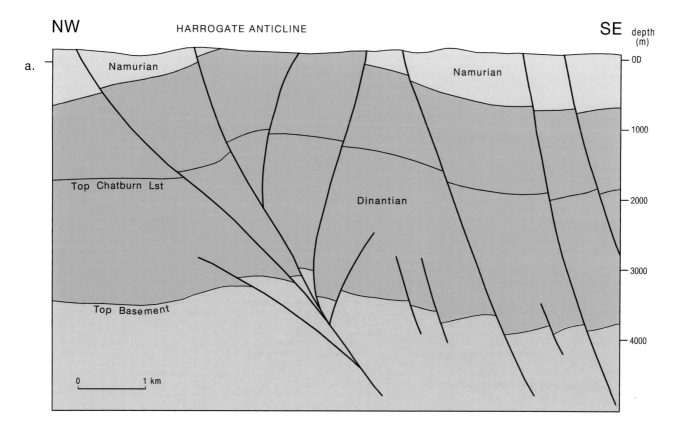

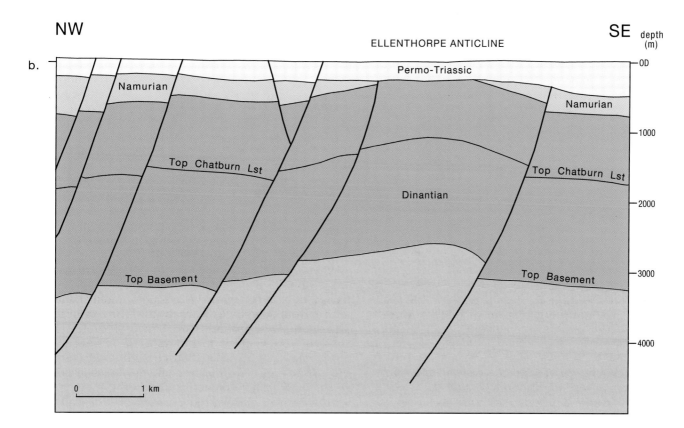

Figure 35 Variscan inversion structures from the Harrogate Basin a) Harrogate Anticline
b) Ellenthorpe Anticline.

W   E

PENNINE MONOCLINE

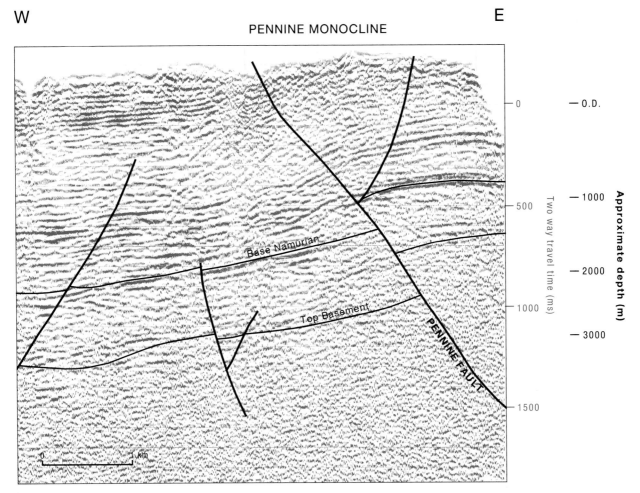

Figure 36 Seismic reflection profile across the Pennine Monocline and underlying reverse fault, near to the Boulsworth Borehole.

Pennine Monocline and neighbouring structures

The north–south-trending Pennine Monocline (Gawthorpe, 1987), also known as the Pennine Anticline (Wright et al., 1927), extends from the southern margin of the Bowland Basin in the north, to near the southern edge of the region (Figure 23). The structure is generally asymmetrical, with steep dips on its western flank and gentle dips on its eastern flank, affecting strata of Namurian age at crop. Seismic reflection data in the north near the Boulsworth Borehole, indicate that the west-facing monocline is underlain by a similarly trending, down-to-the-west reverse fault (Figure 36). Like the Dent Fault, the Pennine Line is unusual here showing net reverse displacements at basement level. Other reverse faults may be present but not imaged in the data. Farther south, the structure takes on a more anticlinal form, swinging into a north-west–south-east orientation near Todmorden. Here it is associated with the Todmorden Smash Belt, a complex series of faults whose strike approximates those of the beds (Wright et al., 1927). South of the Todmorden Smash Belt the structure is less well defined for several kilometres, before appearing again as the Mossley Anticline (Figure 23), a generally asymmetrical, west-verging structure. Locally, where it is cut by the

down-to-the-west Tame Fault, the anticline shows eastwards vergence, with a steeper eastern limb.

Lee (1988), on the basis of gravity data, suggested that the Pennine Monocline overlay an important down-east synsedimentary normal fault between the Rossendale and Huddersfield basins (see Pennine Line above), which suffered subsequent Variscan reversal. This is certainly not the case near the Boulsworth Borehole, but farther south where the subsurface structure is unclear, it cannot be unequivocally demonstrated that earlier normal movements did not occur on the structure and Lee's interpretation of an important basin defining structure may still hold.

To the west of the Pennine Monocline, similarly complex belts of faulting extend north-west–south-east across the Central Lancashire High and the Rossendale Basin. The Darwen Valley Smash Belt (Wright et al., 1927) is a complex fault system which breaks up the character of the Rossendale Anticline (Figure 23). In its northern extent, it shows evidence of scissor movement, the direction of throw on the main fault varying along its length. Scissor motion on the fault may indeed have occurred, but it is most probably a consequence of oblique-reverse displacements along an earlier transfer fault during subsequent compressional or transpressional episodes. The importance of the

Figure 37 Cross-section across the southern margin of the Rossendale Basin. Note gentle inversion anticline and possible small reverse faults in the hanging-wall block of the Heywood Fault.

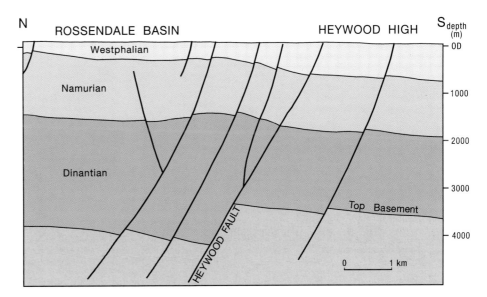

fault zone diminishes to the south and movement may have been transferred onto the Irwell Valley Fault lying to the south-west, another fault in the series of important north-west-trending fault zones dissecting the Rossendale Basin. The generally north-easterly throwing Irwell Valley Fault can be traced southwards to a plexus of faults on the northern margin of the Cheshire Basin near Prestwich, where indications of syn- and post-Permo-Triassic movements are evidenced by its control on the distribution of Permo-Triassic strata. Other north-west– south-east faults of note cutting across the Rossendale Basin, which may have suffered Variscan reversal, are the Great Haigh, Padiham, Shevington–Pemberton and Upholland fault systems. More regional Variscan inversion of the Rossendale Basin is suggested by the Rossendale Anticline (see below).

Heywood Fault

West of its intersection with the Darwen Valley Fault, the Heywood Fault (Figure 23) shows obvious reversal of move-ment, with a hanging-wall anticline clearly imaged on seismic reflection data at the southern margin of the Rossendale Basin (Figure 37).

Rossendale Anticline

The Rossendale Anticline (Wright et al., 1927) marks an area in which strata of early Namurian age (the Fletcher-bank, Helmshore and Brooksbottom grits) are brought to crop in a broadly periclinal structure some way to the north of the Heywood Fault (Figure 23). This may attest to mild Variscan inversion of the northern part of the Rossendale Basin.

FOUR

Dinantian

Dinantian strata crop out in numerous anticlines of the inverted Craven Basin to the north of the Pendle Monocline, over the Askrigg Block, on the southern margin of the Lake District and also in the Harrogate Anticline. They are dominated by limestones of both shallow- and deep-water origin, interbedded with mudstones or siltstones. Sandstones are not common except in the succession in the Stainmore Trough which has strong deltaic influences, and locally on the Askrigg Block. In view of the abundance of carbonate accumulations in the Dinantian succession and the often loosely defined terminology applied by different authors to these accumulations and their environments of deposition, there follows a brief account of the terminology adopted in this report.

A **carbonate platform** is a general term describing an accumulation of carbonates mostly generated in shallow water, with a flat top, extending over areas of several hundred square kilometres and which may possess steep sides (James and Kendal, 1992). Platforms may be **rimmed**, having a continuous or semicontinuous rampart of reefs and/or lime shoals protecting the inner area. The bounding edge of a rimmed platform forms a steeply dipping surface. Alternatively, a platform may be **unrimmed**, with wave action extending substantial distances inwards from the outer edge. In this case the bounding edge of the platform may be steep or may form a gently dipping surface. A carbonate **ramp** is defined as a sloping surface (less than 1° dip) connecting two levels and extending from the surf zone to abyssal depths, with *no break in slope* at the edge of the platform (Ahr, 1973). A **carbonate shelf** is here defined as a platform tied to an adjacent continental area from which terrigenous sediment may be supplied. A **carbonate bank**, in contrast, is an isolated platform surrounded by deeper water and cut off from terrigenous sediment.

The present understanding of the Dinantian stratigraphy of this region has to a large extent resulted from the study of the outcrop sections. However, these areas of outcrop comprise only a small proportion of the area covered by this account, whereas Dinantian strata are thought to exist at depth underneath most of the region. Published information from the concealed Dinantian strata has largely been based on isolated provings in boreholes and is therefore less detailed than, and sometimes difficult to relate to, outcrop sections. Geophysical investigations aimed at elucidating Dinantian stratigraphy have to date mainly relied on an analysis of potential fields (gravity and magnetics); published information from reflection seismic data is very limited (Fraser and Gawthorpe, 1990). It is the aim of this account to integrate all sources of data, including reflection seismic data, to provide as comprehensive a review of the stratigraphy of the whole region as is possible.

The exposed thickness of the Dinantian section ranges up to 1700 m and the oldest strata exposed are of late Courceyan age, whereas geophysical evidence suggests that an additional thickness of up to 2500 m of Courceyan and possibly older strata is concealed at depth. There is therefore an imbalance between the amount of data available from outcrop and that from the concealed strata in this region.

The distinction between 'basinal' and 'block' areas was established at an early stage from the study of rock types, and stratigraphical and structural features in outcrops (Phillips, 1836). The extent of these blocks and basins, commonly buried beneath later cover, was not fully constrained by outcrop evidence however. Information from borehole sections, principally those drilled in the search for hydrocarbons, are of use in this respect. In addition to helping define the extension of known blocks and basins, these borehole data also suggested the presence of other block and basinal areas. However this information was of no direct use in precisely defining the boundaries of these units. Gravity and magnetic data were utilised to postulate (Gawthorpe et al., 1989; Lee, 1988) a number of new highs and lows. The concept of asymmetrical tilt blocks with a sharply defined, commonly faulted boundary between platform and basinal facies on one side and a more gradual boundary on the gently dipping ramp, emerged from this work in combination with other studies of the Dinantian strata of central and northern England (Smith et al., 1985; Grayson and Oldham, 1987; Smith and Smith, 1989).

Interpretation of all available seismic reflection data has enabled further delineation of the subsurface extent and relationships of Dinantian structural and stratigraphical units. The distinction between platform carbonates and deep-water facies is clear and can be reliably tied into outcrop and borehole successions on a number of seismic lines. Figure 38 presents a typical example: the platform carbonates are characterised by a strong event at the top of the succession and a poorly reflective internal seismic signature with weak, low-amplitude reflections showing little continuity. The overall form of this facies is a very broad mound with tapering edges, representing the superposition of successive depositional slopes from shallow to deep water. In contrast, the deep-water facies is typically 'stripy' in appearance, comprising high-amplitude, moderately continuous events which in part overlie, and in part onlap or pass laterally into, the strong event at the top of the carbonate platform facies. The distinction of these seismic facies has permitted the mapping in the subsurface of Dinantian highs which are onlapped and develop successions dominated by platform carbonates, and of surrounding areas with rocks of deeper water-facies.

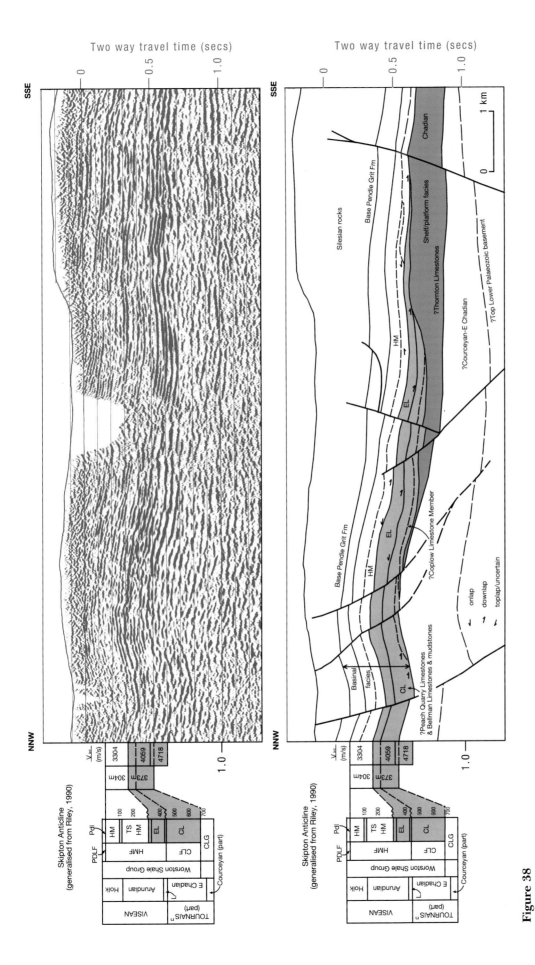

Figure 38

a. Seismic reflection profile from the northern part of the Central Lancashire High to the north-east of the Craven Basin (Skipton Anticline offline to the north-west) illustrating the contrast between the unreflective seismic facies of platform carbonates and the 'stripy' seismic facies of basinal rocks of the Worston Shale Group. Note the overall wedge-like form of the platform carbonates, representing basinward thinning due to the stacking of successive depositional slopes from shallow to deep water.

b. Tentative identification of formation and member boundaries of the Worston Shale Group.

Biostratigraphical determinations from concealed Dinantian sections are often poorly constrained as much data are based on cuttings. Biostratigraphical studies were therefore commissioned on several cores from concealed Dinantian sections.

Lithostratigraphical nomenclature of the Dinantian succession has resulted from the study of outcrop and some cored boreholes located principally in the Craven Basin and on the Askrigg Block and Southern Lake District High. A summary is presented in Table 5. There is, however, no formal nomenclature for the Dinantian successions of the concealed highs or basins.

Because of the uncertainties of the biostratigraphical data, the widely scattered borehole positions and the bias of information to outcrop sections, it was not possible to perform a rigorous stage-by-stage analysis of Dinantian stratigraphy across the whole region. Instead, the account of the Dinantian stratigraphy is based upon the division of the succession established at outcrop in the Craven Basin where the stratigraphy is most complete and best studied.

Table 5 Lithostratigraphical nomenclature of the Dinantian succession within the region.

Stage	STAINMORE TROUGH	SOUTHERN LAKE DISTRICT	NORTHERN ASKRIGG BLOCK	SOUTHERN ASKRIGG BLOCK	Chatburn Limestone Group / Worston Shale Group	BOWLAND BASIN	CENTRAL LANCASHIRE AND HOLME & HEYWOOD HIGHS
BRIGANTIAN	Upper Alston Group	Gleaston Formation	Wensleydale Group	Wensleydale Group	Bowland Shale Group (part)	Lower Bowland Shale Formation	Undivided Platform Carbonates
ASBIAN	Lower Alston Group	Urswick Limestone	Danny Bridge Limestones / Garsdale Limestone	Gordale Limestone (Malham Formation)	Worston Shale Group	Pendleside Limestone Formation	Undivided Platform Carbonates
HOLKERIAN	Sequence not yet formally subdivided	Park Limestone	Fawes Wood Limestone	Cove Limestone (Malham Formation)	Worston Shale Group	Hodderense Limestone Formation	Undivided Platform Carbonates
ARUNDIAN		Dalton Beds	Ashfell Sandstone	Kilnsey Formation	Worston Shale Group	Hodder Mudstone Formation	Undivided Platform Carbonates
ARUNDIAN/CHADIAN		Red Hill Oolite	Tom Croft Limestone		Worston Shale Group	Hodder Mudstone Formation	Undivided Platform Carbonates
CHADIAN		Martin Limestone	Marsett Sandstone	Chapel House Limestone	Chatburn Limestone Group	Clitheroe Limestone Formation	Undivided Platform Carbonates
CHADIAN/COURCEYAN			Raydale Dolomite		Chatburn Limestone Group		Undivided Platform Carbonates
COURCEYAN		Basement Beds		Stockdale Farm Formation / Askrigg Terrace	Chatburn Limestone Group		Basal dolomites, limestones and sandstones

Reference is made, however, to the time-equivalent strata deposited in other basins, on interbasinal highs and basin margins, using all available geological and geophysical data from both outcrop and concealed sections.

TECTONIC SETTING AND PALAEOGEOGRAPHICAL SUMMARY

In late Devonian to Dinantian times, northern England lay in low latitudes to the north of the Equator (Dewey, 1982) with a climate which varied from arid to monsoonal. Following Caledonian deformation and uplift, the region was eroded to form an area of generally low relief. By the start of Dinantian times, the region was subjected to a major period of crustal extension related to back-arc spreading (Leeder, 1982). This resulted in a series of extensional, fault-bounded and rapidly subsiding basins, separated by more slowly subsiding highs. The division between structural and stratigraphical highs and lows was to a large extent controlled by the distribution of structural units resulting from the Caledonian orogeny (Chapters Two and Three). This tectonic regime had a profound effect on deposition, resulting in a relatively complete, usually thick and variably argillaceous sequence in the basins and a sequence of platform limestones or marginal facies elsewhere.

STRATIGRAPHICAL DEVELOPMENT

From the initiation of Dinantian sedimentation until the deposition of the Chatburn Limestone Group in early Chadian times, sedimentation was mostly concentrated in fault-bounded basins and appears in general terms to have kept pace with subsidence. Successions which accumulated outside of these fault-bounded basins are much thinner and of marginal facies. This period was essentially one of 'synextension' sedimentation.

A transitional period then ensued, lasting until the end of Dinantian times, in which intermittent extension punctuated more regional basinal subsidence (Chapter Three). As a result of the more regional basinal subsidence during this transitional period, there was a general rise in relative sea-level which continued throughout the Dinantian in this region and which led to the progressive inundation of areas outside the earlier-formed rifts and previously above sea-level; the Holme and Central Lancashire highs were submerged in Chadian times and the Askrigg Block was finally completely submerged in Holkerian times, strata onlapping and overstepping this high from the north (Dunham and Wilson, 1985. fig. 4). The basin thus became considerably enlarged and deepened. This phase of general subsidence was interrupted in late Chadian and Asbian times by periods in which deep-water conglomeratic and turbiditic deposits accumulated. This, in combination with the association of facies changes across faults, has been taken by many authors (e.g. Gawthorpe, 1987; Ebdon et al., 1990; Riley, 1990) as evidence for periods of extension. This was thought to have enhanced bathymetric differences

creating new intrabasinal highs and lows. Our investigations suggest that the succession deposited after the Chatburn Limestone thickens considerably and changes facies over broad zones associated entirely with the same faults which were active in the earlier extensional phase and therefore this can be regarded as a period of fault reactivation rather than one establishing a new basin architecture.

During this transitional phase, platform carbonates quickly developed with restricted areas of deeper-water sedimentation in between. As relative sea-level continued to rise, these areas of platform carbonates retreated to the margins of the now larger basin, and became areally more restricted on intrabasinal highs such as the Central Lancashire and Holme highs. At the same time, the area of deep-water basinal sedimentation increased and led to the accumulation of sediments of the Worston Shale Group of the Craven Basin and of similar rocks in adjacent basinal areas. By the end of Dinantian times, it is likely that there was still a substantial relief of the basin floor, related both to topographical differences inherited from the early Dinantian extension and those produced by these later phases of fault movement, combined with elevations due to build-ups of platform carbonates. In general the succeeding Namurian strata appear to have infilled this remaining relief.

Chatburn Limestone Group and older rocks (Courceyan to early Chadian)

Strata of this age (Table 5) crop out on the margins of the Southern Lake District High (Adams et al., 1990), the western margin of the Askrigg Block and in the cores of anticlines within the Bowland Basin. They are thought to lie at depth under much of the region but have been proved only in the Swinden and Haw Park boreholes in the Bowland Basin, in the Raydale and Beckermonds Scar boreholes on the northern part of the Askrigg Block and in the Cominco boreholes immediately to the south on the Malham Terrace. Thin basal strata of indeterminate age encountered in boreholes on the Central Lancashire and Holme highs may form part of this succession.

At outcrop and in borehole provings outside of the Bowland Basin, rocks are generally of marginal facies whereas within the Bowland Basin the succession is dominated by marine limestones deposited in moderately shallow water. The stratigraphical range of strata is believed to be from early Courceyan (or possibly Devonian; see below) to early Chadian.

Deposition of these rocks occurred during a period of extension which led to the formation of several rapidly-subsiding fault-bounded depocentres. Surrounding areas remained as positive features, either as land masses or areas accumulating thin sequences of marginal facies. A marine transgression led to the gradual drowning of this land surface which continued throughout the Dinantian.

Seismic data reveal several depocentres, notably the Bowland Basin, in which the succession is up to 2500 m thick (Map 2), although this must remain an estimate as no borehole has yet penetrated to basement. The maximum drilled thickness is the 658 m of marine Courceyan strata of the Swinden Borehole (Charsley, 1984). The remaining succession at depth is undated, but analogy with other northern England basins suggests that strata of Lower Courceyan and possibly Devonian age may be represented. Exposed sections outside the Craven Basin lie in basin margin positions. Thicknesses range up to 250 m on the margin of the Southern Lake District High and to 80 m on the western margin of the Askrigg Block. The unbottomed marginal succession encountered in the Cominco boreholes on the Malham Terrace is 165 m thick.

The Lake District and Askrigg blocks were largely emergent during this time, probably forming one continuous landmass which was progressively inundated by rising sea levels. Sandy and conglomeratic fluviatile and shallow marine rocks were deposited around this landmass.

Rocks of this age in south Cumbria comprise the Basement Beds (Courceyan) and possibly the lowest part of the overlying Martin Limestone (Chadian). Marked lateral variations in both thickness and facies occur in the Basement Beds. Their absence over the Cartmel area indicates a basement ridge here at this time which is believed to have persisted into Chadian times. Conglomerates, sandstones and mudstones dominate the thicker sections around the Duddon estuary with thin argillaceous limestones and gypsum beds also present, the latter indicating periodic desiccation in an arid climate. Limestones thicken southwards and upwards through the succession at the expense of coarse terrigenous clastics, consistent with a northern source for the terrigenous material and a northerly retreating coastline as relative sea-level rose. A late Courceyan influx of fine detritus from the Lake District Block is represented by muddy strata towards the top of the Basement Beds. The overlying Martin Limestone comprises a fairly pure carbonate mudstone with cross-stratified grainstones and represents barrier beach complexes, tidal flats and restricted lagoons, and attests to the establishment of open-marine conditions in early Chadian times.

Rocks of this age also crop out to the east of the Lake District Block, just to the north of the region, between Hawes and Ravenstonedale. The earliest strata are the Pinskey Gill Beds, a 40–50 m thick succession of variably sandy limestones and dolomites interbedded with mudstones, thought to have been deposited in hypersaline conditions. Their precise age is uncertain, but faunas indicate a mid to late Courceyan age (Higgins and Varker, 1982; Holliday et al., 1979). They are overlain by 40 m of fluviatile sandstones and conglomerates of the Shap Conglomerate, indicating a temporary marine regression. Marine beds occur in the top two metres of this conglomerate however and are of Chadian age. The extent of these strata in the subsurface on the northern side of the Askrigg Block is uncertain but they are thought to onlap the block from the north, to a line somewhere north of the Raydale Borehole where late Chadian rocks rest on basement. It may be that part of the Sedbergh Conglomerate, which crops out along the Dent Fault, is in part equivalent to these strata; biostratigraphical control is poor however.

A succession with similarities to that in south Cumbria is encountered in the Cominco S2 and S7 boreholes on the Malham Terrace immediately to the south of the Askrigg Block (Arthurton et al., 1988). This succession, the Stockdale Farm Formation, consists of peritidal and evaporitic deposits and was not bottomed in either borehole. It is of Courceyan age, apart from the topmost 11 m which is Chadian. It comprises the Halstead Shales with Anhydrite, overlain by the Stockdale Farm Sandstones and Shales which in turn are succeeded by the Stockdale Farm Limestones and Shales. Terrigenous components in the limestones, particularly quartz, are ubiquitous and indicative of the marginal location just to the south of the then-emergent Askrigg Block. This formation is unconformably overlain by Arundian platform carbonates.

Seismic data suggest that the Chatburn Limestone reflector may not extend onto the Central Lancashire High which may therefore have been emergent at this time. Thin reddened beds and/or peritidal carbonates underlying Chadian platform carbonates at the base of the Boulsworth Borehole and below Arundian shelf carbonates in the Roddlesworth Borehole on the Central Lancashire High are of a similar facies to the Stockdale Farm Formation seen in the Malham Terrace. Biostratigraphical control is poor however and it is thought possible that these are younger representatives of this presumed diachronous facies.

The main depocentres identified are generally fault controlled (Map 2). Thickest of these is the Bowland Basin which is bounded and controlled by the Pendle Fault to the south, the Bowland Line to the north-west and the Craven Fault system to the north. Seismic data suggest that this unit is approximately 2500 m thick throughout this depocentre. The lithology of the succession is partly revealed by exposures of the Gisburn Coates Beds and Haw Bank Limestones of the Gisburn and Skipton anticlines in the Basin as well as the succession encountered in the Swinden Borehole (Charsley, 1984). These form part of the Chatburn Limestone Group of uppermost Courceyan age (Metcalf, 1981; Aitkenhead et al., 1992) which consists of a sequence of thinly interlayered, bioclastic, grey to dark grey bioturbated limestones and calcareous mudstones. The limestones are thought to have been deposited on a carbonate ramp (Gawthorpe et al., 1989) by storm-generated currents and the clays are thought to have reached the basin from a land source by fluvial action. The Persian Gulf is envisaged by Charsley (1984) as a modern-day analogue. The lithology of the concealed and undrilled part of the succession is unproved. The continuous and subparallel nature of the most of the reflections indicates that the succession is well bedded and the moderate to high amplitude of the reflections suggests interbedded units of reasonably contrasting lithologies. This seismic facies is very similar to that of the section penetrated by the Swinden Borehole and it is therefore thought possible that much of this unproved succession is of a similar nature. The substantial thickness and assumed similarity of rock types throughout this interval, the lack of any evidence of progradation and palaeo-bathymetric evidence from the succession encountered in the Swinden Borehole suggest that deposition was rapid and kept pace with subsidence.

A basal sequence of limited areal extent and wedge-like profile can be recognised on some seismic lines. It has an unreflective seismic facies, suggestive of a poorly bedded succession, and the variations in thickness indicate some degree of fault control as well as infill of earlier topography. These controlling faults, however, appear to trend north-west–south-east in contrast to those controlling the thicker overlying succession and may be related to long-lived basement structures.

To the north-west of the Bowland Basin is the Bowland High, an area including the South Fells Tilt Block of Lawrence et al. (1987), which merges northwards into the South Lancaster Fells Basin. There is no borehole proving of this unit on the Bowland High but the seismic data suggest that a succession of Chatburn Limestone and older rocks appears to be present over all parts of this high. Although subject to significant thickness variations (thickening generally towards the west) and being much thinner than the succession immediately to the south in the Bowland Basin, this interval does not thin to less than 200 to 300 m. Any thinning does not appear to be accompanied by onlap onto the basement surface, suggesting that this high was not emergent for significant periods of time and that the sequence is most probably condensed. It is not possible to ascertain whether all or only part of the Courceyan to early Chadian interval recognised in the Bowland Basin to the south is represented over this high.

Seismic facies are very similar in the Harrogate Basin, and it is thought that lithologies similar to those proposed for the Bowland Basin exist at depth in a succession which ranges up to 2000 m thick. There is no proving of rocks of this age in the Stainmore Trough, but it is thought likely that rocks of broadly similar facies to those developed in the Bowland Basin also exist here.

It was not possible to trace the Chatburn Limestone reflector into the Rossendale Basin to the south of the Central Lancashire High with confidence. There is no borehole proving strata of this age in this part of the region. However the seismic data here reveal Dinantian seismic sequences which display a similar geometry and seismic facies to those observed on the northern margin of this high where some age constraints are available. Comparison with these would suggest that only the very lowermost strata may be of Courceyan and early Chadian age and may comprise a narrow carbonate platform with more basinal facies developed in a narrow zone between this and the Heywood High to the south.

Worston Shale Group and equivalent rocks (early Chadian to late Asbian)

The Worston Shale Group (Earp et al., 1961) ranges in age from early Chadian to late Asbian and has been divided by Riley (1990) into four formations with a total thickness of up to 1700 m. All rocks, with the exception of those belonging to part of the lowest formation, the Clitheroe Limestone Formation, are of basinal facies in the exposed Craven Basin. Lateral variations in facies are rapid and commonplace and are reflected in the large number of component members (Table 5). Rocks of this group

crop out only in anticlines of the inverted Craven Basin. Seismic data, however, suggest that similar rocks are also present in the subsurface in adjacent basinal areas. Seismic lines have been correlated with outcrops of this group in the Skipton and Lothersdale anticlines and reflectors corresponding to some formational boundaries and individual members tentatively identified (Figure 38). There is limited penetration of these strata by two boreholes in the Harrogate Basin, the Whitmoor Borehole in the Lancaster Fells Basin and the Alport Borehole in the Alport Basin, but there are no borehole provings elsewhere.

Rocks spanning the same age-range as the Worston Shale Group are exposed and have been penetrated in boreholes on the Askrigg Block (Arthurton et al., 1988; Dunham and Wilson, 1985) and on the southern margin of the Lake District high (Horbury, 1989), but here are developed predominantly as shallow-water platform carbonates with the local development of fringing reefs during the Asbian. Lithostratigraphical nomenclature and the correlation with rocks of the Worston Shale Group is summarised in Table 5. Seismic data suggest that platform carbonates of this age are also widely developed in the subsurface on inter- and intrabasinal highs. These have been penetrated by boreholes on the Central Lancashire, Holme and Heywood highs, but no formal lithostratigraphical subdivisions have been made.

The detail of lithological variation available from outcrop is superior to any inferences that can be drawn from an analysis of the seismic data. However, despite this detail, the relationship between basinal and shallow-water sediments of this group and their equivalents at outcrop is not entirely clear-cut and has led to various and sometimes conflicting interpretations (Riley, 1990; Gawthorpe, 1987). Many seismic lines reveal the presence of buried platform carbonate margins on the Central Lancashire and Holme highs and provide important information on the spatial and temporal relationships between the platform carbonates and deeper-water sediments. Key relationships seen on these seismic lines, together with available biostratigraphical control, are presented in Figure 39. There are four stacked platform carbonate units which progressively became more restricted in area, and which finally retreated to a position overlying the crest of the basement high. The age of the upper two units is determined from boreholes as Chadian to possibly Holkerian and Asbian to Brigantian respectively. The age of the lowest units is determined as Chadian, by the age of onlapping basinal sedimentary rocks tied in to outcrops in the Skipton Anticline. The age, lithology and subdivision of the Chadian basinal seismic facies is controlled by correlation with outcrop and isolated borehole provings. These relationships are thought to demonstrate progressive sea-level rise during this interval, with three periods of increased rate of relative sea-level rise. In the following account, an attempt is made to use these relationships between different seismic facies in conjunction with the limited biostratigraphical control on these, to provide the overall stratigraphical framework into which the details available from outcrop are integrated.

Riley (1990) recognised four unconformities within this group, the lowest at the base of the Hodder Mudstone

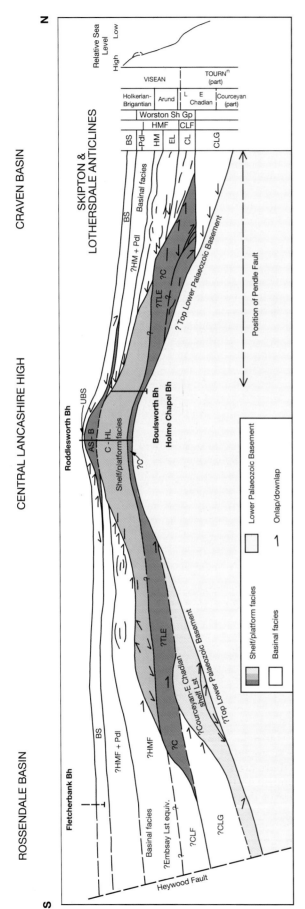

Figure 39 Summary of stratigraphical relationships, as revealed by a composite seismic reflection profile, of platform carbonates (shaded) and surrounding basinal rocks (unshaded) on the Central Lancashire High.

being most profound and widespread and the upper three being confined to the margins of the basin. Examination of the seismic data does not, however, reveal significant and widespread breaks at these levels within a basinal setting. Seismic data does, however, reveal breaks in sedimentation within platform carbonate deposits which are thought to result from pulsed sea-level rises, with periodic temporary restriction of sedimentation basinward of the platform edge.

CLITHEROE LIMESTONE FORMATION AND EQUIVALENT ROCKS (EARLY TO LATE CHADIAN)

The sedimentary rocks of the Clitheroe Limestone Formation range in age from early to late Chadian (Table 5) and record the transition from shallow- to deep-water conditions within the depocentres. The succession is dominated by packestones, wackestones and floatstones which are commonly crinoidal with subordinate mudstones. Waulsortian limestones occur at two levels and the total thickness of this formation ranges up to 1500 m. A summary palaeogeographical map is presented in Figure 40.

The basal Thornton Limestone member is a succession of bioturbated packestones, wackestones and subordinate grainstones with measured thicknesses up to 200 m, which are thought to have been deposited in shallow water. These lithologies extend southwards into the Bowland Basin, to a north-east-trending line within 10 km of the Pendle Fault running just to the north of the Gisburn and Whitewell anticlines (Riley, 1990). There is some seismic evidence for a southward-facing platform edge in approximately this position at this time, and this boundary can be tentatively traced north-eastwards beyond the limits suggested by Riley (1990) towards the Ellenthorpe Borehole. In this area the seismic data provide evidence of a prograding carbonate margin; however there is insufficient biostratigraphical control to be certain that this is of the same age as the Thornton Limestone. The nature of the succession in the Stainmore Trough is uncertain. The overlying Arundian to Brigantian succession proved in the Seal Sands Borehole to the north-east of the region is dominated by deltaic deposits and it is thought possible that these deltas may also have penetrated into the Stainmore Trough during deposition of the Clitheroe Limestone Formation. In this case, the edge of this carbonate platform at this time would have had an approximately north-west orientation on the eastern and northern margin of the Askrigg Block and would have interdigitated with deltaic deposits.

An extensive area of platform carbonates also developed on the Central Lancashire High at this time (Figure 40) with estimated thicknesses substantially greater (up to 850 m) than those measured from outcrop in the Craven Basin. The complex northward-facing margin of this platform carbonate is clearly imaged on seismic data to the south of the Low Bradley and Weeton boreholes (Figure 38) and is onlapped by a seismically 'stripy' facies thought to indicate

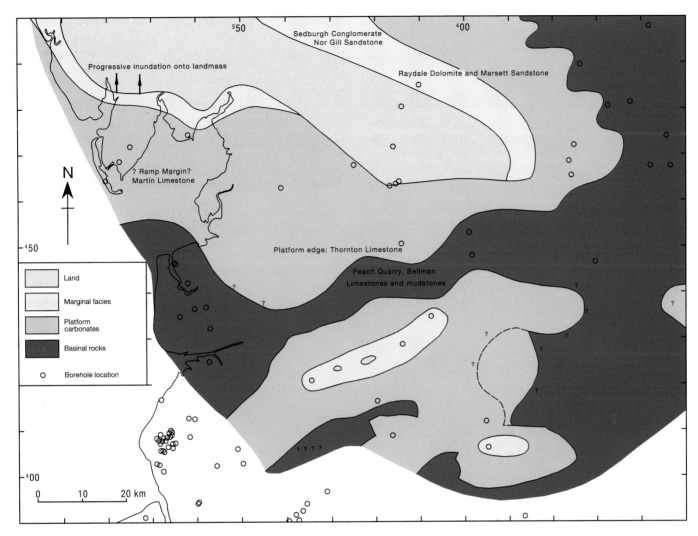

Figure 40 Generalised facies map of early to late Chadian times (Clitheroe Limestone).

rocks of basinal facies. The platform edge trends approximately east to west to the east of Low Bradley and follows the footwall block of the north-east-trending Pendle Fault to the west. A narrow belt of rocks of basinal facies which onlaps these platform margins to the north and south is therefore defined, lying immediately to the north of the Pendle Fault and broadening eastwards into the Harrogate Basin (Figure 40). In the west of the Bowland Basin these basinal rocks comprise the Waulsortian limestones and mudstones of the Coplow Limestone Member overlain in the Clitheroe Anticline by the Peach Quarry Limestones (thought to be storm deposits by Riley, 1990) and the Waulsortian Bellman Limestones and mudstones. The only proving of rocks of basinal facies elsewhere is in the Weeton Borehole in the Harrogate Basin which encountered calcareous shales at this level. It is thought possible that reflectors below the Embsay Limestone on Figure 38 which onlap the platform edge, correspond to these basinal divisions of the Clitheroe Limestone. Unfortunately the nearest outcrop to these seismic lines is the Skipton Anticline, where details of the subdivision of this formation are uncertain (Riley, 1990, fig. 6). Elsewhere at crop, the

Thornton Limestone is generally unconformably overlain by rocks of the Hodder Mudstone Formation. In the Newton Anticline, however, the Coplow Limestones overlie Thornton Limestone attesting to deepening of the basin.

The southern margin of the carbonate platform on the Central Lancashire High is less easy to map using seismic data, due to structural complications, poor-quality data and areas with no data; however, it appears to trend approximately north-east. A southward protuberance onto the Holme and Heywood highs separates the Rossendale and Harrogate basins in which deeper- water sediments are assumed to have been deposited at this time, although there are no firm provings of this. Platform carbonates appear to thin stratigraphically and by onlap on to the crest of the Central Lancashire and Holme highs. Biostratigraphical data is poor, but it is thought possible that the marginal facies of peritidal carbonates, interdigitated with sandstones at the base of the succession here as encountered in the Wessenden and Boulsworth boreholes, are lateral equivalents of these platform carbonates (Riley, 1993, personal communication). A retreat of the northern and southern margin of the Chadian carbonate platform is seen on seismic profiles across the Central Lancashire and Holme highs (Figure 38). The reduction in the area of platform carbonate deposition is thought to indicate a basinwide rise in relative sea-level.

The northern margin of the carbonate platform on the Holme and Heywood highs and the north-western margin of the Central Lancashire High appears to be fault-controlled whereas other margins lie on the dip slope of the highs and their positions are controlled by the local balance of subsidence and carbonate production.

The Lake District and Askrigg blocks were both largely emergent at the start of Chadian times, but were progressively inundated by rising sea-levels and proximal sediments were deposited at their margins. Barrier beach complexes, tidal flats and restricted lagoonal sediments of the Martin Limestone were deposited in a northerly thinning succession on the Southern Lake District High (Adams et al., 1990). Limited seismic evidence suggests that deposition occurred on a southwards deepening surface. Meanwhile to the east of the Lake District Block, the Sedburgh Conglomerate was deposited in what is thought to have been a laterally restricted alluvial fan environment against the Dent Fault (Underhill et al., 1988). The Raydale Dolomite and Marsett Sandstone were deposited on the Askrigg Block (Figure 40) to the north of a line running between the Raydale and Beckermonds Scar boreholes.

HODDER MUDSTONE FORMATION AND EQUIVALENT ROCKS (LATE CHADIAN TO MID HOLKERIAN)

Rocks of the Hodder Mudstone Formation range in age from late Chadian to Holkerian (Table 5). They crop out extensively in the Craven Basin but similar rocks are believed to be present in the subsurface in most of the adjacent basinal areas. This formation is dominated by mudstone, but also includes subordinate limestones, siltstones and sandstones with Waulsortian limestones, limestone breccias and boulder conglomerates near the base. Soft sediment deformation, slumps, debris flows and gravity slides are widespread (Riley, 1981; Gawthorpe and Clemmey, 1985) and thicknesses range up to 900 m. A summary palaeogeographical map is presented in Figure 41.

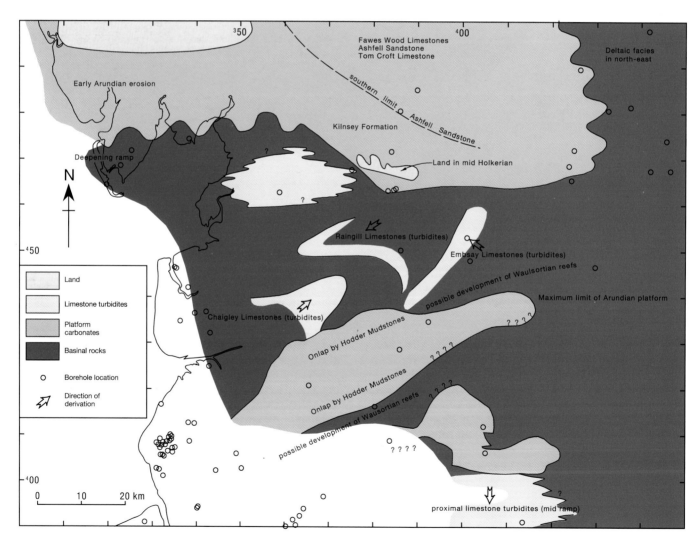

Figure 41 Generalised facies map of late Chadian to mid Holkerian times (Hodder Mudstone Formation).

The Limekiln Wood Limestone, comprising limestone breccias interbedded with mudstones up to 120 m thick, lies at the base of this formation only in the south-west of the Bowland Basin. This limestone was derived from the underlying Clitheroe Limestone and appears to have been deposited by turbidity currents and debris flows. The breccias are overlain by up to 200 m of the hemipelagic Phynis Mudstones which record a general and rapid deepening of the basin hereabouts. Platform carbonate deposition was, however, re-established farther north towards the margin of the Bowland Basin, and resulted in the limestones of the Hetton Beck Formation which range up to 130 m thick. The platform edge at this time ran along, and was in part controlled by the southern faulted margin of the Bowland High. In the Skipton Anticline, however, there appears to have been a hiatus in deposition during the late Chadian and none of the above mentioned rocks are present (Riley, 1990, fig. 7). The carbonate platforms became the source areas for large-scale syndepositional slumps and gravity slides in areas close to the platform edge (such as the Sykes Anticline near to the Bowland High), and for the turbiditic Whitemore Limestones up to 80 m thick, in more distal areas. Rocks of a similar facies have been proved in the Harrogate Basin; an analysis of the seismic facies would suggest that similar rocks occur in other basinal areas at this stratigraphical level.

Arthurton (1988) and Riley (1990) postulate a period of tectonic movements at the end of Chadian times citing evidence of erosion in the Skipton and Eshton–Hetton Beck anticlines and the Southern Lake District High, and also by the local occurrence of the terrigenous Buckbanks Sandstone in the western part of the Bowland Basin. A widespread unconformity with significant overstep occurs at the base of the Hodder Mudstone Formation. Earliest sedimentation appears to have been restricted to depositional 'lows' and commenced in several localities with limestone breccias of the Limekiln Wood Limestone. Syndepositional tectonic activity and associated submarine fault scarp retreat have been cited as the cause of this unconformity (Arthurton et al., 1988; Riley, 1990). Outcrop evidence suggests that the unconformity appears to represent a longer period of time in the east of the Bowland Basin than in the west (Riley, 1990).

Where seismic data clearly resolve details at this stratigraphical level, for example on the northern unfaulted margins of the Central Lancashire High (Figure 38), there is clear evidence of an unconformity, although faulting does not appear to have played a role in its formation here. The lowest part of the Hodder Formation present in the Skipton Anticline is the Embsay Limestone. Correlation with the seismic profile in Figure 38 suggests that this interval thickens towards the south-east, and it is possible that representatives of the Phynis Mudstones and perhaps Limekiln Wood Limestones are present here. It then thins south-eastwards by onlap onto first basinal and then platform facies of presumed Clitheroe Limestone Formation. It then laps out against this carbonate platform (?Thornton Limestone) and is overlapped by the upper part of the Hodder Mudstone Formation. These relationships suggest that the unconformity at the base of the Hodder

Mudstone Formation, is one produced by depositional onlap onto a pre-existing topography and that erosion (at a scale resolvable by seismic data) was not important. In view of the deep-water nature of all the rocks of the Hodder Mudstone Formation, this might imply that the cause of the unconformity is a rapid deepening within the basin which effectively shut down shallow-water carbonate production of the Thornton Limestone. It is possible however, that this deepening was caused by tectonic movements which elsewhere were responsible for fault reactivation noted earlier with the possibility of erosion associated with fault scarp retreat.

The continued rise in relative sea-level into Arundian times resulted in the inundation of all but the very highest parts of the Askrigg Block. Deposition of shallow-water carbonates of the Kilnsey Formation in the south, and the lower part of the Fawes Wood Limestone, the Tom Croft Limestone and Penny Farm Gill Dolomite in the north, ensued (Figure 41). A clastic input from the north in late Arundian times temporarily extended onto the block, resulting in the deposition of the Ashfell Sandstone as far south as the Beckermonds Scar Borehole. The boundary of these platform carbonates with the thick, presumed deltaic deposits in the Stainmore Trough is very poorly constrained, but is thought likely to trend approximately north–south in the eastern part of the block. Platform carbonates elsewhere became increasingly restricted in area, being confined to the crest of the Central Lancashire and Holme highs, which now formed separate banks (Figure 41). On the Southern Lake District High, shallow-water limestones of the Red Hill Oolite are overlain by the Dalton Beds and record a rapid change to deeper-water conditions. Both are interpreted as forming on a southerly tilting ramp (Adams et al., 1990).

The areas of platform carbonates provided the detritus for the turbiditic limestones of the Rain Gill, Chaigley and Embsay Limestones which were deposited in the northern, south-western and eastern part of the Craven Basin, respectively (Figure 41), and are interbedded with thick sequences of undifferentiated Hodder Mudstones. Rocks of similar lithology are proved at this stratigraphical level in the Harrogate Basin (Weeton Borehole) and resedimented shallow-water carbonates interbedded with basinal shales in the Alport Basin derived from the Holme High carbonate platform. The presence of interbedded tuffs and of volcaniclastic particles within the limestones indicates contemporary volcanism here (Alport Borehole–Gutteridge, 1991). The general similarity of seismic facies in other basinal areas suggests the presence of rocks of similar facies. The seismic data around the Central Lancashire High, however, reveals the presence of small mounded features locally at this level. These may represent substantial slumped or gravity slide deposits, consistent with a deep-water environment of deposition or perhaps Waulsortian reefs, although there are no documented occurrences of these at outcrop at this level.

Arundian platform carbonates range in thickness from around 150 m on the Askrigg Block to nearly 700 m on the crest of the Central Lancashire High. These variations in thickness indicate that former structural highs were subsiding at different rates and that subsidence rates were greatest over the Central Lancashire High. The limited data available would suggest that more general postextensional basinal subsidence, involving former interbasinal highs and with a depocentre underlying the better documented Silesian depocentre, may already have begun.

In early Holkerian times there was shallowing over the Southern Lake District High which resulted in the deposition of the Park Limestone. At the same time, the terrigenous Twiston Sandstone was deposited in the Bowland Basin, mostly near the Pendle Fault Zone. The source of these sandstones is uncertain: there is no seismic evidence of deep erosion of the Central Lancashire High to a level whereby basement was exposed. This may point towards fault movements, exposing suitable source rocks for terrigenous sediments, rather than shallowing and consequent erosion.

HODDERENSE LIMESTONE FORMATION AND EQUIVALENT ROCKS (MID TO LATE HOLKERIAN)

The Hodderense Limestone Formation of mid to late Holkerian age, comprises wackestones and floatstones interbedded with thin packestones and mudstones, and outcrops extensively in the Bowland Basin. Local intrabasinal highs such as the Bowland High and South Fells Tilt Block in the Craven Basin, accumulated proportionately more limestone than mudstone. It is a condensed deposit resulting from sediment starvation in basinal areas, with a maximum thickness of 15 m (below the level of seismic resolution). Deposition of shallow-water carbonates continued at this time on the Southern Lake District High (upper part of the Park Limestone), the Askrigg Block (the basal Cove Limestone Member of the Malham Formation in the south and the upper part of the Fawes Wood Limestone in the north) and on the Central Lancashire and Holme highs. A period of erosion and karstification at the end of Holkerian times is recorded on the Southern Lake District High (Adams et al., 1990). A thick succession of deltaic rocks continued to be deposited in the Stainmore Trough and these presumably interdigitate with platform carbonates along an approximately north-west-trending line of uncertain location on the eastern margin of the Askrigg Block.

PENDLESIDE LIMESTONE FORMATION AND EQUIVALENT ROCKS (LATE HOLKERIAN TO LATE ASBIAN)

The Pendleside Limestone Formation of late Holkerian to Asbian age (Table 5) is dominated by fine- to coarse-grained packestones with variable amounts of interbedded mudstones and locally sandstones. Many of the limestones show evidence of deposition by turbidity and massflow processes suggestive of slope instability and substantial palaeowater depths. Thicknesses range up to 300 m.

During latest Holkerian to early Asbian times, there was local erosion at the margin of the Craven Basin, resulting in the removal of the Hodderense Limestone in the Eshton–Hetton and Skipton anticlines (Riley, 1990). Erosion also occurred on the Southern Lake District High resulting in a hiatus below the Urswick Limestone. There is also limited seismic evidence for a temporary cessation of platform carbonate deposition on the Central Lancashire High at this time followed by the establishment of a carbonate platform of much-reduced extent (Figure 39).

The limestone turbidites of the Pendleside Limestone Formation were fed from the platform carbonates on the Askrigg Block (the Cove and Gordale Limestones of the Malham Formation in the south, Garsdale and Danny Bridge limestones in the north), and the Southern Lake District (Urswick Limestone), Holme and Central Lancashire highs, the latter now of much reduced extent. Turbidites are absent on intrabasinal highs (Riley, 1990). This formation covers the earlier platform carbonates of the Central Lancashire High and laps out at the toe of the smaller Asbian–Brigantian carbonate mound (Figure 39).

In early Asbian times in the Craven Basin, these turbidites were dominated by pellet-oolite grains, but in late Asbian times, the dominant carbonate supply changed to lithoclastic limestone. This is thought to have resulted from the establishment of fringing reefs to the south of the middle Craven Fault near the southern margin of the Askrigg Block (the 'Craven reef belt') which effectively acted as a block to the direct supply of carbonates from the platforms. The lithoclastic limestones are thought to have been sourced from these reefs by gulleying and erosion during repeated periods of subaerial exposure. Palaeokarstic horizons are common throughout all Asbian platform carbonates. Tectonic and eustatic cycles are recognised by Horbury (1989) in the Urswick Limestone of the Southern Lake District High and it is thought that both processes may have played a role in the formation of these breccias. The thickness of these limestone breccias and the size of the clasts is greatest near to the reef belt. They are also particularly thick along the northern margin of the Catlow Anticline, and this has led to the suggestion that the reef belt continues in the subsurface along the southern margin of the Bowland High (Arthurton et al., 1988). The platform margin must, however, change to a north-westerly trending feature towards the west, as basinal Asbian facies are encountered in the Whitmoor Borehole. On the Southern Lake District High a reef-fringed margin is thought to have extended in a north-east–south-west direction approximately along the line of the Hutton Monocline (Adams et al., 1990). This would suggest that for at least part of its course, this boundary ran close to the trace of the Craven faults on the south-western margin of the Askrigg Block, as indicated in Figure 42. Evidence for the presence of this rimmed platform margin to the east of the exposed is lacking, but it is assumed that it lay approximately along the line of the subsurface continuation of the North and Middle Craven faults (Figure 14), to the south of the Sawley Borehole. A marked decrease in the amount of platform-derived carbonates is noted in the Alport Basin (Gutteridge, 1991) from mid-Asbian times onwards, resulting in a succession of basinal shales and distal carbonate turbidites. This is also attributed to periodic platform emergence combined with the establishment of accretionary rimmed shelves, but in this case, along the northern margin of the Derbyshire carbonate platform and the southern margin of the Holme platform. Limestone breccias are also noted locally just to the north of the Central Lancashire High (Riley, 1990, fig. 17) and

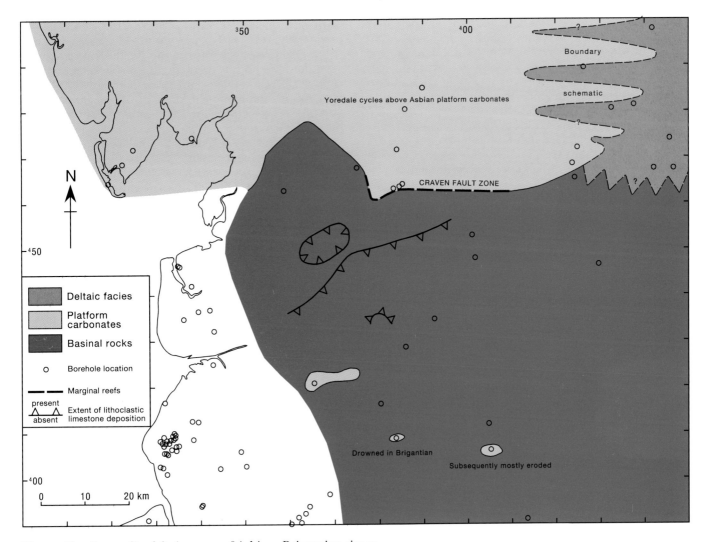

Figure 42   Generalised facies map of Asbian–Brigantian times.

presumably indicate derivation from the carbonate banks on this high.

Rocks in the Stainmore Trough comprise alternations of deltaic sandstones, siltstones and mudstones, with inter-digitated limestones indicating periodic open-marine influences. The boundary between the platform carbonates developed on the Askrigg Block and the rocks in the Stainmore Trough therefore became very diffuse at this time.

Bowland Shale Group: Lower Bowland Shale Formation and equivalent rocks (late Asbian to Brigantian)

The Lower Bowland Shale Formation (Table 5) is dominated by mudstone but also contains variable amounts of interbedded sandstone and limestone. It includes strata up to the *Cravenocerous leion* marine band which marks the base of the Namurian. Rocks of this formation are present in all basinal areas within the region and thicknesses are highly variable, up to 400 m, much of the variation being attributed to the presence or absence of sandstone. These rocks were deposited in basins fringed by reefs which

effectively cut off the supply of detrital carbonates from the platforms for much of the time and allowed the water column to become stratified and oxygen-depleted.

The mudstones are black, calcareous, foetid, rich in organic material and micaceous in part. Mudstone breccias are reported from the Alport Basin (Gutteridge, 1991) and Harrogate Basin (Cooper and Burgess, 1993). They are very fossiliferous and contain a dysaerobic benthic fauna. The limestones are turbiditic and comprise transported shallow-water limestone clasts, crinoid debris and some contain slump structures. One major limestone unit is distinguished in the Craven Basin, comprising interbedded limestone and mudstone and known as the Park Styles or Ravenholme Limestone. Elsewhere the limestones are thinner and of a more distal turbiditic facies. The sandstones which are also interbedded with mudstones are collectively known as the Pendleside Sandstone Member in the Craven Basin and the Harlow Hill Sandstone in the Harrogate Basin. They are dark grey and quartz-rich but with minor feldspar and lithic fragments, together with comminuted plant material. Individual beds are variable, from thin and planar to thick and variable units, and commonly show sole marks at the base and structures indicative of slumping. These sandstones are turbidites which were derived from coastal deltas to the north (possibly from the Askrigg Block). Consequently they are absent in the south of the region, in the southern part of the Bowland Basin and the Rossendale and Alport basins (Gutteridge, 1991).

The presence of basinal mudstones and turbiditic limestones and sandstones throughout this formation suggests that at the end of Brigantian times water depths were still significant and the basins had not yet been infilled.

At the same time that the Lower Bowland Shale Formation was being deposited in the Craven Basin, a series of at least 11 cyclic repetitions of limestone, mudstone and sandstone, the Yoredale facies, were deposited on the Askrigg Block. These are thought to result from periodic small rises of relative sea-level resulting in deposition of the limestones which are the most persistent of these lithologies, followed by progradation of deltas producing the shale and sandstone beds which are laterally more impersistent. The Yoredale facies spread later to adjacent parts of the Southern Lake District High. On the Southern Lake District High the start of Brigantian times is marked by an increase in water depths and deposition of

deep-water limestones. This facies of thinly bedded, muddy limestones and cherts with interbedded mudstones persisted throughout the Dinantian over the Furness peninsula, but elsewhere is succeeded by shallow-marine limestones with subordinate interbeds of shale and sandstone. Palaeokarsts are developed in grainstones to the north of Lancaster (Adams et al., 1990) and are indicative of periodic emergence.

On the crest of the Central Lancashire High, restricted carbonate banks survived until the end of Dinantian times but were then blanketed by terrigenous sediments of the overlying Namurian succession which effectively ended carbonate deposition in this area. The Brigantian succession on the Holme High is missing and Asbian platform carbonates are directly overlain by Kinderscoutian rocks. It is not certain whether this results from non-deposition or erosion although the change from a carbonate-dominated succession in early Asbian times to a mudstone-dominated one in late Asbian and Brigantian times may suggest that carbonate production ended with uplift in Asbian times, and thereby imply no deposition of the Brigantian succession here (Gutteridge, 1991). Lower Bowland Shales overlie platform carbonates on the Heywood High demonstrating Brigantian drowning of this structural feature.

FIVE

Namurian

Namurian rocks are widely distributed in the region (Figure 2). They crop out on either side of the inverted Bowland Basin, along the north–south-trending Pennine Anticline, over much of the Harrogate Basin northwards into the Stainmore Trough and the eastern Askrigg Block. Namurian rocks also form outliers on the Askrigg Block to the west and outcrop in the Rossendale Anticline to the south of the Pendle Monocline. Namurian rocks are present beneath all occurrences of Westphalian rocks in the region, and those areas where Dinantian rocks outcrop and subcrop are thought originally to have been covered by Namurian rocks. The sub-Permian distribution in the west of the region continues the Caledonide trend of the Bowland Basin. In the east, Namurian rocks subcrop on the western flank of the inverted Carboniferous Cleveland Basin.

The thickest preserved Namurian succession is on the flanks of the Rossendale Anticline. Because of severe erosion over much of the region, it is difficult to deduce depositional thickness variations. However, seismic data from the preserved margins of the Craven Basin suggest that the succession originally thickened to over 2000 m in the basin (Map 6). This depocentre probably extended north-eastwards into the southern margin of the Stainmore Trough and south-eastwards into the Alport Basin. This study confirms that substantial thickness variations are largely confined to the lower Namurian. The Askrigg Block continued to exert an influence throughout this time and resulted in a thinner succession which was of a markedly different facies in earliest Namurian times. The Holme High also appears to have influenced depositional thickness at least until Kinderscoutian times. The dominant controls on these thickness variations were a combination of regional thermal relaxation subsidence, topographical relief of the basin floor and distance from the sediment source. The basin floor relief resulted from a combination of incomplete infilling of basins during the Dinantian, differential compaction of underlying platform and basinal rocks and locally also due to active faulting along basin-margin faults. Variations in the thickness of early Namurian strata were also locally controlled by tectonic inversion, for example east of Formby. Here, local inversion of the concealed Bowland Basin against the controlling Pendle Fault formed an anticline against which early Namurian rocks are banked (Figure 43).

STRATIGRAPHICAL DEVELOPMENT

Namurian rocks in the region are the deposits of a delta, slope and turbidite fan complex associated with rivers draining southwards from Scandinavia (Jones,

1980). These deltas had already reached the Midland Valley of Scotland and northern England during Dinantian times, and their appearance in Namurian times in the region was a consequence of their continued southward progradation. This progradation was interrupted by marine incursions resulting in marine bands which are used extensively to correlate the succession. These marine incursions divide the succession into three main progradational phases, Pendelian, Kinderscoutian and Marsdenian, each with depocentres progressively farther south (Figure 44). By Yeadonian times the basin had essentially been filled. Three delta types have been described, namely turbidite-fronted, sheet (classic Millstone Grit cycles) and elongate (Collinson, 1988). Basinal mudstones and turbidites are recognised in the areas beyond the limits of the delta, and delta-slope mudstones separate turbiditic sandstones from the delta-top channel sandstones with thin coals in the resulting successions. Growth faulting, thought to result from gravitational collapse of these deltaic sequences, is recorded in several places (Chisholm, 1977; 1981).

In early Namurian times, there was a substantial topographical relief of the sea floor. Highs inherited from Dinantian times included the Askrigg Block, the Holme High and, at a very early stage only, the Central Lancashire High. The relief of these highs may have affected the course of the deltas prograding in from the north. This effect is well documented outside the region in Derbyshire, where the Ashover Grit delta is interpreted to follow a tortuous path around basin highs (Jones, 1980). Deltas appear to have entered the region via the Stainmore Trough in the north-east and possibly also from the northwest. The early Pendle Grit and Grassington Grit deltas in the region avoided the highs, except on the south-east margin of the Askrigg Block.

No agreement has been reached on the applicability of sequence stratigraphical concepts to the Namurian deltas (Read, 1991; Collinson et al., 1992) and this study has not clarified matters further.

Pendleian (E1)

Pendleian strata are found at crop, in the inverted Bowland Basin and on the south-east margin of the Askrigg Block.

During this time, the south of the region which was farthest away from the advancing deltas received little sediment, and condensed mudstone successions resulted, for example in the Edale Basin. Rare distal turbidites may have reached this area and the Huddersfield Basin, although none have yet been proved. The Bowland Basin in the north of the region was much nearer the source of

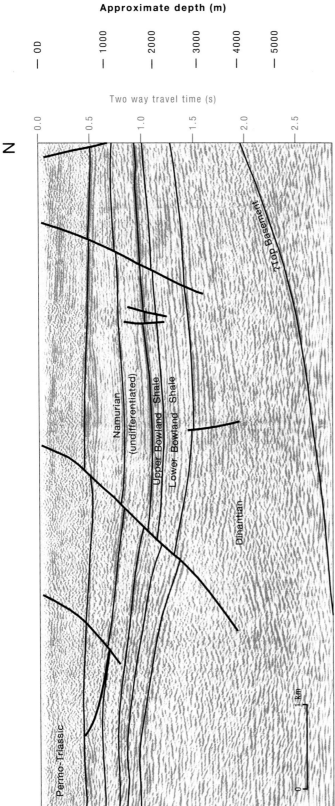

Figure 43 Seismic reflection profile illustrating late Dinantian inversion of the Formby Basin. The Dinantian succession thickens southwards towards the Pendle Fault System (just beyond the southern end of the section). The Bowland Shale thins on to the crest of an anticline, suggestive of Brigantian inversion. South-dipping normal fault suffered reversal at this time and also in Namurian times.

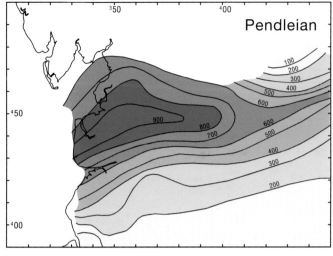

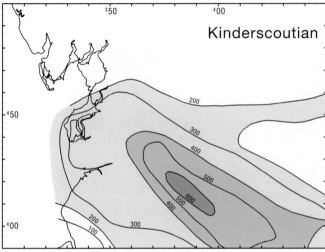

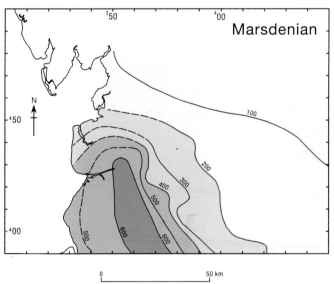

Figure 44 Restored isopachs (metres) of the main Namurian progradational phases.

the deltas and consequently there is a thick basal mudstone and turbidite succession with goniatite faunas (Upper Bowland Shale and Pendle Grits). Log correlation suggests that the Pendle Grit extended as far south as the Croxteth and Heywood boreholes. Similar facies occur in the Harrogate Basin, where the turbidites thin northwards and pinch-out just south of the North Craven Fault (Collinson, 1988). These turbidites are overlain by the Pendle Shales, thought to have been deposited on a delta slope (Collinson, 1988), and fluvial distributary sandstones of the Brennand and Warley Wise grits, recording the infilling of the basin hereabouts to sea-level. Coals are found locally in these uppermost sandstones (Aitkenhead et al., 1992). A similar succession accumulated on the former Southern Lake District High, although sandstone units are thinner there, indicating a more distal position. In marked contrast to these basinal successions, a 'Yoredale' facies of cyclic limestones, mudstones and sandstones continued to accumulate in a thinner succession on the Askrigg Block, which remained a positive area at this time (Dunham and Wilson, 1985).

An unconformity at the base of the Grassington Grit on the south-east margin of the Askrigg Block cuts down to Brigantian strata towards Pateley Bridge (Dunham and Wilson, 1985). This unconformity is thought to be related to footwall uplift of the southern part of the Askrigg Block, associated with active faulting along the North Craven Fault at this time.

Upper Bowland Shales onlap the isolated Brigantian carbonate banks on the Central Lancashire High (Figure 40), but the turbiditic Pendle grits cover these mounds and demonstrate foundering of this high, in early Pendleian times. Higher Grits in this area are very variable in thickness (e.g. the Warley Wise Grit is three times thicker in the Boulsworth borehole than in the Holme Chapel Borehole).

Arnsbergian

This period was marked by northward retreat of most of the deltas in the region, and led to the deposition of the Sabden Shales. These shales have a very characteristic geophysical log signature of high gamma-ray values and abnormally low sonic velocity, with little variation even in the presence of interbedded sandstones. This distinctive log character is however absent on the Holme High and more difficult to distinguish in the thinner, less sandy sections, for example at Kirk Smeaton Borehole. Arnsbergian rocks thicken from the Askrigg Block into the Harrogate Basin with the appearance of more marine bands (Cooper and Burgess, 1993). In the north of the Garstang district, the Roeburndale and Caton Shale formations replace the Sabden Shales and grits (Aitkenhead et al., 1992). In the south of the region, the Edale Shales continued to accumulate throughout this period.

Chokierian to Alportian

Rocks of this age are very thin or absent, leading to interpretations of a non-sequence or unconformity at this stratigraphical level (Ramsbottom et al., 1978). Fluvial sandstones (Upper Follifoot Grit, Silver Hills Sandstone) are present on the Askrigg Block, and in the Harrogate Basin and northern part of the Bowland Basin, whereas in the south of the region, the Edale Shales continued to accumulate.

Kinderscoutian

In Kinderscoutian times, deltas again advanced southwards across the region. In the north in the Craven Basin, Stainmore Trough and northern part of the Rossendale High, where deposition occurred at or near base level, the resulting succession is thin and overlies a generally thick Pendleian succession. In the south, however, where the basin was largely unfilled, the resultant succession is thick and overlies a thin Pendleian succession (Figure 44).

The lowest sandstones are mostly turbiditic and variously called Parsonage Sandstone, Cobden Sandstone (Lancashire), Addlethorpe Grit (Harrogate Basin), Libishaw Sandstone (Askrigg Block), Todmorden Grit, Shale Grit and Mam Tor Sandstones. Variations in thickness of these turbidites appears to have been controlled by basin floor relief. They are overlain by the Gridslow Shales, of delta slope facies (Walker, 1966) which also show thickness variations attributable to basin floor topography. This in turn is overlain by the Lower Kinderscout Grit which becomes coarser upwards and is characterised by 10–20 m shale interbeds. The overlying Upper Kinderscout Grit is a widespread fluviatile deposit and again indicates filling of the basin to just above sea-level. It has a sheet-like form caused by amalgamation of braided channels up to 35 m deep (McCabe, 1977).

Marsdenian

The delta front at this time lay in the south-west of the region and extended well to the south into the Widmerpool–Staffordshire sub-basin (Collinson et al., 1977). The Alum Crag Grit which forms the basal turbiditic phase is overlain by thin shales which in turn are overlain by fluvial sandstones (Brooksbottom, Helmshore, Revidge, Fletcherbank, Hazel Greave, Pule Hill, Middle and Holcombe Brook grits, Huddersfield White Rock) which locally include coals. Palaeocurrents and lithofacies distribution indicate derivation mostly from the north-east, across the earlier Kinderscout delta, although in late Marsdenian times the main deltaic activity may have been to the south-east of the region with progradation from the south-east (Jones, 1980). There is local evidence for marine reworking of these deltaic sediments (Okolo, 1983; Benfield, 1969).

Yeadonian

The Haslingden Flags form an elongate, eastward-prograding delta between Blackburn and Halifax (Collinson, 1988). The suggested westerly source from the East Irish Sea Basin may indicate that this basin had been filled by this time. Bristow (1988) interpreted the east-to-west trend of the delta as being formed in a graben but the presence of contemporary faulting is not supported by this study.

The Rough Rock, a sheet sandstone at the top of the Namurian succession, is the product of large axial braided rivers with extensive crevasse splay and overbank flows (Bristow, 1988). In the Rossendale area, the Rough Rock is split by the Sand Rock Mine Coal, which thickens southwards. The connection with the Stainmore Trough via the Harrogate Basin had been abandoned, and the Craven Basin became essentially part of the northern margin of the basin.

SIX

Westphalian

Westphalian strata in the region comprise all beds between the base of the Subcrenatum Marine Band and the Base Permian unconformity.

The term Coal Measures is applied to coal-bearing rocks of Westphalian age which consist of laterally and vertically variable cycles of mudstones, siltstones, sandstones, seat-earths and coals. In this region, Coal Measures crop out in three main areas: the Lancashire Coalfield, the Yorkshire Coalfield and the Ingleton Coalfield (Map 8). Additionally, small outliers of basal Coal Measures crop out near Kirby Malzeard, west of Ripon. The Yorkshire and Lancashire coalfields have substantial concealed extensions which continue beyond the margins of the region. The central part of the Ingleton Coalfield is also concealed by Permian strata. Excellent summaries of the geology of these coalfields are given by Goosens et al., (1974) for the Yorkshire Coalfield, by Poole and Whiteman (1955) for the Lancashire Coalfield and by Ford (1954, 1958) for the Ingleton Coalfield. The following account is based largely on these sources and a summary of local stratigraphical names is presented in Figure 45.

Ammonoid-bearing marine bands are used extensively to subdivide Westphalian strata. These beds extend over much of north-west Europe and are assigned different local names in Yorkshire and Lancashire (Figure 45). On this basis, strata of Langsettian (Westphalian A), Duckmantian (Westphalian B), Bolsovian (Westphalian C) and Westphalian D age are defined (Figure 45). Division into Lower, Middle and Upper Coal Measures is also made on the basis of these marine bands.

Strata of Langsettian, Duckmantian and Bolsovian age are widespread throughout the region. It is likely that Westphalian D strata are also present, but as diagnostic fossils are lacking in the strata above the Cambriense Marine Band, this cannot be proved. Deposition during Langsettian times took place in a shallow-water delta or lower delta plain environment that was periodically inundated by the sea to shallow depths. Upper Langsettian and Duckmantian rocks were deposited in an upper delta plain environment, resulting in thicker and more laterally continuous coals and hence the most productive measures. Upper Bolsovian and younger rocks were deposited under oxidising, possibly fluvial conditions, and the strata are commonly multicoloured and devoid of coal. In the Ingleton Coalfield, they rest unconformably on earlier strata and may be indicative of the early stages of uplift associated with the Variscan orogeny.

Westphalian strata of the Yorkshire Coalfield attain a maximum preserved thickness of greater than 1500 m east of Rotherham and Barnsley (Goosens et al., 1974). In the Lancashire Coalfield it has been postulated that they attain a maximum preserved thickness of 2500 m in the area immediately south of Manchester (Smith et al., 1984) although this study indicates that preserved thicknesses are substantially thinner (that is 1500 m) than this (Map 8). In the Ingleton Coalfield, Westphalian strata are approximately 1000 m thick (Goosens et al., 1974).

Reconstructed isopachs for the Lower and Middle Coal Measures (Figure 46), suggest that the Coal Measures of Yorkshire, Lancashire and Ingleton were deposited in a single postextensional 'sag' basin, the 'Pennine Basin' (Calver, 1968). The preserved thickness of Coal Measures is estimated to range up to 1500 m near the basin depocentre. The original thickness of strata overlying the Cambriense Marine Band is more difficult to estimate due to varying degrees of erosion. It is over 300 m thick near Badsworth in the east of the region and at various places at subcrop in the Yorkshire Coalfield (Goosens et al., 1974) and nearly 600 m thick in the Lancashire Coalfield. The total thickness of Westphalian strata in the centre of the basin was therefore likely to have exceeded 2100 m. The dominant control on Westphalian sedimentation is thought to be regional thermal relaxation and compaction-induced subsidence. Seismic data examined during this study are unable to resolve any significant contemporary faulting.

YORKSHIRE COALFIELD

The Yorkshire Coalfield and its southerly continuation, the Nottingham–Derbyshire coalfields, are essentially similar and have been taken as the standard succession for the coalfields of the Pennine Basin (Figure 45) (Ramsbottom et al., 1978). More than 1500 m of easterly dipping Westphalian strata are preserved in the exposed coalfield east of Rotherham and Barnsley, although this succession thins to the south and east.

Earliest Langsettian depositional environments were transitional between those of Namurian and Westphalian times, and resulted in the deposition of thin and economically insignificant coals. In contrast, upper Langsettian and lower Duckmantian strata are the most productive Coal Measures with only minor amounts of sandstone and numerous mussel bands. Upper Duckmantian strata, that is those strata above the Maltby Marine Band, contain many marine bands, an increased proportion of sandstone and only a few economically useful coals. Mussel beds are well developed except in the upper beds. The base of the Bolsovian Stage is marked by the Aegiranum (Mansfield) Marine Band, which is up to 10 m thick in parts of Yorkshire. There are only two coals of Bolsovian age which have been worked on a large scale in this succession, which also includes three thick sandstones and a number of mussel bands.

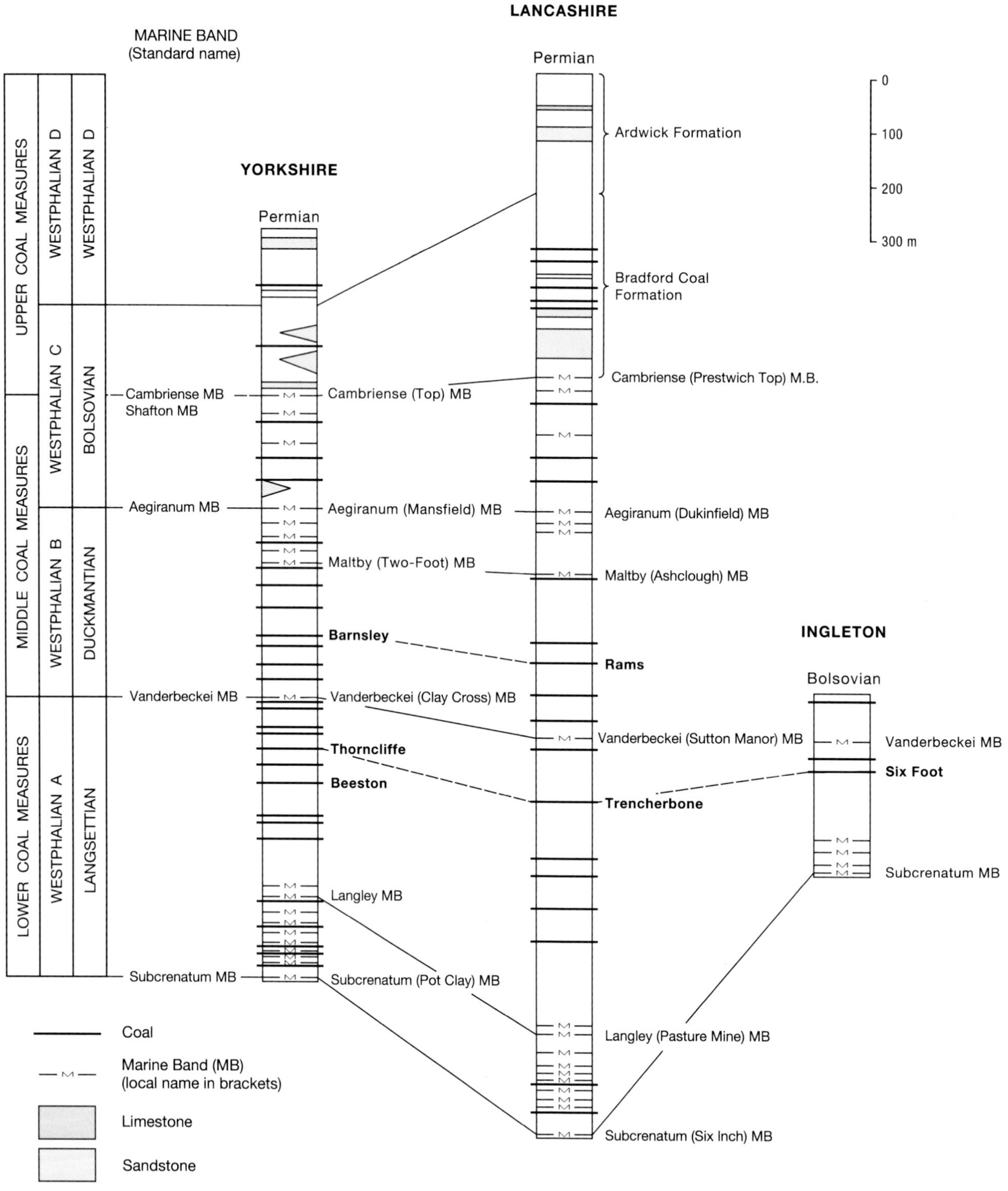

Figure 45   Correlation of Westphalian strata of the Yorkshire, Lancashire and Ingleton coalfields.

The Cambriense (Top) Marine Band represents the last marine incursion into north-west Europe in Westphalian times. Rocks deposited after this are preserved in the exposed coalfield around Badsworth and South Kirkby where there are only two workable coal seams. Sedimen-

tation was still cyclical, although the highest beds are intermediate in facies between the grey measures below and the red Etruria Marl of the Midlands (Goosens et al., 1974). These are believed to have been deposited under oxidising conditions in shallow water. Several major,

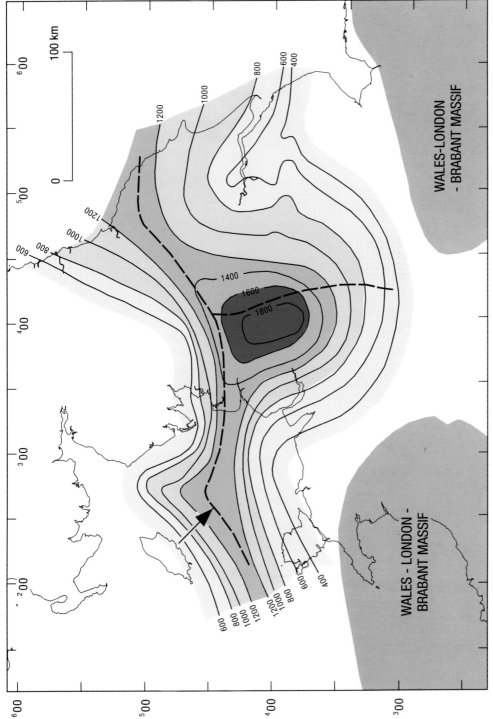

Figure 46 Restored and generalised isopachs of the Lower and Middle Coal Measures (modified from Calver, 1989).

—————— Isopachs at intervals of 200 m

— — — — Inversion axes and Silesian depocentres

▲——— Thickening directions on seismic profiles

massive, medium-grained sandstones were deposited above the Cambriense Marine Band, each locally exceeding 40 m in thickness. The lowest of these sandstones, the Ackworth Rock has an erosive base and cuts out the Cambriense Marine Band in places.

LANCASHIRE COALFIELD

The Westphalian strata of Lancashire (Figure 45) can be conveniently separated into two areas of outcrop: the Burnley and South Lancashire coalfields (Map 8). These are almost separated by an inlier of Namurian strata, the Rossendale Anticline.

In broad terms, the outcrop of the South Lancashire Coalfield forms an arc around the northern and north-western margin of the Permo-Triassic Cheshire Basin. Its concealed extension dips beneath the Cheshire Basin and there is little reason to doubt that it is continuous at depth with the Westphalian strata of North Wales and North Staffordshire. For example, Westphalian strata were proved in the Knutsford Borehole below a depth of 2775.8 m below OD, in the northern Cheshire Basin, well south of the southern limit of deep mining in the Lancashire Coalfield. Strata of Langsettian, Duckmantian, Bolsovian and Westphalian D age are present and Lower, Middle and Upper Coal Measures are recognised. The facies of the Lower and Middle Coal Measures is typical of those found throughout the Pennine Basin. However, reddened Middle and Upper Coal Measures are present in the Lancashire Coalfield, for example in the St Helens area (Trotter, 1954). In the Prestwich area the aggregate thickness of coal (excluding seams less than 0.6 m thick) in the Lower and Middle Coal Measures is around 22.5 m (Poole and Whiteman, 1955).

The Bradford Coal Formation of the Upper Coal Measures consists of a rhythmic succession of coals and coaly shales overlain by dark, highly fossiliferous mudstones with abundant carbonaceous ironstones, sandstones and fireclays. Some of the fireclays towards the top of this formation contain limestone (Poole and Whiteman, 1955).

The base of the Ardwick Group of the Upper Coal Measures is conventionally placed in the highest part of the Bolsovian stage (Ramsbottom et al., 1978) and its top within the Westphalian D. The succession consists predominantly of red, purple, green, brown and yellow blocky mudstones. Towards the top of the group, grey beds and thin limestones are commonly present and sandstones are also found. The deposition of this group marks the end of coal-forming conditions in the Lancashire area. It may have been caused by compression and uplift of the Pennine Basin in the early stages of the Variscan orogeny. If this is the case, it is analogous to the unconformity between the red and grey measures in the Ingleton Coalfield (see below), although this does not imply that they are necessarily the same age.

The Burnley Coalfield crops out between the Rossendale Anticline and the Pendle Monocline and consists entirely of strata of Langsettian and Duckmantian age which attain a maximum thickness of about 650 m. It has no concealed extension.

INGLETON COALFIELD

The Ingleton Coalfield is a small (approximately 50 km^2) outlier of Westphalian rocks lying close to the villages of Ingleton and Burton-in-Lonsdale. The structure of the coalfield is an east–west-trending syncline, plunging to the east and truncated to the north-east by the South Craven Fault. Exposure in the Ingleton Coalfield is limited because of thick Quaternary deposits, but it is believed to consist of over 940 m of strata of Langsettian to Bolsovian/Westphalian D age overlain by Permian breccias. The succession consists of up to 520 m of lower Grey Measures, which are the productive strata containing up to six coal seams, unconformably overlain by nearly 580 m of unproductive Red Measures, which cut out the Grey Measures in the centre of the coalfield. Apart from the South Craven Fault, the Hollintree Fault, lying parallel to and half a mile south-west of the former, is the main fault in the coalfield, with a throw of probably more than 300 m. There are few other faults within the coalfield.

AUSTWICK OUTLIER

Up to 150 m of Coal Measures conformably overlies the Namurian in this small faulted outlier which is a south-east extension of the Ingleton Coalfield. It is truncated to the north-east by the Lawkland Fault (Figure 2), which is parallel to but south-west of the South Craven Fault. The lowest 50 m of this succession was proved by the Waters Farm Borehole (Arthurton et al., 1988).

SEVEN

Post-Variscan structure and structural evolution

PERMO-TRIASSIC STRUCTURAL EVOLUTION

By earliest Permian times, Variscan continental collision had led to final suturing and consolidation of the Pangaean supercontinent (Ziegler, 1982). The region lay deep within this continental mass. Variscan basin inversion and regional uplift resulted in considerable elevation of the land surface. During Permian times this underwent progressive peneplanation, and, contemporaneously, regional sag basins developed in the North Sea region. By late Permian, and particularly, early Triassic times, the north-west European region formed an isthmus between the rapidly developing Arctic–North Atlantic rift system to the north, and the Tethys–Central Atlantic–Gulf of Mexico rift-wrench system to the south; regional extension, directed roughly east–west, became established as the dominant tectonic process.

Principal Permo-Triassic structural features

Because of markedly incomplete preservation of the sedimentary succession, details of the Permo-Triassic structures of the region are partly a matter for conjecture. Nevertheless, sufficient evidence remains to draw firm conclusions about many aspects of the structure.

The principal Permo-Triassic structural features of the region are illustrated in Map 9 and Figure 47. Strongly contrasting structural styles characterise the eastern and western parts of the region, separated by the poorly understood Pennine High. In the east, subsidence was of a regional nature, close to the western margin of the Southern North Sea Basin. In the west, subsidence was associated with extensional basin development manifest as the East Irish Sea, the West Lancashire and the Cheshire basins, forming part of a major rift system extending southwards to the English Channel and northwards into Scottish waters. It is likely that many of the major Dinantian basin-controlling normal faults were reactivated in extensional mode during Permo-Triassic basin development. The Dinantian fault network was by no means perfectly reactivated however; many new north–south-trending faults appear to have developed in Permo-Triassic times, reflecting the east–west extension direction. It is likely that a significant component of the normal displacements which presently affect Namurian and Westphalian strata may well have developed in post-Carboniferous times.

SOUTHERN NORTH SEA BASIN

The whole Permo-Triassic outcrop at the eastern part of the region was deposited close to the western feather-edge of the Southern North Sea Basin. This landward part of the Southern North Sea Basin is also variously known as the Cleveland Basin and East Midlands Shelf (Kent, 1980) and the Eastern England Shelf (Whittaker, 1985). Permian strata rest unconformably on the Carboniferous sequence in the north-east of the region, with a gentle regional eastward dip. Although relatively minor, some structures which affect the Permo-Triassic sequence hereabouts give important clues to the style of Permo-Triassic, and subsequent, structural evolution in the region. They are therefore discussed in some detail. Faults are of three main types:

Subplanar normal faults

Dominantly east-trending, these faults are subparallel to the structures in the underlying Carboniferous sequence. They have small normal displacements, are subplanar with moderate to steep dips, and also affect the underlying Carboniferous rocks (Figure 16). Some of the faults appear to be Carboniferous structures reactivated in post-Triassic times. Other faults displace both Permo-Triassic and Carboniferous beds by the same amount, implying an entirely post-Carboniferous age.

The Bilton–Scriven Monocline (Cooper and Burgess, 1993) is mapped at surface as an east-trending, south-facing, faulted fold affecting Permo-Triassic strata and causing the base of the Permo-Triassic outcrop to swing from a north–south strike to east to west over a distance of some 5 km [^{4}38000 ^{4}63000]. Seismic reflection data show that the structure resembles a faulted syncline which directly overlies the Variscan Ellenthorpe Anticline (Figure 48). It appears to have formed by extensional reactivation and collapse of the anticline, and illustrates how the reactivation of pre-existing structures is likely to have played an important role in post-Carboniferous basin development throughout the region.

Curved detached normal faults

These faults are markedly curved ('listric') in profile, flattening at depth on to subhorizontal *décollement* surfaces within the Permian sequence (Figures 16 and 49). The faults appear to be effectively detached from the underlying Carboniferous rocks as they do not penetrate into them (consequently they do not appear on Map 9). Examples of this type of structure include the Kirkby Sigston–Cotcliffe Graben (Figure 49) of the Northallerton district (Frost, 1998) and the Asenby–Coxwold Graben of the Thirsk District (Powell et al., 1992). It is likely that beds of soluble anhydrite and halite present within the Permian sequence provided the weak layers necessary for this type of faulting to develop. It may be that gravity-sliding down the south-easterly dipping palaeoslope was a prime factor in the development of detached normal faulting hereabouts. A side-effect of this detached normal faulting, was severe localised structural attenuation of the

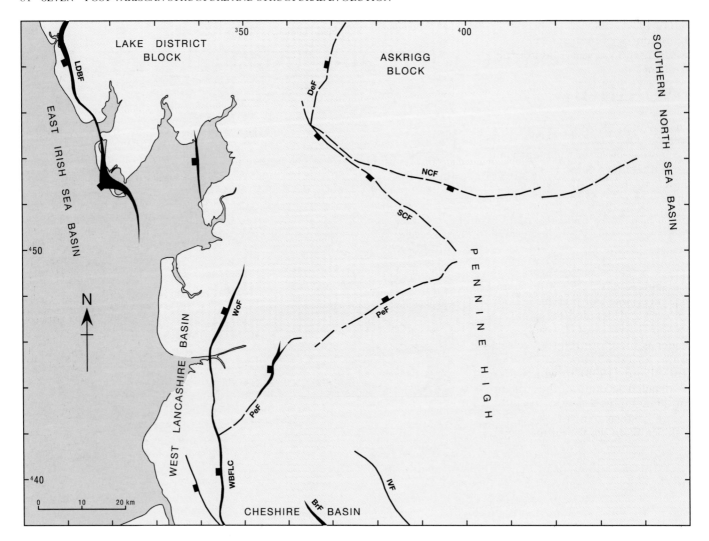

Figure 47   Principal Permo-Triassic structures of the region.

BrF Brook House Fault; DeF Dent Fault; IVF Irwell Valley Fault; LDBF Lake District Boundary Fault
System; NCF North Craven Fault; PeF Pendle Fault; SCF South Craven Fault; WBFLC Western Boundary
Fault of the Lancashire Coalfield; WoF Woodsford Fault. Dashed ornament indicates faults thought likely
to have been active during Permo-Triassic times, but for which movement casnnot be proven.

Permo-Triassic sequence (see Figure 49). The age of this
faulting is uncertain; it was at least, in part, post-middle
Jurassic (p.89).

Folds

As well as the extension-related structures discussed above,
localised minor folds affecting the Permo-Triassic sequence
are visible on the seismic reflection data (Figure 52).
These appear to be associated with the reversal of underlying faults and may be indicative of post-Triassic compressional stresses associated with basin inversion (89).

LAKE DISTRICT BLOCK

In Permo-Triassic times the Lake District Block was separated from the East Irish Sea Basin to the west by the Lake
District Boundary Fault System (Figure 50). To the east of
this the block is likely to have dipped gently towards the

Dent Fault. It is believed that the block has remained a
structurally high area since Carboniferous times, receiving
a markedly attenuated Permo-Triassic sequence (Holliday,
1993) which has been subsequently eroded. Depth of
burial studies based upon geophysical logs and the thermal modelling of apatite fission-track palaeotemperatures
(Chadwick et al., 1994), indicate that less than 1000 m of
Permo-Triassic strata were deposited over the central parts
of the block. This contrasts with over 4000 m deposited
offshore in the East Irish Sea Basin. Thicker strata are also
likely to have been deposited over the eastern part of the
block, on the hanging-wall block of the Dent Fault.

ASKRIGG BLOCK

In Permo-Triassic times the Askrigg Block is likely to have
been bounded to the west by the Dent Fault, and to the
south by the North Craven Fault System. Sedimentary

Figure 48   Cross-section through the Bilton–Scriven structure, overlying the Variscan Ellenthorpe Anticline.

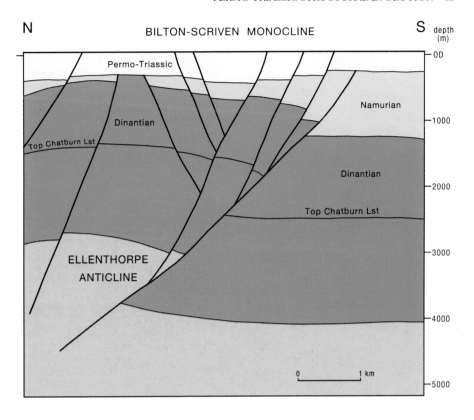

thicknesses on the block are very poorly constrained. In the west, on the footwall-block of the Dent Fault, the sedimentary cover was probably similar to that on the Lake District Block, with gradual eastward thickening towards the South North Sea Basin.

East Irish Sea Basin

This is a major sedimentary basin containing a very thick Permo-Triassic sequence. Much of this lies offshore however and detailed description is beyond the remit of this report; the reader is therefore referred to Jackson et al. (1987) and Jackson and Mulholland (1993) in which there are detailed accounts of the structure and stratigraphy.

The eastern margin of the East Irish Sea Basin lies within the region, in west Cumbria, and is marked by the Lake District Boundary Fault (Figure 50). Offshore in the basin depocentre, more than 4000 m of Permo-Triassic strata were deposited, a full sequence being locally preserved. In the region, close to the eastern basin margin, up to about 2000 m of Permo-Triassic strata are preserved.

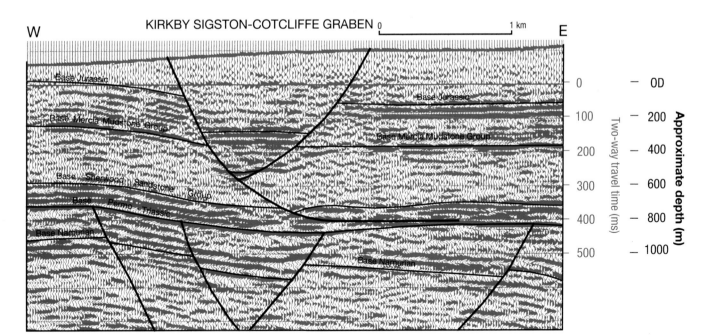

Figure 49   Seismic reflection profile across the Kirkby Sigston–Cotcliffe Graben. Note severe structural attenuation of the Permo-Triassic sequence by detached normal faulting. Note pre-late Permian normal faults cutting the Carboniferous succession.

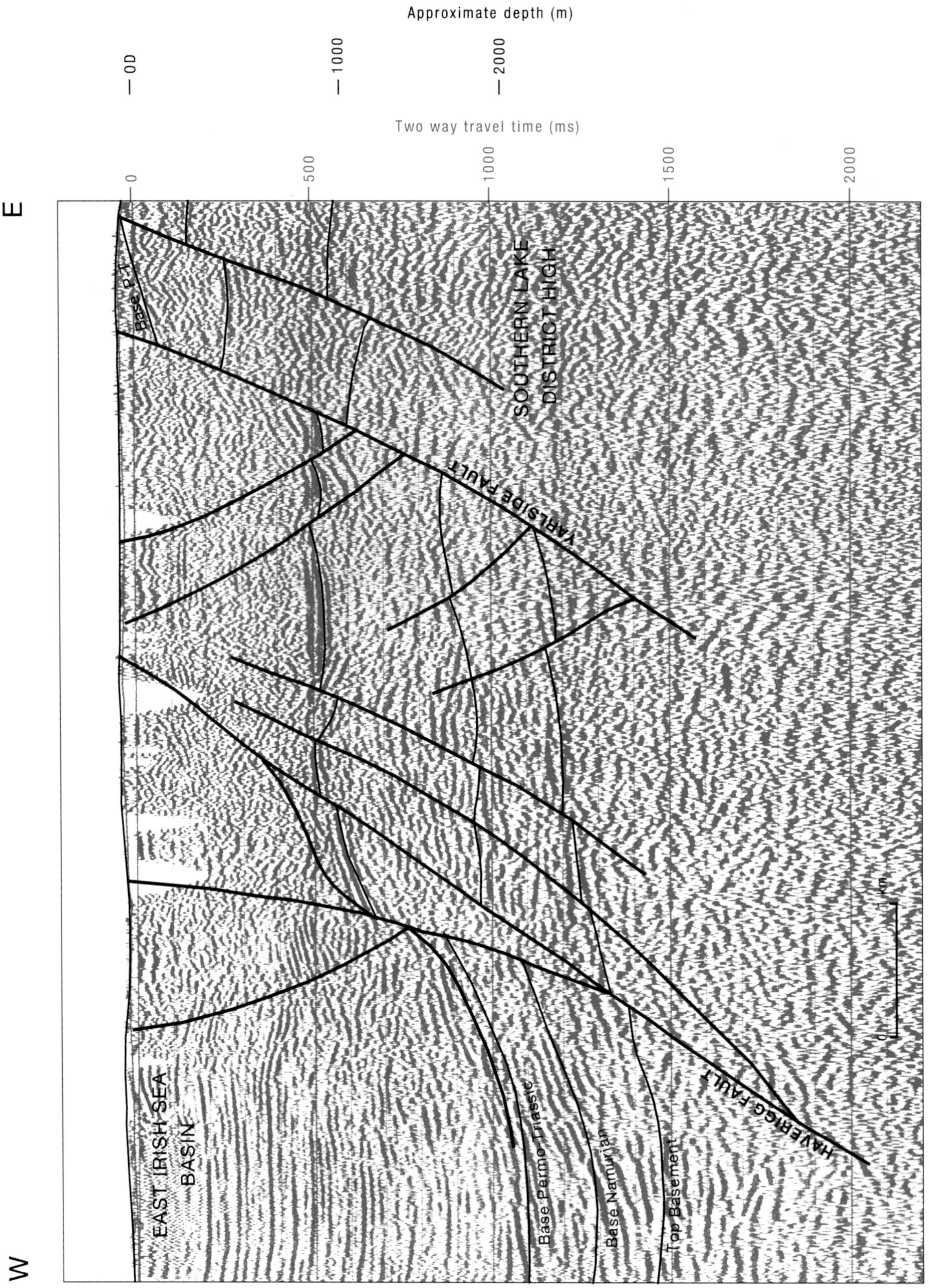

Figure 50   Seismic reflection profile across the Lake District Boundary Fault System near to Barrow-in-Furness. Note that Base Namurian is closer to base Permo-Triassic in hanging-wall block of Haverigg Fault than in its foot-wall block. This suggests Variscan reversal of the fault.

WEST LANCASHIRE BASIN

The West Lancashire Basin forms the landward portion of the East Irish Sea Basin (Figure 47, Map 9, Regional Cross-section B–B'). The eastern margin of the basin is partially fault-bounded and partially an unconformable contact between the Permo-Triassic basin-fill and the underlying Carboniferous rocks. Permo-Triassic thicknesses are typically in the order of 1000 m and locally in excess of 2000 m. Nowhere in the basin is a full sequence preserved, so initial thicknesses were undoubtedly much greater than this. Dominant fault trends in the basin are north–south, roughly perpendicular to the presumed Permo-Triassic extension direction (see above). Major basin-controlling faults (Figure 49) include the Western Boundary Fault (of the Lancashire Coalfield), the Pendle Fault (reactivating the earlier Carboniferous structure) and the Woodsford Fault; all large normal faults downthrowing west, with some associated antithetic faults. The Woodsford Fault (Figure 51) appears to have in part controlled the distribution of the Collyhurst Sandstone.

CHESHIRE BASIN

Only the northernmost part of this important Permo-Triassic basin impinges upon the region (Figure 47, Regional Cross-section A–A'. Permo-Triassic sedimentary thicknesses locally reach 2000 m at the southern edge of the region (Map 9), but thicken markedly to nearly 4000 m some 30 km farther south in the basin depocentre (Evans et al., 1993). Within the region, the basin is cut by north-north-west-trending normal faults, typified by the Brook House and Irwell Valley faults (Figure 47). These faults cut the basin hereabouts into a system of tilted fault-blocks (Figure 19). Thickness changes across these faults indicate that they were active throughout the deposition of much of the Permo-Triassic succession (Evans et al., 1995).

PENNINE HIGH

The Permo-Triassic evolution of this large and rather ill-defined area is very poorly understood, as, for the most part, post-Carboniferous strata are not preserved. It is likely that the Pennine High received markedly thinner

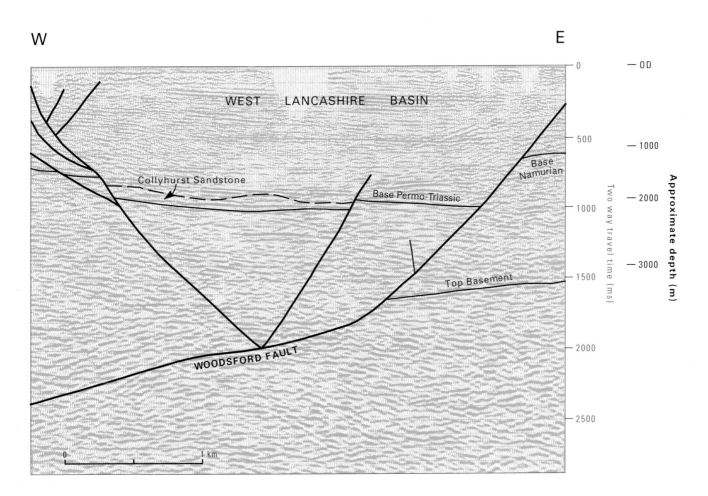

Figure 51   Seismic reflection profile across the Woodsford Fault, near to the eastern edge of the West Lancashire Basin. Note apparent banking of Collyhurst Sandstone against the east-dipping antithetic fault.

Permo-Triassic deposits than the surrounding basinal areas, but thicknesses are difficult to quantify. Fraser and Gawthorpe (1990), from regional geological considerations, estimate that the post-Variscan succession hereabouts is less than 500 m thick. Conversely, Lewis et al. (1992) estimate thicknesses of up to 2700 m from apatite fission-track data. More rigorous analysis of the fission-track palaeotemperatures encountered hereabouts (90–100°C), using the method of Chadwick et al. (1994), indicate typical thicknesses in the order of 2000 m. Local variations in Permo-Triassic depositional thicknesses are likely to have occurred. For example the sites of the Carboniferous Bowland and Harrogate basins may well have had rather thicker sequences, whereas sites above the Central Lancashire and Holme highs probably had very thin post-Variscan cover successions. On a smaller scale the Heywood and Holme faults may also have experienced some movement with relatively thicker sequences above the Rossendale and Huddersfield basins.

Principal Permo-Triassic faults

LAKE DISTRICT BOUNDARY FAULT SYSTEM

This major structural feature forms the present-day boundary between the Permo-Triassic strata of the East Irish Sea Basin and the Lower Palaeozoic rocks at outcrop in the Lake District Block (Figures 2 and 47). The fault system extends some 20 km to the north of the region, giving it a total length of about 70 km. The fault system downthrows to the west and has a large, net, normal displacement, which reaches more than 1800 m close to the northern edge of the region, where it juxtaposes the higher parts of the Sherwood Sandstone Group against the Eskdale Granite. Here, much of the displacement is likely to be across a single structure with a very large throw (the Haverigg Fault). Farther south, in the Barrow-in-Furness district, the fault system branches into at least three separate smaller faults, the Haverigg, Gleaston and Yarlside faults (Figure 50). These faults are subplanar, normal and downthrow west, with moderate to moderately steep dips and a cumulative throw approaching 2000 m (Map 9).

DENT FAULT SYSTEM

The post-Variscan history of this fault is largely a matter of speculation. Underhill et al. (1988) suggest displacements were small, though Permo-Triassic oblique-normal slip may have occurred at its northern end in order to accommodate development of the Vale of Eden half-graben (to the north of the region). The authors of this memoir believe that normal (or oblique-normal) down-to-the-west displacements may well have been significant, with development of relatively thick (now eroded) Permo-Triassic deposits on its hanging-wall block.

NORTH CRAVEN FAULT SYSTEM

Permo-Triassic displacement on the North Craven Fault System probably did occur, but firm evidence of such is lacking. Dunham and Wilson (1985) estimate that more than 600 m of down-to-the-south normal displacement

occurred cumulatively at the western end of the North and South Craven faults, as evidenced by the nearby Permo-Triassic outlier above the Ingleton Coalfield (Maps 8 and 9). Much of this throw was probably of Permo-Triassic age, though considerable younger displacements cannot be ruled out. Farther east, in the Pateley Bridge area, down-to-the-south displacements of Namurian strata (Figure 20) may well have been of Permo-Triassic age.

SOUTH CRAVEN FAULT SYSTEM

The South Craven Fault was regarded by Hudson (1930) 'as definitely post-Carboniferous in age'. This is not wholly the case (see Chapter Three), but a significant post-Carboniferous displacement has undoubtedly occurred. The fault marks the north-east margin of the Permo-Triassic outlier of the Ingleton Coalfield and clearly has a large post-Carboniferous down-to-the-south displacement. How much of this displacement was of Permo-Triassic age, and how much was younger, cannot be estimated. Recent movement has also occurred on the South Craven Fault System. Versey (1948) recorded a seismic event known as the Skipton or Settle Earthquake, in 1944. He regarded the epicentre as 'in all probability' lying along the Gargrave Fault.

PENDLE FAULT SYSTEM

The degree to which the Pendle Fault System was reactivated in Permo-Triassic times appears to have varied along its length (Figure 47), possibly as a function of its trend relative to the dominant east–west extension direction. Where it forms the east-north-east-trending southern margin of the Carboniferous Bowland Basin, movements on the fault system were probably strongly oblique, with little evidence of dip-slip reactivation. Farther west, where it swings into a north-north-east-trend, significant oblique-normal displacement occurred, with a downthrow to the west locally in excess of 1000 m (Map 9).

WOODSFORD FAULT

The Woodsford Fault (Figures 47 and 51) lies near the eastern margin of the West Lancashire Basin splaying northward from the Western Boundary–Pennine Fault System. Downthrow, to the west, is generally around 800 m at the base of the Permo-Triassic, but it attains a maximum throw of 1400 m, to the east of the Elswick Borehole (Figure 3). It extends for approximately 20 km in a south-south-west direction before assuming a north–south trend near the Ribble from where it extends a farther 20 km southwards to merge with the Western Boundary Fault of the Lancashire Coalfield. To the north of the Ribble it has associated antithetic faults (including the Thistleton Fault) which define a narrow graben where early Permian rocks are believed to be thicker (see Chapter Eight).

WESTERN BOUNDARY FAULT OF THE LANCASHIRE COALFIELD

This steeply dipping, major fault, as the name suggests, defines the western margin of the Lancashire Coalfield. Downthrow to the west is in excess of 600 m, and it juxtaposes Sherwood Sandstone against Coal Measures. It trends north–south for approximately 15 km before merging to the north with the Woodsford Fault near the intersection with the Pendle Fault. Permo-Triassic strata are not preserved in its footwall block and therefore its displacement history cannot be determined.

BROOK HOUSE FAULT

The Brook House Fault (Figure 47) constitutes the principal structure in the northern part of the Cheshire Basin. Downthrow to the east exceeds 600 m at the base of the Permo-Triassic (Map 9), and is greater than this to the south of the region. All units of the Permo-Triassic sequence thicken eastwards across the fault, indicating that it was active throughout much of Permo-Triassic basin evolution.

IRWELL VALLEY FAULT

The Irwell Valley Fault (Figure 47) lies in the northern part of the Cheshire Basin. Because Permo-Triassic strata are no longer preserved in its footwall-block, its displacement history cannot be determined. It is likely however to have been a similar feature to the subparallel Brook House Fault.

POST-TRIASSIC STRUCTURAL EVOLUTION

The youngest strata preserved in the region are of upper Jurassic age, occurring in the far north-east. These rocks were deposited towards the western edge of the Southern North Sea Basin and are described more fully in the Northallerton (Frost, 1998) and Thirsk (Powell et al., 1992) memoirs. The post-Triassic structural evolution of the region is divided into three main phases, which are described below.

Jurassic and early Cretaceous extension

Prior to the onset of North Atlantic sea-floor spreading in mid-Cretaceous times, the post-Triassic development of the region was characterised by episodes of regional crustal extension. Comparison with more complete sequences in basins to the south and east (for example Whittaker, 1985; Kirby and Swallow, 1987; Badley et al., 1989) indicates that extension occurred principally in the early Jurassic and again in late Jurassic to early Cretaceous times. The early extension was probably a remnant of the Permo-Triassic tectonic regime and was still directed roughly east–west. Later, in late Jurassic and early Cretaceous times, a new, north–south-directed extension direction became established.

For much of this time a depositional regime prevailed in which thick successions were deposited in fault-controlled extensional basins in the west of the region. Paradoxically, post-Triassic faulting in the region can only be unequivocally demonstrated in the east, where middle Jurassic strata of the Southern North Sea Basin are cut by normal faults to form such structures as the Kirkby–Sigston–Cotcliffe and the Asenby–Coxwold grabens (Figure 49 and Powell et al., 1992). Most of these faults are low-angle structures, with a tendency to detach on the basal Permian evaporites (see p.90). Their most likely age is early Cretaceous, as they are very similar to the structures which controlled early Cretaceous development of the Cleveland Basin (Kirby and Swallow, 1987), a few kilometres to the east of the region. This phase of early Cretaceous extension, and localised basin development, was also accompanied by considerable erosion, particularly of the block areas between the basins. This led to development of the widespread late-Cimmerian unconformity (Rawson and Riley, 1982, Whittaker, 1985). Considerable thicknesses of Jurassic and Permo-Triassic strata were probably removed from much of the region at this time.

Mid Cretaceous to Early Palaeocene regional shelf subsidence

By mid-Cretaceous times extension had effectively ceased (Whittaker, 1985), as sea-floor spreading propagated northwards into the North Atlantic region. Postextensional regional shelf subsidence became established, with much diminished structural demarcation between blocks and basins and deposition of a relatively uniform Upper Cretaceous sequence (the Chalk). Deposition probably continued into early Palaeocene times which, according to apatite fission-track data (Lewis et al., 1992), probably marked the maximum post-Variscan burial of much of the region.

Mid-Palaeocene to Present regional uplift and basin inversion

Regional uplift, commencing in early Palaeocene times (for example Lewis et al., 1992), triggered a period of erosion which has probably continued, certainly onshore, to the present day. It is likely that basin inversions, with associated fault reversals and local folding were superimposed upon this regional uplift. Because insufficient younger strata are preserved in the region, firm evidence for basin inversion is scarce, and is limited to minor folding observed in the Thirsk district (Figure 52). Some of these minor folds overlie earlier pre-Permian (Variscan) folds, which affect Carboniferous strata. This is indicative of repeated fault reversal, similar to, though on a smaller scale than, the 'double inversion' of the Cleveland area envisaged by Kent (1980). A small distance to the east of the region, the Cleveland Basin was strongly inverted (Kirby et al., 1987) with more than 2000 m of axial uplift. Apatite fission-track palaeotemperatures, coupled with low heat flow values indicate considerable uplift in the Craven Basin area. It may be, therefore, that strong inversion affected a roughly east–west region coincident with the underlying Ribblesdale Foldbelt, reactivating again, this fundamental line of crustal weakness. Inversion of the East Irish Sea Basin probably also occurred at this time (for example Knipe et al., 1993; Chadwick et al., 1994), but in the region direct evidence is lacking. Complex structures, including minor folds, in the hanging-wall blocks of the Lake District Boundary Fault System (Figure 50) may attest to oblique-reversal, associated with basin inversion. Just south of the region, Fraser and Gawthorpe (1990) cite evidence for reversal of major structures such as the Hoton and Barton faults.

Basin inversion was not necessarily coeval with the regional uplift and may have corresponded to one or more of three inversion episodes documented in southern Britain: the late-Cretaceous inversion in the southern North Sea (Glennie and Boegner, 1981; Badley et al., 1989), the Palaeocene inversion of the Wessex Basin (Lake and Karner, 1987) or the main Oligo-Miocene inversion of southern Britain and the southern North Sea (Badley et al., 1989). Well-documented cases of basin inversion reasonably close to the region include the Sole Pit Trough (Van Hoorn, 1987) and the Wessex Basin (Lake and Karner, 1987), where the main phase of inversion occurred in Oligo-Miocene times, corresponding to major Alpine nappe development. It is considered that this probably also constituted the principal inversion event in the region, though earlier, minor, phases cannot be ruled out.

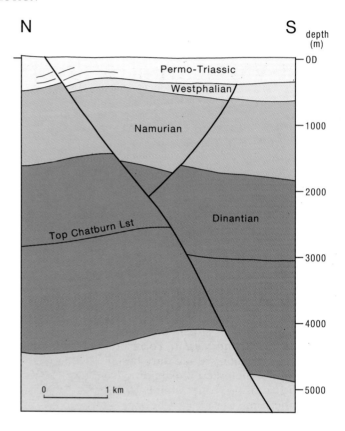

Figure 52 Cross-section close to the southern end of the Stainmore Trough, illustrating post-Permo-Triassic hanging-wall anticline, possibly formed during Alpine compression.

EIGHT

Post-Variscan stratigraphy

Permian and Triassic rocks are the youngest strata to crop out in the region. They are the remnants of a once much more extensive cover of Mesozoic rocks which was uplifted and eroded during Cenozoic times. The thickness and extent of Permo-Triassic, Jurassic and younger rocks, formerly present but now eroded away, is unknown although depth of burial studies based on the state of compaction of sediments and apatite fission track studies suggest that the eroded cover was typically some 2000 m thick over the region (Chapter Seven).

PERMIAN AND TRIASSIC

Permian and Triassic strata cover about a quarter of the region (Figure 2 and Map 9), corresponding to the margins of three major sedimentary basins. To the west of the Pennines, the outcrop extending from west Cumbria to south Lancashire fringes the East Irish Sea Basin, and the northern margin of the Cheshire Basin extends into the southern part of the region. To the east of the Pennines, the outcrop corresponds to the western margin of the North Sea Basin. The chronostratigraphical and lithostratigraphical classification of strata in these areas is shown in Table 6. Permo-Triassic rocks rest everywhere with profound angular unconformity on Carboniferous strata ranging widely in age from early Viséan to late Westphalian. This reflects the great amount of erosion that took place during and after Variscan folding and the extensional rifting that followed.

Permian

In early Permian times, the region formed a small part of a vast desert. Clastic rocks (Appleby Group) were deposited from sheet floods, debris flows and desert winds, accumulating locally to considerable thicknesses to the west of a probable Pennine barrier (Smith and Taylor, 1992). Some of these rocks accumulated in valleys, but the thicker sequences were probably deposited in developing grabens or half grabens. Evidence of this is present, for example, in Lancashire (e.g. Figure 51), where the aeolian Collyhurst Sandstone has been proved to be 715 m thick in Formby No. 1 Borehole, but is absent nearby in No. 4 (Kent, 1948; Wray and Cope, 1948), and also in the Elswick Borehole where this section is very thick but is absent in the nearby Thistleton Borehole. The largely aeolian Kinnerton Sandstone deposition was similarly affected by fault control. The highest relief in the region was probably formed by the fault-bounded Lake District massif (Figure 47) flanked by proximal breccias and conglomerates (Brockram). In contrast, to the east of the Pennine barrier, the mainly aeolian Basal

Permian Sands formed a thin cover on a relatively even pediment (Smith and Taylor, 1992). Another barrier or divide separated the East Irish Sea and Cheshire basins and has been named the Llyn–Rossendale Ridge by Jackson and Mulholland (1993). However, its effect on sedimentation is less clear than that of the Pennine barrier.

In late Permian times, a marine transgression formed the 'Bakevellia' and 'Zechstein' seas with depocentres in the East Irish Sea and North Sea basins, respectively. A shallow arm of the 'Bakevellia Sea' also entered the Cheshire Basin. The deposits in these seas show a major cyclical pattern, which can be idealised and simplified as a repeated upwards succession of couplets comprising dolomite and/or marl overlain by evaporites. Five such cycles (plus some subcycles) have been recognised by Smith (1980) in the North Sea Basin, and named successively EZ1 (English Zechstein 1) to EZ5. Each is attributed, by Smith, to a rapid flooding event, followed by carbonate shelf progradation (Cadeby and Brotherton formations), and then evaporation to produce hypersaline conditions in the basin in which land-derived calcareous mud and silt (marl) was also being deposited. The evaporites in these cyclical sequences thin towards the basin margin and, in addition, are partially or wholly removed by groundwater dissolution at outcrop including those of the Marl Slate, Edlington and Roxby formations in the region. Similar cycles, tentatively correlated, for example by Jackson and Mulholland (1993), with the EZ1 to EZ5 cycles, appear to be present in the East Irish Sea Basin but are not represented by the stratigraphical nomenclature. The detailed repeated sequences of carbonates, mudstones or siltstones, and evaporites have been well-documented by Arthurton and Hemingway (1972) in the main formation where they are developed in west Cumbria and north Lancashire, namely the St Bees Evaporites. Carbonates and evaporites are poorly represented in the succeeding St Bees Shales, and in the main Upper Permian formation of south Lancashire, the Manchester Marls, except in the Southport and Formby district. Here, Wray and Cope (1948) state that 'thin beds of anhydrite and gypsum associated with massive dolomite occur at several horizons in the formation'.

Triassic

At the end of Permian times, a major regression of the sea caused the three main fault-controlled basins to become landlocked. A period of general intracontinental subsidence and red-bed sedimentation ensued, but with the three basins continuing as the main depocentres.

Fluvial sand deposition (Sherwood Sandstone Group) dominated the earliest Triassic Scythian Stage, deposited

Table 6   Stratigraphy of the Permian and Triassic rocks of the region using representative sections from selected districts.

PERIOD	Series	STAGE	WEST OF PENNINES — West Cumbria (Sellafield)	WEST OF PENNINES — Lancashire (Blackpool and Garstang)	GROUP	WEST OF PENNINES — North Cheshire Basin	GROUP	EAST OF PENNINES — Yorkshire (Harrogate District)	GROUP
TRIASSIC	Upper	NORIAN		Breckells Mudstones	MERCIA MUDSTONE GROUP	Bollin Mudstone (LKM)	MERCIA MUDSTONE GROUP	undivided	MERCIA MUDSTONE GROUP
		CARNIAN		Kirkham Mudstones					
		LADINIAN		Singleton Mudstones		Tarporley Siltstone (KW)			
		ANISIAN	Ormskirk Sandstone	Hambleton Mudstones		Helsby Sandstone (KS)	SHERWOOD SANDSTONE GROUP	undivided	SHERWOOD SANDSTONE GROUP
			Calder Sandstone	undivided	SHERWOOD SANDSTONE GROUP	Wilmslow Sandstone (UMS)			
		SCYTHIAN	St Bees Sandstone			Chester Pebble Beds (PB)			
PERMIAN	Upper		St Bees Shales	Manchester Marls	CUMBRIAN COAST GROUP	Manchester Marls / Kinnerton Sandstone	CUMBRIAN COAST GROUP	Roxby (UPM)	(MAGNESIAN LIMESTONE GROUP) STAINTONDALE / TEESIDE / AISLABY / DON
			St Bees Evaporites					Brotherton (UML)	
								Edlington (MPM)	
								Cadeby (LML)	
								Marl Slate	
	Lower		Brockram	Collyhurst Sandstone	APPLEBY GROUP	Collyhurst Sandstone	APPLEBY GROUP	Basal Permian Sands/Basal Breccia	

No thickness values are implied. All names in lower case are formations but the word 'Formation' has been omitted for clarity. Previous nomenclature is indicated by symbols in parentheses: LKM = Lower Keuper Marl, KW = Keuper Waterstone, KS = Keuper Sandstone, UMS = Upper Mottled Sandstone, PB = Bunter Pebble Beds, UPM = Upper Permian Marl, UML = Upper Magnesian Limestone, MPM = Middle Permian Marl, LML = Lower Magnesian Limestone.

on the flood plains of river systems located on either side of the by then partially overstepped Pennine barrier. The general northerly flow of these rivers is reflected by a general northwards-fining of the clastic rocks, and the quartzitic pebbly sand sequences, that characterise the Midlands, occur only in the south of the region, in southernmost Lancashire (Audley-Charles, 1970; Warrington, 1974).

Differences from the usual fluvial sandstone facies form the basis for the definition of local formations, for example the pebbly Chester Pebble Beds, the Wilmslow Sandstone which shows a general transition from fluvial to aeolian, and the Helsby Sandstone which shows alternating fluvial and aeolian facies (Thompson, 1991). The contrast between these facies also serves to distinguish the three formations in the Sherwood Sandstone Group in west Cumbria namely St Bees Sandstone (fluvial), Calder Sandstone (mixed) and Ormskirk Sandstone (aeolian).

Minor tectonism and erosion are marked by a disconformity at the base of the Mercia Mudstone Group followed by a possible marine incursion represented by the intertidal Tarporley Siltstone Formation in the Cheshire Basin. Thereafter, on the margins of the East Irish Sea Basin, numerous changes of facies are thought to represent the repeated advance, and retreat or drying out, of a very shallow and frequently hypersaline sea over an extensive, low-lying, muddy, coastal plain which was often emergent (Wilson and Evans, 1990). The four formations recognised in the Fylde area, namely the Hambleton, Singleton, Kirkham and Breckells mudstones, reflect these facies changes (Wilson and Evans, 1990; Aitkenhead et al., 1992).

POST-TRIASSIC

A small area of Jurassic strata are preserved in the far north-east of the region (e.g. Figure 49), the youngest of which are of late Jurassic age. These rocks, predominantly mudstones and limestones, were deposited in a marine environment in the western part of the southern North Sea Basin and are described more fully in the Northallerton (Frost, 1998) and Thirsk (Powell et al., 1992) memoirs.

The former distribution of post-Triassic strata elsewhere in the region is a matter for conjecture, but it is likely that its post-Triassic evolution was largely controlled by the structural template established in Permo-Triassic times. Thus the thickest post-Triassic sequences are likely to have been deposited in the west, south and eastern parts of region, associated with the East Irish Sea, Cheshire and southern North Sea basins respectively. Thinner sequences were probably deposited over the Pennine High, and the Askrigg and Lake District blocks (Holliday, 1993, Chadwick, et al., 1994).

NINE

Economic geology

The presence of a wide variety of economic deposits, particularly in rocks of Carboniferous age, has been both a major stimulus to the economy and prosperity of the region and an important spur to geological research and exploration. The mining or quarrying of coal, galena, sphalerite, ironstone, roadstone and building materials were once important industries. A small quantity of oil, was produced from the Formby Oilfield in the period 1939–65 (Huxley, 1983).

In recent years the acquisition of seismic reflection profiles and the drilling of several deep hydrocarbon exploration wells has provided new insights into the geology of the region, and thrown new light on its economic potential. These aspects of the subsurface geology are discussed in this chapter. More detailed local accounts of the economic geology of the region can be found in the published Geological Survey Memoirs (Appendix 1).

COAL

The high ground of the Central Pennines separates the Yorkshire and Lancashire coalfields. In both areas the coal-bearing Westphalian rocks are partially concealed by younger Permo-Triassic rocks (Smith, 1985). Little additional information relating to the economic geology of these has been revealed by the current work. The seismic data suggest that there may be an isolated area of probable early Westphalian (Lower Coal Measures) rocks, up to 200 m thick, not shown by Smith (1985), in the north-east of the region (Map 8). These rocks are probably too deep, and lacking the main productive parts of the Coal Measures, to be considered as an economic prospect.

CONVENTIONAL HYDROCARBONS

The hydrocarbon prospectivity of the Carboniferous rocks of northern England in general has been studied in some detail by Fraser et al. (1990), and Scott and Colter (1987) have published a comprehensive review of prospects within the region. Both of these studies were essentially based on data available prior to the most recent phase of hydrocarbon exploration (1984–91) which has encompassed most the region (Figure 3), and it is now pertinent to review once more the hydrocarbon prospectivity of the Central Pennine Basin and environs in the light of the new exploration data.

Many oil and gas seepages and shows have been recorded in coal mines and in boreholes in Lancashire, notably in the areas of Wigan and Runcorn. The abandoned Formby Oilfield, discovered in 1939, remains the main hydrocarbon discovery in the region, but there has also been limited commercial production of gas from coal mines, notably Parkside Colliery, near Warrington, Lancashire. However, significant commercial production of oil and gas has been achieved in nearby areas from rocks of comparable lithology and burial histories to those in the region. Offshore, to the west, major oil and gas discoveries have been made in the adjacent areas of the East Irish Sea Basin, including the Morecambe Bay, Hamilton and Douglas fields. The important East Midlands oilfields are located to the south-east of the region, and the Eskdale and Lockton gasfields of the Cleveland Basin to the east.

The Formby Oilfield

Between 1939 and 1965, the Formby Oilfield produced at rates between 10 and 100 barrels of oil per day, with a cumulative total of about 76 000 barrels, or about 10 000 tons (Huxley, 1983). The field is located in an area where oil shows had been recognised for many centuries. Production came from unusually shallow depths, of around 30–40 m, from Holocene peat and silt, and the underlying fractured Mercia Mudstone. An unsuccessful search was made in the 1950s for the assumed deeper source from which the shallow accumulation had leaked (Falcon and Kent, 1960).

This oilfield is located where a north-east–south-west-trending Dinantian structural high is cut by north–south-trending Mesozoic faults. It had been thought that hydrocarbons migrated north-westwards from the concealed Carboniferous Rufford Syncline, where a thickened late Dinantian to early Namurian (Bowland Shale), source-rock kitchen is preserved. However this may need review in the light of recent oil discoveries a few kilometres offshore. The north–south faulting of Triassic or later age has disrupted the Carboniferous structures and led to oil migrating up the faults into the Triassic Ormskirk Sandstone and ultimately into the Holocene peat and silt deposits. The faults are apparently not sealing, probably because the Mercia Mudstone Group is thinner here than offshore.

Source rocks and maturity

The main organic-rich units, with source potential, are believed to be the late Dinantian–early Namurian Bowland Shales, and the Coal Measures. Similar strata of the same age are thought to be the main hydrocarbon source in the East Irish Sea Basin. The Permo-Triassic rocks of the region have no known source potential.

Vitrinite reflectance, spore colour determinations, TOC (total organic carbon) measurements and pyrolysis have been undertaken on samples of Carboniferous age from numerous outcrops in the Craven Basin region and from several boreholes. The quality and quantity of these data are highly variable and most are presented in confidential reports. Maturity of samples from any one formation appears to increase eastwards and southwards. There is a marked increase in maturity across the Pendle Fault. Higher reflectance gradients are seen south of this line, as for example in the Boulsworth-1 Borehole.

The Bowland Shales are regarded as the most important source rocks in the area (Lawrence et al., 1987). Maturation data (based on spore colour and vitrinite reflectance) for the Bowland Shales indicate that they are generally equivalent to high-volatile bituminous coal rank, and therefore fall within the oil window. In Boulsworth-1 and Holme Chapel-1 boreholes, the Bowland Shales are of significantly higher maturity, being mature with respect to gas generation. Visual kerogen analysis indicates that they usually have mixed hydrocarbon potential and are therefore capable of producing both oil and gas. However, Lawrence et al. (1987) suggested that the condensed lower part of the Bowland Shale may be entirely oil prone. TOC values are quite variable, ranging from 0.75 per cent to 9.46 per cent.

Sparse maturity data for the Sabden Shales (and their equivalents, the Caton Shales near Settle) reveal them to be submature to mature with respect to oil generation. Visual kerogen analysis of the Sabden Shales in Boulsworth-1 indicates a predominance of amorphous organic matter, which is regarded as oil prone. TOC values are around 4 per cent and generally pyrolysis yields are low.

Coals by definition have high TOC, and values of 18–76 per cent have been measured from Langsettian coal in this region. Most banded bituminous coals are rich in humic matter and consequently are gas prone. However, vitrinite reflectance values for these coals range from 0.54 to 0.99 per cent inferring that they that they are below peak maturity for gas generation, but that some gas may have been produced. More deeply buried coals are likely to be good gas source rocks. Any cannel coals present are likely to be good oil source rocks as they are composed largely of sapropelic kerogen which is oil prone.

Reservoir rocks

There is a wide variety of potential reservoir rocks within the region, ranging from Lower Carboniferous to Triassic in age. Namurian and Westphalian sandstones form the reservoirs in the East Midlands oilfields, and Permo-Triassic sandstones, particularly those of the Ormskirk Sandstone, near the top of the Sherwood Sandstone Group, form the hydrocarbon traps in the East Irish Sea Basin.

The Dinantian limestones of the region, as elsewhere in Britain, in general do not form attractive reservoir rocks, with porosity values less than 5 per cent (Holliday, 1986), although permeability may be enhanced locally by fracturing or by dissolution. Somewhat better reservoir characteristics are found in the sandstones of the Mill-stone Grit and Lower and Middle Coal Measures (Namurian and Westphalian), although porosity and permeability rarely exceed 15 per cent or 50 mD respectively (Holliday, 1986). Similar rocks have proved adequate reservoirs in the East Midlands (Fraser et al., 1990), but they are preserved over only a relatively restricted part of the region. Higher porosity and permeability values are to be expected in the Upper Coal Measures and Barren Measures, but these are even more restricted in their occurrence.

Permo-Triassic rocks are restricted to the eastern and western parts of the region. Those in the east are relatively thin and have little reservoir potential, although late Permian carbonates have reservoired gas to the east in the Cleveland Basin. Of much greater significance are the Permo-Triassic sandstones of western coastal areas and the adjacent offshore. Despite a complex diagenetic history (Burley, 1987; Burley and Kantorowicz, 1986; Rowe et al., 1993; Strong, 1993; Strong et al., in press), these rocks commonly yield relatively high porosity and permeability values (Lovelock, 1977; Colter and Ebbern, 1978; Smith, 1986), particularly in sandstones of aeolian origin. The main potential reservoir levels, where sandstone is overlain by probable sealing rocks, are at the top of the Collyhurst Sandstone, immediately below the Manchester Marls/St Bees Evaporites, and more especially the Ormskirk Sandstone, below the argillaceous and halite-bearing Mercia Mudstone Group. Porosity and permeability values of more than 15 per cent and 150 mD respectively are not uncommon in the Ormskirk Sandstone and its lateral equivalents.

Burial history

There are likely to have been two main periods when hydrocarbons could have been generated from the Carboniferous source rocks within the region, in late Carboniferous and late Cretaceous times (Kirby et al., 1987; Fraser et al., 1990). These were both times of regional subsidence and maximum burial following extensional basin development (Chapter Seven).

It is probable, in the areas of greater Upper Carboniferous subsidence and thicker sedimentation, that parts, or all, of the Bowland Shales entered the oil window in Westphalian times. Evidence of this period of burial is seen in Harlsey 1 Borehole (Figure 3), where vitrinite reflectance values in Mesozoic rocks are significantly lower than those from the underlying Carboniferous succession. This suggests that maximum maturation levels were reached during late Carboniferous times and were never exceeded during subsequent burial. The Coal Measures were probably nowhere sufficiently mature for gas generation within the region. Prior to Variscan basin inversion and uplift, there would be insufficient cover to trap any hydrocarbons generated at this time and prevent their escape. Closed structural traps were first formed by Variscan transpression, but, as hydrocarbon generation would have largely ceased as a result of the accompanying regional uplift, it is unlikely that significant oil accumulations formed at this time. Of those that did form, few would have survived for long because of the deep erosion of much of the region at this time. In late Carboniferous and early Permian times, potential Silesian sandstone reservoir rocks were stripped off many of the Variscan anticlines in the region.

A new period of extensional basin formation began in Permian times, continuing into the Cretaceous. The dominantly north to south faults in the west, on the margins of the East Irish Sea and Cheshire basins, were active at this time, and the seals on any earlier formed hydrocarbon traps may have been breached. The east was little effected by extensional faulting, being more influenced by regional subsidence on the margin of the North Sea Basin. In central parts of the region, including the Pennines, the Askrigg Block and the Lake District, the Mesozoic cover was probably relatively thin (Holliday, 1993; Chadwick et al., 1994), and in all probability less than the thickness of Carboniferous rocks eroded during Variscan inversion and uplift (Figure 24). In such areas, renewed hydrocarbon generation in Cretaceous times would not have been possible. By late Cretaceous times, the thickness of cover in both the east and west became so great that further oil, and even gas generation, from the Bowland Shales became possible, particularly where they were preserved in synclinal areas and were buried more deeply than in late Carboniferous times. Rocks of the Coal Measures were also locally deeply buried, but probably did not enter the gas generating zone (Fraser et al., 1990).

In Cretaceous times, the structures developed in Carboniferous rocks by Variscan deformation were available to trap contemporaneously formed hydrocarbons which could migrate from the synclinal areas of Bowland Shales towards the adjacent highs. However, because of the absence or local unsuitability of the Silesian reservoir rocks in these anticlinal areas, the hydrocarbons may have migrated more generally into the Permo-Triassic cover sequence. Whether there were suitable trapping structures in the cover is uncertain, but it is probable that some closed anticlinal features were locally formed during Mesozoic times as a result of tilting, faulting and footwall uplift associated with the late Jurassic to early Cretaceous Cimmerian tectonism (Knipe et al., 1993). It is possible that some migration of hydrocarbons into the cover rocks resulted from the breaching of the seals in Carboniferous reservoirs brought about by these deformational events.

Deformation of the cover rocks during Cenozoic basin inversion and regional uplift brought subsidence to an end, and hydrocarbon generation ceased in most onshore areas. The effects of the deformation on the trapping of hydrocarbons are likely to have been mixed. Old structures, particularly in Carboniferous rocks, may have been breached (Fraser et al., 1990), but this could have allowed migration into Mesozoic or newly created closures in the Permo-Triassic sandstones. However, the extensive erosion of the Mesozoic cover rocks across the whole region at this time (Lewis et al., 1992; Holliday, 1993; Chadwick et al., 1994), and of the underlying Carboniferous rocks, is likely to have caused the widespread breaching of seals and allowed significant volumes of previously trapped hydrocarbons to escape. Major hydrocarbon accumulations are most likely to be present in Permo-Triassic sandstone reservoirs, but these can only form traps in the relatively small part of the onshore area where a sufficient thickness of sealing Mercia Mudstone has also been preserved.

Prospectivity summary

This review suggests that the most promising area for hydrocarbon exploration is that part of the coastal zone of west Lancashire where significant thicknesses of Mercia Mudstone have been preserved. This is in keeping with the proximity of the area to the offshore discoveries in the East Irish Sea Basin, and with the large number of oil and gas shows in the vicinity, including the former small oilfield at Formby. The main targets are closed structures at Top Ormskirk Sandstone Level. Concealed Variscan anticlines probably only have potential where Silesian sandstones have been preserved in axial areas. Exposed Variscan anticlines elsewhere in the region are generally too deeply eroded to have much potential.

COAL-BED METHANE

Methane is a by-product of the coalification process, that is the low-grade metamorphism of peat through lignite to coal and anthracite. Some of this methane may migrate from the source rock, but that which remains within the coal is known as coal-bed methane (CBM). It is either adsorbed onto maceral surfaces or held as free gas within the cleat system of the coal. Coal is known to have a very large internal surface area and consequently can hold large quantities of methane, with maximum British in-situ methane measurements of $18m^3$/tonne recorded by Creedy (1991). CBM is produced from the seam by reducing the pressure which results in desorption of the methane and diffusion through the fracture system to the point of lowest pressure, usually a borehole. Pressure reduction is usually brought about by pumping water from the coals.

Factors controlling CBM formation, preservation and production include: coal rank and composition, tectonic history (especially basin inversion), coal permeability, in-seam gas pressure and in-situ stress. The region contains several areas of Coal Measures that may be prospective for CBM development, namely the Yorkshire, Lancashire and Ingleton coalfields.

The Yorkshire Coalfield covers a large area but is unlikely to have any potential for CBM production as it is largely exposed and coals have been worked extensively. However, the eastward, concealed extension of the coalfield may have some CBM potential where coals are unworked.

The Lancashire Coalfield can be separated into two areas of outcrop, the South Lancashire and Burnley coalfields. The relatively small, exposed Burnley Coalfield in the north has little potential for CBM exploitation as it is extensively mined with a low total coal thickness and the prospect is compartmentalised by faults. The southern part of the South Lancashire Coalfield, beneath Permo-Triassic strata, is much more prospective for CBM exploration. It covers a large area and has a total coal thickness of 20–25 m. High- to medium-volatile bituminous coals are present at depths of up to 1500 m and a gas content of 8.2 m³/tonne has been measured by Creedy (1991).

The Ingleton Coalfield is likely only to have poor potential for CBM production due to the small size of the coalfield, lack of unworked coal, shallow depth of coals and removal of productive Coal Measures by faulting. The rank and gas content of the coals is unknown.

GEOTHERMAL ENERGY

Some parts of the region, notably the Lake District, presently are areas with heat flow and geothermal gradients significantly in excess of the national averages (Rollin, 1987). Because of this, the region has figured in UK geothermal energy programmes (Downing and Gray, 1986; BGS, 1988). Two main methods of heat extraction from the rocks of the region have been considered, 'hot dry rock' and low enthalpy systems.

In a hot dry rock system, cold water from the surface is pumped down a borehole into hot, fractured, impermeable rocks at depth. There, it is warmed and then returned to the surface where its newly acquired heat can be used for space heating or, if the temperature exceeds 200°C, electricity generation. The largely concealed granites of the Lake District have been the main potential targets within the region for this kind of system. Full reviews of these studies are given elsewhere (Lee, 1986; Evans et al., 1988). The present work provides no new relevant details.

Low enthalpy systems attempt to extract hot groundwater directly from deep aquifers. The review of Holliday (1986) concluded that Carboniferous and older rocks are generally impermeable at the necessary depths (about 2 km) and have little potential as a source of low enthalpy energy, although some local exceptions cannot be ruled out. The thickness and subsurface structure of the Carboniferous rocks of the region are now much better constrained, but the borehole data have shown that the porosity of the sandstones and limestones at depth is generally very low (about 5 per cent). Carboniferous strata of the region are essentially tight and compact, and the sandstones discontinuous and lenticular. It must be concluded that they have no foreseeable potential as a source of low enthalpy geothermal energy.

UNDERGROUND STORAGE/DISPOSAL OF FLUIDS

Storage or disposal of fluids, such as toxic waste or CO_2, in closed and sealed structures formed in deep aquifers, has been considered in a number of areas of the UK. A recent CEC investigation into the CO_2 storage potential of aquifers and reservoirs provided estimates of storage capacity for many stratigraphical horizons both onshore and offshore Britain (Holloway et al., 1993). The potential for this kind of use in the region is thought to be extremely poor in view of the limited number of closures so far demonstrated, their restricted extent, and, as detailed below, the generally poor porosity and permeability characteristics of the putative reservoir rocks.

The Permo-Triassic sandstones of the western part of the region are estimated to have a potential storage capacity of approximately 6×10^{10} m³ of CO_2, at a temperature of 38°C and a pressure of 111 bar. However, both these and sandstones of similar age on the eastern edge of the region are used for water extraction and consequently are not available for fluid disposal.

The East Midlands oilfields lie just to the east of the region. The main reservoir sandstones are Silesian in age with low permeability (less than 50 mD). Enhanced oil recovery using CO_2 flooding has been attempted in some parts of the field with a view to extending the producing life of the field. The project was abandoned due to the very slow injection rates achieved and the consequent long period before extra oil was recovered at the well head. It therefore seems unlikely that these Silesian rocks and their equivalents in the region are suitable for storage or disposal of fluids or gas.

EVAPORITES

There is no clear evidence of evaporite minerals in surface exposures of Carboniferous rocks in the region. There are, however, a few records of evaporites in some of the scattered boreholes that have penetrated the earliest (Courceyan) synrift part of the Dinantian carbonate shelf sequences. These include firstly, minor thicknesses of gypsum in the Basement Beds of Tournaisian age on the Southern Lake District High and laminated anhydrite and secondary gypsum in the Halsteads Shales-with-Anhydrite Member of the Stockdale Farm Formation on the Malham Terrace. Evaporite sequences at a similar stratigraphical level and palaeogeographical situation are also known from boreholes at Eyam and Hathern in the adjacent region to the south and it is possible that such deposits are widespread in the subsurface of the region. However, the considerable depth of such deposits largely precludes them being regarded as a resource.

Evaporite minerals occur extensively in the region in both the Upper Permian and Triassic sequences, but the major resources lie outside the region in the East Irish Sea, Cheshire and North Sea basins. Gypsum, anhydrite and alabaster have been worked in the Upper Permian St Bees Evaporites at the disused Barrowmouth Alabaster Mine and the Marchon (Sandwith) Drift Mine in west Cumbria (Shipp, 1992). The latter mine worked seams of anhydrite up to 20 m thick (Arthurton et al., 1978). In south Cumbria, a basal member of the St Bees Evaporites, the Haverigg Hawes Anhydrite, attains a thickness of nearly 40 m in Rampside Borehole (Rose and Dunham, 1977). The feather edges of these evaporites have been proved in north Lancashire at Heysham, and the parent formation is inferred to crop out out beneath drift around Morecambe (Brandon et al., 1998). The existence of a resource here and elsewhere in the Upper Permian of Lancashire is unlikely, however, but cannot be entirely ruled out.

East of the Pennines, Permian evaporites are mostly only thinly represented either because of the basin margin situation or because of removal by dissolution. Where they do occur, they are dominantly in the form of gypsum beds, locally over 30 m thick. Gypsum has been mined just east of the region at Sherburn-in-Elmet. However, the main economic effect of the mineral's presence in the region may not be its intrinsic value as a resource, but as a cause, through subsurface dissolution, of subsidence affecting land, buildings and roads at the surface (Cooper, 1988; Cooper and Burgess, 1993).

Economically significant evaporite deposits in the Triassic succession of the region are confined to the Mercia Mudstone Group west of the Pennines in the Fylde area of Lancashire and the Walney Island area of south Cumbria. Salt occurs mainly at three levels: the Rossall Salts and Mythop Salts in the Singleton Mudstones, and the Preesall Salt in the Kirkham Mudstones. One hundred metres of rock salt was penetrated by a shaft at Preesall (Preesall Salt) in 1885 (Wilson and Evans, 1990). Extraction was initially by mining and later by brine pumping which continues to the present day. The salt occurs in a restricted structural basin that limits the long-term prospects of the brine-field, though other possibilities exist offshore and in similar overall sequence under Walney Island (Rose and Dunham, 1977). The Preesall Salt here is over 100 m thick at wet rock head and was formerly pumped for brine.

MINERAL DEPOSITS

A full review of mineral deposits in the region is beyond the scope of this account. Most of the important known mineralisation in the region occurs in areas peripheral to the Craven Basin, namely the Askrigg Block and the South Pennine Orefield. Several multidisciplinary studies on northern England have been carried out, mainly with a view to locating 'Irish-style' mineral deposits, that is syngenetic, carbonate-hosted, base metal deposits of early Dinantian age (Plant and Jones, 1989). These deposits are formed during the early synextension stage of basin evolution. Active syndepositional faults acted as channels for the mineralising fluids and largely controlled the location of the deposits. No mineral occurrences of this kind are known within the regon, but the present-day disposition of outcrops is not generally favourable for their location. The greater detail and greater areal extent of the new structure contour and isopach maps (Maps 1–9) should allow exploration targets to be located with greater precision.

By comparison with the Northern Pennine Orefield, mines in the Craven Basin were less productive, being few in number and generally small in size. Base metals have been extracted from 12 sites over the last 500 years and more than 20 other mineralised sites are known (Gott, 1990). None of these mines are working today. Galena and baryte are the most common minerals in the Craven Basin, with subordinate zinc and copper minerals. Pyrite and calcite are the most common gangue minerals. Most mineralisation occurs in thin, laterally restricted veins associated with joints or minor faults. One exception to this was the smithsonite deposit which was incorporated in silt, lining the floor of natural caverns. Lead/zinc mineralisation has also been recorded in brecciated, Waulsortian, mud-mound, facies rocks within the Craven Basin.

The main vein mineralisations on the Askrigg Block are galena and calcite with subsidiary fluorite, baryte and quartz. Mineralisation is hosted in limestones and grits of Asbian to Kinderscoutian age. Mineralisation is believed to be strongly structurally controlled and generally takes the form of vertical veins up to several kilometres long. The timing of mineralisation is poorly constrained but it has been suggested to be of Lower Permian age (Dunham and Wilson, 1985). There are no contemporaneous igneous rocks (Plant and Jones, 1989) but the Askrigg Block is cored by a Caledonian pluton, the Wensleydale Granite the emplacement of which pre-dated mineralisation (Chapter Two). It is believed, however, that the granite may have had a localising role in the formation of some ore deposits in the area.

There are two main areas of mineralisation in the Askrigg Block, at the northern edge of the granite and an area associated with the Craven Faults. The mineral reconnaissance programme begun in 1973 by IGS (BGS) involved the taking of geophysical measurements across the North Craven Fault. A Very Low Frequency (VLF) anomaly was noted to coincide with the hanging-wall side of this fault zone and it was speculated that disseminated sulphides may be trapped against the Lower Palaeozoic basement on the downthrown side (Wadge et al., 1983).

The South Pennine Orefield lies on the south-eastern edge of the region. The main mineralisation is calcite, fluorite, galena and baryte with subordinate sphalerite and quartz. Mineralisation is largely vein hosted in the Monsal Dale Limestone which is Brigantian in age. There are no major structures in the South Pennine Orefield but unlike the Askrigg Orefield, there are contemporaneous igneous rocks, mainly tholeiitic basalts and tuffs. Again the timing of mineralisation is not easily constrained but is believed to have occurred after dolomitisation (possibly Upper Permian in age) of the Asbian and Brigantian limestones in the south of the area.

REFERENCES

Most of the references listed below are held in the Library of the British Geological Survey at Keyworth, Nottingham. Copies of the references can be purchased subject to current copyright legislation.

ADAMS, A E, HORBURY, A D, and ABDEL AZIZ, A A. 1990. Controls on Dinantian sedimentation in south Cumbria and surrounding areas of northwest England. *Proceedings of the Geologists' Association*, Vol. 101, 19–30.

AHR, W M. 1973. The carbonate ramp: an alternative to the shelf model. *Transactions of Gulf Coast Association Geological Society*, Vol. 23, 221–225.

AITKENHEAD, N, BRIDGE, D McC, RILEY, N J, and KIMBELL, S F. 1992. Geology of the country around Garstang. *Memoir of the British Geological Survey*, Sheet 67 (England and Wales).

AKHURST, M C, CHADWICK, R A, HOLLIDAY, D W, McCORMAC, M, McMILLAN, A A, MILLWARD, D, and YOUNG, B. 1997. Geology of the west Cumbria district. *Memoir of the British Geological Survey*, Sheets 28, 37 and 47 (England Wales).

ALLSOP, J M. 1987. Patterns of late Caledonian intrusive activity in eastern and northern England from geophysics, radiometric dating and basement geology. *Proceedings of the Yorkshire Geological Society*, Vol. 46, 335–353.

ANDERTON, R, BRIDGES, P H, LEEDER, M R, and SELLWOOD, B W. 1979. *A dynamic stratigraphy of the British Isles.* (London: Allen and Unwin.)

ARCULUS, R J. 1987. The significance of source versus process in the tectonic controls of magma genesis. *Journal of Volcanology and Geothermal Research*, Vol. 32, 1–12.

ARTHURTON, R S. 1983. The Skipton Rock Fault — an Hercynian wrench fault associated with the Skipton Anticline, northwest England. *Geological Journal*, Vol. 18, 105–114.

ARTHURTON, R S. 1984. The Ribblesdale fold belt, NW England — a Dinantian–early Namurian dextral shear-zone. 131–138 *in* Variscan tectonics of the North Atlantic region. HUTTON, D W H and SANDERSON, D J (editors). *Special Publication of the Geological Society of London*, Vol. 14.

ARTHURTON, R S, BURGESS, I C, and HOLLIDAY, D W. 1978. Permian and Triassic. 189–206 *in* The geology of the Lake District. MOSELEY, F (editor). *Yorkshire Geological Society Occasional Publication*, No. 3.

ARTHURTON, R S, and HEMINGWAY, J E. 1972. The St Bees Evaporites — a carbonate–evaporite formation of Upper Permian age in West Cumberland, England. *Proceedings of the Yorkshire Geological Society*, Vol. 38, 565–592.

ARTHURTON, R S, JOHNSON, E W, and MUNDY, D J C. 1988. Geology of the country around Settle. *Memoir of the British Geological Survey*, Sheet 60 (England and Wales).

AUDLEY-CHARLES, M G. 1970. Triassic palaeogeography of the British Isles. *Quarterly Journal of the Geological Society of London*, Vol. 126, 49–89.

BADLEY, M E, PRICE, J D, and BACKSHALL, L C. 1989. Inversion, reactivated faults and related structures: seismic examples from the southern North Sea. 201–219 *in* Inversion tectonics.

COOPER, M A, and WILLIAMS, G D (editors). *Special Publication of the Geological Society of London*, No. 44.

BAINES, J G. 1977. The stratigraphy and sedimentology of the Skipton Moor Grits (Namurian E1c) and their lateral equivalents. Unpublished PhD thesis, University of Keele.

BANHAM, P H, HOPPER, F M W, and JACKSON, J B. 1981. The Gillbrea Nappe in the Skiddaw Group, Cockermouth, Cumbria, England. *Geological Magazine*, Vol. 118, 509–516.

BARNES, R P, LINTERN, B C, and STONE, P. 1989. Short paper: timing and regional implications of deformation in the Southern Uplands of Scotland. *Journal of the Geological Society of London*, Vol. 146, 905–908.

BATHURST, R G C. 1959. The cavernous structure in some Mississippian *Stromatactis* reefs in Lancashire, England. *Journal of Geology*, Vol. 67, 506–521.

BEDDOE-STEPHENS, B, and MASON, I. 1991. The volcanogenetic significance of garnet-bearing minor intrusions within the Borrowdale Volcanic Group, Eskdale area, Cumbria. *Geological Magazine*, Vol. 128, 505–516.

BENFIELD, A C. 1969. The Huddersfield White Rock cyclothem in the Central Pennines: Report of field meeting. *Proceedings of the Yorkshire Geological Society*, Vol. 37, 181–187.

BERRIDGE, N G. 1982. Petrography of the pre-Carboniferous rocks of the Beckermonds Scar Borehole in the context of the magnetic anomaly at the site. *Proceedings of the Yorkshire Geological Society*, Vol. 44, 89–98.

BESLY, B M, and KELLING, G (editors). 1988. *Sedimentation in a synorogenic basin complex: the Upper Carboniferous of Northwest Europe.* (Glasgow: Blackie.)

BEVINS, R E, KOKELAAR, B P, and DUNKLEY, P N. 1984. Petrology and geochemistry of early to mid-Ordovician igneous rocks in Wales: a volcanic arc to marginal basin transition. *Proceedings of the Geologists' Association*, Vol. 95, 337–347.

BINNEY, E W. 1841a. Sketch of the geology of Manchester and its vicinity. *Transactions of the Manchester Geological Society*, Vol. 1, 35–62.

BINNEY, E W. 1841b. Observations on the Lancashire and Cheshire Coalfield, with a section. *Transactions of the Manchester Geological Society*, Vol. 1, 67–79.

BISAT, W S. 1924. The Carboniferous goniatites of the north of England and their zones. *Proceedings of the Yorkshire Geological Society*, Vol. 20, 40–124.

BLACK, W W. 1954. Diagnostic characters of the Lower Carboniferous knoll-reefs in the north of England. *Transactions of the Leeds Geological Association*, Vol. 6, 262–297.

BOIS, C, LEFORT, J-P, LE GALL, B, SIBUET, J-C, GARIEL, O, PINET, B, and CAZES, M. 1990. Traces of Caledonian and Proterozoic crustal features in deep seismic profiles recorded between France and the British Isles. *Tectonophysics*, Vol. 185, 21–36.

BOND, G. 1950. The Lower Carboniferous reef limestones of Cracoe, Yorkshire. *Quarterly Journal of the Geological Society of London*, Vol. 105, 157–188.

BOTT, M H P. 1961. Geological interpretation of magnetic anomalies over the Askrigg Block. *Quarterly Journal of the Geological Society of London*, Vol. 117, 481–495.

BOTT, M H P. 1967. Geophysical investigations of the northern Pennine basement rocks. *Proceedings of the Yorkshire Geological Society*, Vol. 36, 139–168.

BOTT, M H P, ROBINSON, J, and KOHNSTAMM, M A. 1978. Granite beneath Market Weighton, east Yorkshire. *Journal of the Geological Society of London*, Vol. 135, 535–543.

BRANDON, A, AITKENHEAD, N, CROFT, R G C, ELLISON, R A E, EVANS, D J, and RILEY, N J. 1998. Geology of the country around Lancaster. *Memoir of the British Geological Survey*. Sheet 59 (England and Wales).

BRANNEY, M J, KOKELLAR, B P, and McCONNELL, B J. 1992. The Bad Step Tuff: a lava-like rheomorphic ignimbrite in a calc-alkaline piecemeal caldera, English Lake District. *Bulletin of Volcanology*, Vol. 54, 187–199.

BRANNEY, M J, and SOPER, N J. 1988. Ordovician volcano-tectonics in the English Lake District. *Journal of the Geological Society of London* Vol. 145, 367–376.

BRENNER, R L, and MARTINSEN, O J. 1990. The Fossil Sandstone — a shallow marine sand wave complex in the Namurian of Cumbria and North Yorkshire, England. *Proceedings of the Yorkshire Geological Society*, Vol. 48, 149–162.

BRISTOW, C S. 1988. Controls on the sedimentation of the Rough Rock Group (Namurian) from the Pennine Basin of northern England. 114–131 in *Sedimentation in a synorogenic basin complex: the Upper Carboniferous of Northwest Europe*. BESLY, B, and KELLING, G (editors). (Glasgow and London: Blackie.)

BRITISH GEOLOGICAL SURVEY. 1988. *Geothermal energy in the United Kingdom: review of the British Geological Survey's Programme 1984–1987. Investigation of the geothermal potential of the UK.* (Keyworth, Nottingham: British Geological Survey.)

BROADHURST, F M, and FRANCE, A A. 1986. Time represented by coal seams in the Coal Measures of England. *International Journal of Coal Geology*, Vol. 6, 43–54.

BROADHURST, F M, and LORING, D H. 1970. Rates of sedimentation in the Upper Carboniferous of Britain. *Lethaia*, Vol. 3, 1–9.

BROMEHEAD, C E N, EDWARDS, W, WRAY, D A, and STEPHENS, J V. 1933. The geology of the country around Holmfirth and Glossop. *Memoir of the Geological Survey*, Sheet 86 (England and Wales).

BROWN, G C, IXER, R A, PLANT, J A, and WEBB, P C. 1987. Geochemistry of granites beneath the North Pennines and their role in mineralization. *Transactions of the Institute of Mining and Metallurgy (Section B)*, Vol. 96, B65–76.

BUNTEBARTH, G, KOPPE, I, and TEICHMULLER, M. 1982. Palaeogeothermics in the Ruhr Basin. 45–55 in *Geothermics and geothermal energy*. CERMAK, V, and HAENEL, R (editors). (Stuttgart: Schweizerbart's sche.)

BURGESS, I C, and HOLLIDAY, D W. 1979. The geology of the country around Brough-under-Stainmore. *Memoir of the British Geological Survey of Great Britain*, (Sheet 31 and part of sheets 25 and 30. (England and Wales).

BURLEY, S D. 1984. Patterns of diagenesis in the Sherwood Sandstone (Triassic), UK. *Clay Minerals*, Vol. 19, 403–440

BURLEY, S D, and KANTOROWICZ, J D. 1986. Thin section and SEM criteria for the recognition of cement-dissolution porosity in sandstones. *Sedimentology*, Vol. 33, 587–604.

BUSBY, J P, KIMBELL, G S, and PHARAOH, T C. 1993. Integrated geophysical/geological modelling of the Caledonian and Precambrian basement of southern Britain. *Geological Magazine*, Vol. 130, 593–604.

CALVER, M A. 1968. The distribution of Westphalian marine faunas in northern England and adjoining area. *Proceedings of the Yorkshire Geological Society*, Vol. 44, 479–496.

CANN, J R. 1982. In discussion of BERRIDGE, 1982 (see p.99).

CARNEY, J N, GLOVER, B W, and PHARAOH, T C. 1992. Pre-conference field excursion: Precambrian and Lower Palaeozoic rocks of the English Midlands. *British Geological Survey, Technical Report* WA/92/72.

CHADWICK, A, KIRBY, G A, and BAILY, H E. 1994. The post-Triassic structural evolution of northwest England and adjacent parts of the East Irish Sea. *Proceedings of the Yorkshire Geological Society*, Vol. 50 part 1, 91–102.

CHADWICK, R A, HOLLIDAY, D W, HOLLOWAY, S, and HULBERT, A G. 1995. The structure and evolution of the Northumberland–Solway Basin and adjacent areas. *Subsurface Memoir of the British Geological Survey*.

CHARSLEY, T J. 1984. Early Carboniferous rocks of the Swinden No.1 Borehole, west of Skipton, Yorkshire. *British Geological Survey Report*, Vol. 16, No. 1.

CHISHOLM, J I. 1977. Growth faulting and sandstone deposition in the Namurian of the Stanton Syncline, Derbyshire. *Proceedings of the Yorkshire Geological Society*, Vol. 41, 305–323.

CHISHOLM, J I. 1981. Growth faulting in the Almscliff Grit (Namurian E1) near Harrogate, Yorkshire. *Transactions of the Leeds Geological Association*, Vol. 9 (No. 5), 61–70.

CHISHOLM, J I. 1990. The Upper Band–Better Bed sequence (Lower Coal Measures, Westphalian A) in the central and south Pennine area of England. *Geological Magazine*, Vol. 127 (No. 1), 55–74.

CHROSTON, P N, ALLSOP, J M, and CORNWELL, J D. 1987. New seismic refraction evidence on the origin of the Bouguer anomaly low near Hunstanton, Norfolk. *Proceedings of the Yorkshire Geological Society*, Vol. 46, 323–333.

CHUBB, L J, and HUDSON, R G S. 1925. The nature of the junction between the Lower Carboniferous and the Millstone Grit in north-west Yorkshire. *Proceedings of the Yorkshire Geological Society*, Vol. 20, 257–291.

COCKS, L R M, and FORTEY, R A. 1982. Faunal evidence for oceanic separations in the Palaeozoic of Britain. *Journal of the Geological Society of London*, Vol. 139, 465–478.

COCKS, L R M, HOLLAND, C H, and RICKARDS, R B. 1992. A revised correlation of Silurian rocks in the British Isles. *Special Report of the Geological Society of London*, No. 21.

COLLIER, R E L. 1991. The Lower Carboniferous Stainmore Basin, N. England: extensional basin tectonics and sedimentation. *Journal of the Geological Society of London*, Vol. 148, 379–390

COLLINSON, J D. 1988. Controls on Namurian sedimentation in the Central Province basins of northern England. 85–101 in *Sedimentation in a synorogenic basin complex: the Upper Carboniferous of Northwest Europe*. BESLY, B M, and KELLING, G (editors). (Glasgow: Blackie.)

COLLINSON, J D, and BANKS, N L. 1975. The Haslingden Flags (Namurian, G1) of south-east Lancashire: bar finger sands in the Pennine Basin. *Proceedings of the Yorkshire Geological Society*, Vol. 40, 431–458.

COLLINSON, J D, HOLDSWORTH, B K, JONES, C M, and MARTINSEN, O J. 1992. Discussion of: 'The Millstone Grit (Namurian) of the southern Pennines viewed in the light of eustatically controlled sequence stratigraphy. *Geological Journal*, Vol. 27, 173–180.

COLLINSON, J D, JONES, C M, and WILSON, A A. 1977. The Marsdenian (Namurian R2) succession west of Blackburn; implications for the evolution of Pennine delta systems. *Geological Journal*, Vol.12, 59–76.

COLTER, V S, and EBBERN, J. 1978. The petrography and reservoir properties of some Triassic sandstones of the Northern Irish Sea Basin. *Journal of the Geological Society of London*. Vol. 135. 57–62.

CONEYBEARE, W D, and PHILLIPS, W. 1822. *Outlines of the geology of England and Wales, with an introductory compendium of the general principles of that science, and comparative views of the structure of foreign countries, Part 1.*

CONIL, R, LONGERSTAEY, P J, and RAMSBOTTOM, W H C. 1980. Materiaux pour l'etude micropalaeontologique du Dinantien de Grande-Bretagne. *Memoirs de l'Institute Geologique de l'Universite de Louvain*, Vol. 30, 1–187.

COOPER, A H. 1988. Subsidence resulting from the dissolution of Permian gypsum in the Ripon area; its relevance to mining and water abstraction. 387–390 in Engineering geology of underground movements. BELL, F G, CULSHAW, M G, CRIPPS, J C, and LOVELL, M A (editors). *Special Publication of the Geological Society of London*, No. 5.

COOPER, A H, and BURGESS, I C. 1993. Geology of the country around Harrogate. *Memoir of the British Geological Survey*, Sheet 62 (England and Wales).

COOPER, A H, MILLWARD, D, JOHNSON, E W, and SOPER, N J. 1993. The Early Palaeozoic evolution of northwest England. *Geological Magazine*, Vol. 130, 711–724.

COPE, F W. 1939. Oil occurrences in south-west Lancashire. *Bulletin of the Geological Survey*, No. 2, 18–25.

COPE, J C W, INGHAM, J K, and RAWSON, P F. 1992. *Atlas of palaeogeography and lithofacies.* (Geological Society of London.)

CORNWELL, J D, and WALKER, A S D. 1989. Chapter 4. Regional geophysics. 25–52 in *Metallogenic models and exploration criteria for buried carbonate-hosted ore deposits — a multidisciplinary study in eastern England.* PLANT, J A, and JONES D G (editors). (London: The Institution of Mining and Metallurgy and British Geological Survey.)

CRAIG, G Y (editor), McINTYRE, D B, and WATERSON, C D. 1978. *James Hutton's Theory of the earth: the lost drawings.* (Edinburgh: Scottish Academic Press.)

CREANEY, S. 1980. Petrographic texture and vitrinite reflectance variation on the Alston Block, north-east England. *Proceedings of the Yorkshire Geological Society*, Vol. 42, 553–580.

CREANEY, S. 1982. Vitrinite reflectance determinations from the Beckermonds Scar and Raydale boreholes, Yorkshire. *Proceedings of the Yorkshire Geological Society*, Vol. 44 , 99–102.

CREEDY, D P. 1991. An introduction to geological aspects of methane occurrence and control in British deep coal mines. *Quarterly Journal of Engineering Geology*, Vol. 24, 209–220.

DEWEY, J F. 1982. Plate tectonics and the evolution of the British Isles. *Journal of the Geological Society of London*, Vol. 139, 371–412.

DICKINSON, J. 1905. Heaton Park Borehole, near Manchester, with notes on the surroundings. *Transactions of the Manchester Geological Society*, Vol. 28, 69–84.

DONATO, J A, MARTINDALE, W, and TULLY, M C. 1983. Buried granites within the Mid North Sea High. *Journal of the Geological Society of London*, Vol. 140, 825–837.

DONATO, J A, and MEGSON, J B. 1990. A buried granite batholith beneath the East Midlands Shelf of the Southern North Sea Basin. *Journal of the Geological Society of London*, Vol. 147, 133–140.

DOWNING, R A, and GRAY, D A (editors). 1986. *Geothermal energy — the potential in the United Kingdom.* (London: HMSO.)

DUNHAM, K C. 1974. Granite beneath the Pennines in North Yorkshire. *Proceedings of the Yorkshire Geological Society*, Vol. 40, 191–194.

DUNHAM, K C, DUNHAM, A C, HODGE, B L, and JOHNSON, G A L. 1965. Granite beneath Viséan sediments with mineralization at Rookhope, Northern Pennines. *Quarterly Journal of the Geological Society of London*, Vol. 121, 383–417.

DUNHAM, K C, and WILSON, A A. 1985. Geology of the Northern Pennine Orefield: Vol. 2, Stainmore to Craven. *Economic Memoir of the British Geological Survey*, Sheets 40, 41, 50, etc.

EARP, J R, MAGRAW, D, POOLE, E G, LAND, D H, and WHITEMAN, A J. 1961. Geology of the country around Clitheroe and Nelson. *Memoir of the Geological Survey of Great Britain*, Sheet 68. (England and Wales).

EBDON, C C, FRASER, A J, HIGGINS, A C, MICHENER, B C, and STRANK, A R E. 1990. The Dinantian stratigraphy of the East Midlands: a seismostratigraphic approach. *Journal of the Geological Society of London*, Vol. 147, 519–536.

EDEN, R A, STEVENSON, I P, and EDWARDS, I P. 1957. Geology of the country around Sheffield. *Memoir of the Geological Survey of Great Britain*, Sheet 100 (England and Wales).

EDWARDS, W, WRAY, D A, and MITCHELL, D H. 1940. Geology of the country around Wakefield. *Memoir of the Geological Survey of Great Britain*, Sheet 78 (England and Wales).

EDWARDS, W N. 1951. The concealed coalfield of Yorkshire and Nottinghamshire (3rd edition). *Memoir of the Geological Survey of Great Britain.*

EDWARDS, W N, and TROTTER, F M. 1954. *British regional geology: The Pennines and adjacent areas (3rd edition).* (London: HMSO.)

EVANS, C J, and ALLSOP, J M. 1987. Some geophysical aspects of the deep geology of eastern England. *Proceedings of the Yorkshire Geological Society*, Vol. 46, 323–333.

EVANS, C J, KIMBELL, G S, and ROLLIN, K E. 1988. *Hot dry rock potential in urban areas. Investigation of the geothermal potential of the UK.* (Keyworth, Nottingham: British Geological Survey.)

EVANS, D J, REES, J G, and HOLLOWAY, S. 1993. The Permian to Jurassic stratigraphy and structural evolution of the central Cheshire Basin. *Journal of the Geological Society of London*, Vol. 150, 857–870.

EVANS, D J, REES, J G, HOLLOWAY, S, SMITH, N J P, and CHADWICK, R A. 1994. Discussion on the Permian to Jurassic stratigraphy and structural evolution of the central Cheshire Basin — reply to E G. POOLE. *Journal of the Geological Society of London*, Vol. 151, 894–895.

FALCON, N L, and KENT, P E. 1960. Geological results of petroleum exploration in Britain 1945–1957. *Memoir of the Geological Society of London*, No. 2.

FAREY, J. 1811. *A general view of the agriculture and minerals of Derbyshire.* Vol. 1. (London: B Macmillan.)

FEARNSIDES, W G. 1933. A correlation of structures in the coalfields of the Midland Province. *Report of the British Association for the Advancement of Science (Leicester).* 57–80.

FETTES, D J, LONG, C B, BEVINS, R E, MAX, M D, OLIVER, G J H, PRIMMER, T J, THOMAS, L J, and YARDLEY, B W D. 1985. Grade and time of metamorphism in the Caledonide Orogen of Britain and Ireland. 41–53 *in* The nature and timing of orogenic activity in the Caledonian rocks of the British Isles. HARRIS, A L (editor). *Memoir of the Geological Society of London*, No. 9.

FETTES, D J, LONG, C B, MAX, M D, and YARDLEY, B W D. 1985. Grade and time of metamorphism in the Caledonide Orogen of Britain and Ireland. Plate 3 in The nature and timing of orogenic activity in the Caledonian rocks of the British Isles. HARRIS, A L (editor). Memoir of the Geological Society of London, No. 9.

FEWTRELL, M D, and SMITH, D G. 1980. Revision of the Dinantian stratigraphy of the Craven Basin, N England. Geological Magazine, Vol. 117, 37–49.

FIRMAN, R J, and LEE, M K. 1986. The age and structure of the concealed English Lake District batholith and its probable influence on subsequent sedimentation, tectonics and mineralisation. 117–127 in Geology in the real world — the Kingsley Dunham volume. NESBITT, R W, and NICHOL, I (editors). (London: Institution of Mining and Metallurgy.)

FORD, T D. 1954. The Upper Carboniferous rocks of the Ingleton Coalfield. Quarterly Journal of the Geological Society of London, Vol. 110, 231–265.

FORD, T D. 1958. Mining in the Ingleton Coalfield. Colliery Guardian, Vol. 197, 347–352.

FORTNEY, N J, ROBERTS, B, and HIRONS, S R. 1993. Relationship between metamorphism and structure in the Skiddaw Group, English Lake District. Geological Magazine, Vol. 130, 631–638.

FRASER, A J, and GAWTHORPE, R L. 1990. Tectono-stratigraphic development and hydrocarbon habitat of the Carboniferous in northern England. 49–86 in Tectonic events responsible for Britain's oil and gas reserves. HARDMAN, R F P, and BROOKS, J (editors). Special Publication of the Geological Society of London, No. 55.

FRASER, A J, NASH, D F, STEELE, R P, and EBDON, C C. 1990. A regional assessment of the intra-Carboniferous play of northern England. 417–439 in Classic petroleum provinces. BROOKS, J (editor). Special Publication of the Geological Society of London, No. 50.

FREEMAN, B, KLEMPERER, S L, and HOBBS, R W. 1988. The deep structure of northern England and the Iapetus Suture zone from BIRPS deep seismic reflection profiles. Journal of the Geological Society of London, Vol. 145, 727–740.

FROST, D V. 1998. Geology of the country around Northallerton. Memoir of the Geological Survey of Great Britain, Sheet 42 (England and Wales).

GARWOOD, E J. 1913. The Lower Carboniferous succession in the north-west of England. Quarterly Journal of the Geological Society of London, Vol. 68, 449–586.

GARWOOD, E J, and GOODYEAR, E. 1924. The Lower Carboniferous succession of the Settle district. Quarterly Journal of the Geological Society of London, Vol. 80, 184–273.

GAWTHORPE, R L. 1986. Sedimentation during carbonate ramp-to-slope evolution in a tectonically active area: Bowland Basin (Dinantian), northern England. Sedimentology, Vol. 33, 185–206.

GAWTHORPE, R L. 1987. Tectono-sedimentary evolution of the Bowland Basin, N England, during the Dinantian. Journal of the Geological Society of London, Vol. 144, 59–71.

GAWTHORPE, R L, and CLEMMEY, H. 1985. Geometry of submarine slides in the Bowland Basin (Dinantian) and their relation to debris flows. Journal of the Geological Society of London, Vol. 142, 555–565.

GAWTHORPE, R L, GUTTERIDGE, P, and LEEDER, M R. 1989. Late Devonian and Dinantian basin evolution in northern England and North Wales. 1–23.

GEORGE, T N, JOHNSON, G A L, MITCHELL, M, PRENTICE, J E, RAMSBOTTOM, W H C, SEVASTOPULO, G D, and WILSON, R B. 1976. A correlation of Dinantian rocks in the British Isles. Special Report of the Geological Society of London, No. 7.

GIBBONS, W. 1987. Menai Strait fault system: an early Caledonian terrane boundary in north Wales. Geology, Vol. 15, 744–747.

GIBBS, A D. 1984. Structural evolution of extensional basin margins. Journal of the Geological Society of London, Vol. 141, 609–620.

GILES, J R A. 1989. Evidence of syn-depositional tectonic activity in the Westphalian A and B of West Yorkshire. 201–206 in The role of Devonian and Carboniferous Sedimentation in the British Isles. ARTHURTON, R S, GUTTERIDGE, P, and NOLAN, S C (editors). Occasional Publication of the Yorkshire Geological Society, No. 6.

GILLIGAN, A. 1920. The petrography of the Millstone Grit of Yorkshire. Quarterly Journal of the Geological Society of London, Vol. 74, 251–294.

GLENNIE, K W, and BOEGNER, P. 1981. Sole Pit inversion tectonics. 110–120 in Petroleum geology of the continental shelf of NW Europe. ILLING, L V, and HOBSON, G D (editors). (London: Heyden.)

GLOVER, B W, POWELL, J H, and WATERS, C N. 1993. Etruria Formation (Westphalian C) palaeoenvironments and volcanicity on the southern margins of the Pennine Basin, South Staffordshire, England. Journal of the Geological Society of London, Vol. 150, 737–750.

GOOSSENS, R F, SMITH, E G, and CALVER, M A. 1974. Westphalian. 87–108 in The geology and mineral resources of Yorkshire. RAYNER, D H, and HEMINGWAY, J E (editors). (Leeds: W S Maney and Son Limited for the Yorkshire Geological Society.)

GOTT, A. 1990. Base metal mineralisation in the Craven Basin — with particular reference to the Cow Ark and Newton areas of north-east Lancashire. Unpublished BSc thesis, Luton College of Higher Education.

GRAYSON, R F, and OLDHAM, L. 1987. A new structural framework for the northern British Dinantian as a basis for oil, gas and mineral exploration. 33–59 in European Dinantian environments. MILLER, J, ADAMS, A E, and WRIGHT, V P (editors) (Chichester: John Wiley and Sons Ltd.)

GREEN, A H, RUSSELL, R, DAKYNS, J R, WARD, J C, FOX-STRANGEWAYS, C, DALTON, W H, and HOLMES, T V. 1878. The geology of the Yorkshire coalfield. Memoir of the Geological Survey (England and Wales).

GUION, P D, and FIELDING, C R. 1988. Westphalian A and B sedimentation in the Pennine Basin, UK. 153–177 in Sedimentation in a synorogenic basin complex: the Upper Carboniferous of Northwest Europe. BESLY, B M, and KELLING, G (editors). (Glasgow: Blackie.)

GUTTERIDGE, P. 1991. Aspects of Dinantian sedimentation in the Edale Basin, north Derbyshire. Geological Journal, Vol. 26, 245–269.

HALL, E. 1832. A mineralogical and geological map of the Coalfield of Lancashire, with parts of Yorkshire, Cheshire and Derbyshire. 1:65 000 scale. (Manchester)

HARDING, T P. 1985. Seismic characteristics and identification of negative flower-structures, positive flower-structures and positive structural inversion. American Association of Petroleum Geologists' Bulletin, Vol. 69, No. 4, 582–600.

HARLAND, W B, ARMSTRONG, R L, COX, A V, CRAIG, L E, SMITH, A G, and SMITH, D G. 1989. A geologic timescale 1989. (Cambridge: Cambridge University Press.)

HELM, D G. 1970. Stratigraphy and structure in the Black Combe inlier, English Lake District. Proceedings of the Yorkshire Geological Society, Vol. 38, 105–148.

HICKLING, G. 1918. The geology of Manchester as revealed by borings. Transactions of the Institution of Mining Engineers, Vol. 54, 367–417.

HIGGINS, A C, and VARKER, W J. 1982. Lower Carboniferous conodont faunas from Ravenstonedale, Cumbria. *Palaeontology*, Vol. 25, 145–166.

HOLDSWORTH, B K, and COLLINSON, J D. 1988. Millstone Grit cyclicity revisited. 132–152 in *Sedimentation in a synorogenic basin complex: the Upper Carboniferous of Northwest Europe*. BESLY, B M, and KELLING, G (editors). (Glasgow and London: Blackie.)

HOLLIDAY, D W. 1986. *Devonian and Carboniferous basins*. 84–110 in *Geothermal energy — the potential in the United Kingdom*. DOWNING, R A, and GRAY, D A (editors). (London: HMSO.)

HOLLIDAY, D W. 1993. Mesozoic cover over northern England: interpretation of apatite fission track data. *Journal of the Geological Society of London*, Vol. 150, 657–660.

HOLLIDAY, D W, EVANS, D J, CORNWELL, J D, BARR, M C, McDONALD, A J W, and CHADWICK, R A. 1999. Regional syntheses of geological and geophysical data. 35–93 in Development of regional exploration criteria for buried carbonate-hosted mineral deposits a multidisciplinary study in northern England. PLANT, J A, and JONES, D G (editors). *British Geological Survey Technical Report*, WP/91/1C.

HOLLIDAY, D W, NEVES, R, and OWENS, B. 1979. Stratigraphy and palynology of early Dinantian (Carboniferous) strata in shallow boreholes near Ravenstonedale, Cumbria. *Proceedings of the Yorkshire Geological Society*, Vol. 42. 343–356

HOLLOWAY, S, BAILY, H, ELEWAUT, E, KOELEWIJN, RIEKS VAN DER STRAATEN, LINDEBERG, E, GAIDA, K H, and MOELLER, H. 1993. The underground disposal of carbon dioxide, Area 2, inventory of the theoretical CO_2 storage capacity of the European Communities and Norway. Confidential report for the JOULE II Non-nuclear Energy R and D programme.

HORBURY, A D. 1987. Sedimentology of the Urswick Limestone in south Cumbria and north Lancashire. Unpublished PhD thesis, University of Manchester.

HORBURY, A D. 1989. The relative roles of tectonism and eustacy in the deposition of the Urswick Limestone in south Cumbria and north Lancashire. 153–169 in The role of tectonics in Devonian and Carboniferous sedimentation in the British Isles. ARTHURTON, R S, GUTTERIDGE, P, and NOLAN, S C (editors). *Yorkshire Geological Society Occasional Publication*, No. 6.

HORBURY, A D. 1992. A late Dinantian peloid cementstone-palaeoberesellid buildup from north Lancashire, England. *Sedimentary Geology*, Vol. 79, 117–137.

HUDSON, R G S. 1924. On the rhythmic succession of the Yoredale Series in Wensleydale. *Proceedings of the Yorkshire Geological Society*, Vol. 20, 125–135.

HUDSON, R G S. 1930. The Carboniferous of the Craven reef belt; and the Namurian unconformity at Scaleber, near Settle. *Proceedings of the Geologists' Association*, Vol. 41, 290–322.

HUDSON, R G S. 1932. The pre-Namurian knoll topography of Derbyshire and Yorkshire. *Transactions of the Leeds Geological Association*, Vol. 5, 49–64.

HUDSON, R G S. 1933. The scenery and geology of north-west Yorkshire. 228–255 in The geology of the Yorkshire Dales. *Proceedings of the Geologists' Association*, Vol. 44, 227–269.

HUDSON, R G S. 1937. The Lower Carboniferous of Carnforth. *British Association for the Advancement of Science, Report of the Annual Meeting*, Blackpool, 1936, 344–345.

HUDSON, R G S. 1938a. 295–330 in The geology of the country around Harrogate. *Proceedings of the Geologists' Association*, Vol. 49, 293–352.

HUDSON, R G S. 1938b. An exploratory boring in the Lower Carboniferous of the Skipton Anticline. *Geological Magazine*, Vol. 75, 512–514.

HUDSON, R G S, BISAT, W S, WADSWORTH HAYWOOD, H, and RAISTRICK, A. 1933. The geology of the Yorkshire Dales. *Proceedings of the Geologists' Association*, Vol 44, 227–255.

HUDSON, R G S, and MITCHELL, G H. 1937. The Carboniferous geology of the Skipton Anticline. *Summary of progress of the Geological Survey of Great Britain* for 1935, 1–45. (London: HMSO.)

HUGHES, R A, COOPER, A H, and STONE, P. 1993. Structural evolution of the Skiddaw Group (English Lake District) on the northern margin of eastern Avalonia. *Geological Magazine*, Vol. 130, 621–629.

HULL, E, DAKYNS, J R, TIDDEMAN, R H, WARD, J C, GUNN, W, and DE RANCE, C E. 1875. The geology of the Burnley Coalfield and of the country around Clitheroe, Blackburn, Preston, Chorley, Haslingden and Todmorden. *Memoir of the Geological Survey*, (England and Wales) Old Series One-inch Quarter Sheets 88NW, 89NE, 89NW and 92SW.

HUTTON, D H W, and MURPHY, F C. 1987. The Silurian rocks of the Southern Uplands and Ireland as a successor basin to the end-Ordovician closure of Iapetus. *Journal of the Geological Society of London*, Vol. 144, 765–772.

HUXLEY, J. 1983. *Britains onshore oil industry*. (London: MacMillans Publishers.)

JACKSON, D I, and MULHOLLAND, P. 1993. Tectonic and stratigraphic aspects of the East Irish Sea Basin and adjacent areas: contrasts in their post-Carboniferous structural styles. 791–808 in *Petroleum geology of Northwest Europe: Proceedings of the 4th Conference*. PARKER, J R (editor). (Belfast: The Universities Press for the Geological Society of London.)

JACKSON, D I, MULHOLLAND, P, JONES, S M, and WARRINGTON, G. 1987. The geological framework of the East Irish Sea Basin. 191–203 in *Petroleum geology of North West Europe*. BROOKS, J, and GLENNIE, K (editors). (London: Graham & Trotman.)

JOHNSON, G A L. 1967. Basement control of Carboniferous sedimentation in northern England. *Proceedings of the Yorkshire Geological Society*, Vol. 6, 175–194.

JONES, C M. 1980. Deltaic sedimentation in the Roaches Grit and associated sediments (Namurian R2b) in the southwest Pennines. *Proceedings of the Yorkshire Geological Society*, Vol. 43, 39–67.

JONES, R C B, TONKS, L H, and WRIGHT, W B. 1938. Wigan district. *Memoir of the Geological Survey of Great Britain*, Sheet 84 (England and Wales).

KEMP, A E S. 1987. Evolution of Silurian depositional systems in the Southern Uplands of Scotland. 124–155 in *Marine clastic sedimentology: concepts and case studies*. LEGGETT, J K, and ZUFFA, G G (editors). (London: Graham & Trotman.)

KENDALL, P F, and WROOT, H E. 1924. *The geology of Yorkshire*. 2 Vols. (Vienna: printed privately.)

KENT, P E. 1948. A deep borehole at Formby, Lancashire. *Geological Magazine*, Vol. 85, 253–264.

KENT, P E. 1980. Subsidence and uplift in East Yorkshire and Lincolnshire: a double inversion. *Proceedings of the Yorkshire Geological Society*, Vol. 42, 505–524.

KING, W B R, and WILCOCKSON, W H. 1934. The Lower Palaeozoic rocks of Austwick and Horton-in-Ribblesdale, Yorkshire. *Quarterly Journal of the Geological Society of London*, Vol. 90, 7–31.

KIRBY, G A, SMITH, K, SMITH, N J P, and SWALLOW, P W. 1987. Oil and Gas generation in eastern England. 171–180 in *Petroleum* geology of north west Europe Vol. 1. BROOKS, J, and GLENNIE, K W (editors). (London: Graham & Trotman.)

KIRBY, G A, and SWALLOW, P. 1987. Tectonism and sedimentation in the Flamborough Head region of north-east England. Proceedings of the Yorkshire Geological Society, Vol. 46, 301–309.

KLEMPERER, S L, and HOBBS, R. 1992. The BIRPS Atlas. Deep seismic reflection profiles around the British Isles. (Cambridge: Cambridge University Press).

KNELLER, B C. 1991. A foreland basin on the southern margin of Iapetus. Journal of the Geological Society of London, Vol. 148, 207–210.

KNELLER, B C, KING, L M, and BELL, A M. 1993. Foreland basin development and tectonics on the northwest margin of eastern Avalonia. Geological Magazine, Vol. 130, 691–697.

KNIPE, R J, COWAN, G, and BALENDRAN, V S. 1993. The tectonic history of the East Irish Sea Basin with reference to the Morecambe fields. 857–866 in Petroleum geology of northwest Europe: Proceedings of 4th Conference. PARKER, J R (editor). (Belfast: The Universities Press for the Geological Society of London.)

KOKELAAR, B P, HOWELLS, M F, BEVINS, R E, ROACH, R A, and DUNKLEY, P N. 1984. The Ordovician marginal basin of Wales. 245–270 in Volcanic and associated sedimentary and tectonic processes in modern and ancient marginal basins. KOKELAAR, B P, and HOWELLS, M F (editors). Special Publication of the Geological Society of London, No. 16.

LAKE, S D, and KARNER, G D. 1987. The structure and evolution of the Wessex Basin, southern England: an example of inversion tectonics. Tectonophysics, Vol. 137, 347–378.

LAWERENCE, S R, COSTER, P W, and IRELAND, R J. 1987. Structural development and petroleum potential of the northern flanks of the Bowland basin (Carboniferous), North-west England. 225–233 in Petroleum geology of north west Europe, Volume 1. BROOKS, J, and GLENNIE, K (editors). (London: Graham & Trotman.)

LEAT, P T, and THORPE, R S. 1989. Snowdon basalts and the cessation of Caledonian subduction by the Longvillian. Journal of the Geological Society of London, Vol. 146, 965–970.

LEE, A G. 1988. Carboniferous basin configuration of central and northern England modelled using gravity data. 69–84 in Sedimentation in a synorogenic basin complex: the Upper Carboniferous of Northwest Europe. BESLY, B M, and KELLING, G (editors). (Glasgow: Blackie.)

LEE, M K. 1986. Hot dry rock. 21–41 in Geothermal energy — the potential in the United Kingdom. DOWNING, A, and GRAY, D A (editors). (London: HMSO.)

LEE, M K, PHARAOH, T C, and GREEN, C A. 1991. Structural trends in the concealed Caledonide basement of eastern England from images of regional potential field data. 45–62 in Proceedings of the International Meeting on the Caledonides of the Midlands and the Brabant Massif. ANDRE, L, HERBOSCH, A, VANGUESTAINE, M, and VERNIERS, J (editors). Annales de la Société, Géologique de Belgique, Vol. 114.

LEE, M K, PHARAOH, T C, and SOPER, N J. 1990. Structural trends in central Britain from images of gravity and aeromagnetic fields. Journal of the Geological Society of London, Vol. 147, 241–258.

LEE, M K, PHARAOH, T C, WILLIAMSON, J P, GREEN, C A, and DE VOS, W. 1993. Evidence on the deep structure of the Anglo-Brabant Massif from gravity and magnetic data. Geological Magazine, Vol. 130, 575–582.

LEEDAL, G P, and WALKER, G P L. 1950. A restudy of the Ingletonian Series of Yorkshire. Geological Magazine, Vol. 87, 57–66.

LEEDER, M R. 1982. Upper Palaeozoic basins of the British Isles — Caledonide inheritance verses Hercynian plate margin processes. Journal of the Geological Society of London, Vol. 139, 479–491.

LEEDER, M R, and HARDMAN, M. 1990. Carboniferous of the Southern North Sea Basin and controls on hydrocarbon prospectivity. 87–105 in Tectonic events responsible for Britain's oil and gas reserves. HARDMAN, R F P, AND BROOKS, J (editors). Special Publication of the Geological Society of London, No. 55.

LEEDER, M R, and McMAHON, A H. 1988. Upper Carboniferous (Silesian) basin subsidence in northern Britain. 43–52 in Sedimentation in a synorogenic basin complex: the Upper Carboniferous of Northwest Europe. BESLY, B M, and KELLING, G (editors). (Glasgow: Blackie.)

LEES, A, and MILLER, J. 1985. Facies variation in Waulsortian buildups, Part 2; Mid-Dinantian buildups from Europe and North America. Geological Journal, Vol. 20, 159–180.

LEGGETT, J K, McKERROW, W S, and EALES, M H. 1979. The Southern Uplands of Scotland, a lower Palaeozoic accretionary prism. Journal of the Geological Society of London, Vol. 136, 755–770.

LEWIS, C L E, GREEN, P F, CARTER, A, and HURFORD, A J. 1992. Elevated K/T palaeotemperatures throughout northwest England: three kilometres of Tertiary erosion? Earth and Planetary Science Letters, Vol. 112, 131–145.

LISTER, S W, and WARD, H E. 1983. Confidential report for BP: Petroleum geochemistry of the East Midlands wells Alport and Gun Hill.

LYNAS, B D T. 1988. Evidence for dextral oblique-slip faulting in the Shelve Ordovician inlier, Welsh Borderland: implications for the south British Caledonides. Geological Journal, Vol. 23, 39–57.

MAGRAW, D. 1957. New boreholes into the Lower Coal Measures below the Arley Mine of Lancashire and adjacent areas. Bulletin of the Geological Survey, No. 13, 14–38.

MAGRAW, D. 1961. Exploratory boreholes in the central part of the South Lancashire Coalfield. The Mining Engineer, Vol. 120, 432–445.

MAGRAW, D, and RAMSBOTTOM, W H C. 1956. A deep borehole for oil at Croxteth Park, near Liverpool. Liverpool and Manchester Geological Journal, Vol. 1, 512–535.

MARR, J E. 1921. The rigidity of north-west Yorkshire. Naturalist, Hull, 63–72.

MARTINSEN, O J. 1990a. Interaction between eustacy, tectonics and sedimentation with particular reference to the Namurian E1c-H2c of the Craven–Askrigg area, northern England. Unpublished Dr Scient. thesis, Universitetet i Bergen.

MARTINSEN, O J. 1990b. Fluvial, inertia-dominated deltaic deposition in the Namurian (Carboniferous) of northern England. Sedimentology, Vol. 37, 1099–1113.

MARTINSEN, O J. 1993. Namurian (late Carboniferous) depositional systems of the Craven–Askrigg area, northern England: implications for sequence stratigraphic models. Special publication of the International Association of Sedimentologists, No. 18, 247–281.

MASON, P C, and JACKSON, R G. 1981. Confidential BP report: A geochemical study of Lancashire outcrops of Carboniferous age.

MAYNARD, J R. 1992. Sequence stratigraphy of the Upper Yeadonian of northern England. Marine and Petroleum Geology, Vol. 9, 197–207.

MAYNARD, J R, and LEEDER, M R. 1992. On the periodicity and magnitude of Late Carboniferous glacio-eustatic sea level changes. *Journal of the Geological Society of London*, Vol. 149, 303–311.

McCABE, P J. 1978. The Kinderscoutian delta (Carboniferous) of northern England; a slope influenced by density currents. 116–126 in *Sedimentation in submarine canyons, fans and trenches*. STANLEY, D J, and KELLING, G (editors). (Stroudsburg: Dowden, Hutchinson and Ross.)

McCAFFREY, W D, BARON, H, MOLYNEUX, S G, and KNELLER, B C. 1992. Recycled achritarchs provenance indicators: implications for Caledonian terrane reconstruction. *Geological Magazine*, Vol. 129, 457–464.

McKENZIE, D P. 1978. Some remarks on the development of sedimentary basins. *Earth and Planetary Science Letters*, Vol. 40, 25–32.

MERRIMAN, R J, PHARAOH, T C, WOODCOCK, N H, and DALY, P. 1993. The metamorphic history of the concealed Caledonides of eastern England and their foreland. *Geological Magazine*, Vol. 130, 613–620.

METCALFE, I. 1981. Conodont zonation and correlation of the Dinantian and early Namurian strata of the Craven lowlands of Northern England. *Report of the Institute of Geological Sciences*, No. 80/10, 1–70.

MILLER, J. 1986. Facies relationships and diagenesis in Waulsortian mudmounds from the Lower Carboniferous of Ireland and N England. 311–335 in *Reef diagenesis*. SCHRODER, J H, and PURSER, B H (editors). (Berlin: Springer-Verlag.)

MITCHELL, G H. 1956. The Borrowdale Volcanic Series of the Dunnerdale Fells, Lancashire. *Liverpool and Manchester Geological Journal*, Vol. 1, 428–449.

MITCHELL, G H. 1967. The Caledonian Orogeny in northern England. *Proceedings of the Yorkshire Geological Society*, Vol. 36, 135–138.

MOLYNEUX, S G. 1991. The contribution of palaeontological data to an understanding of the Early Palaeozoic framework of eastern England. 93–106 in *Proceedings of the International Meeting on the Caledonides of the Midlands and the Brabant Massif*. ANDRE, L, HERBOSCH, A, VANGUESTAINE, M, and VERNIERS, J (editors). *Annales de la Société Géologique de Belgique*, Vol. 114.

MOORE, D. 1959. Role of deltas in the formation of some British Lower Carboniferous cyclothems. *Journal of Geology*, Vol. 67, 522–539.

MOORE, D. 1960. Sedimentation units in sandstones of the Yoredale Series (Lower Carboniferous) of Yorkshire, England. *Journal of Sedimentary Petrology*, Vol. 30, 218–227.

MOSELEY, F. 1956. The geology of the Keasden area, west of Settle, Yorkshire. *Proceedings of the Yorkshire Geological Society*, Vol. 30, 331–352.

MOSELEY, F. 1962. The structure of the south-western part of the Sykes Anticline, Bowland, west Yorkshire. *Proceedings of the Yorkshire Geological Society*, Vol. 33, 287–314.

MOSELEY, F. 1972. A tectonic history of north-west England. *Journal of the Geological Society of London*, Vol. 128, 561–598.

MUNDY, D J C. 1978. Reef communities. 157–167 in *The ecology of fossils*. MCKERROW, W S (editor). (London: Duckworth.)

MURPHY, F C, and HUTTON, D W H. 1986. Is the Southern Uplands of Scotland really an accretionary prism? *Geology*, Vol. 14, 354–357.

MURRAY, D W. 1983. The limestone and dolomite resources of the country around Settle and Malham, North Yorkshire (with notes on the hard-rock resources of the Horton-in-Ribblesdale area). Description of parts of 1:50 000 geological sheets 50 and 60. *Mineral Assessment Report, Institute of Geological Sciences*, No. 126.

MYERS, J O, and WARDELL, J. 1967. The gravity anomalies of the Askrigg Block south of Wensleydale. *Proceedings of the Yorkshire Geological Society*, Vol. 36, 169–173.

NOBLE, S R, TUCKER, R D, and PHARAOH, T C. 1993. Lower Palaeozoic and Precambrian igneous rocks from eastern England, and their bearing on late Ordovician closure of the Tornquist Sea: constraints from U-Pb and Nd isotopes. *Geological Magazine*, Vol. 130, 738–747.

O'BRIEN, C, PLANT, J A, SIMPSON, P R, and TARNEY, J. 1985. The geochemistry, metasomatism and petrogenesis of the granites of the English Lake District. *Journal of the Geological Society of London*, Vol. 142, 1139–1157.

OKOLO, S A. 1983. Fluvial distributary channels in the Fletcher Bank Grit (Namurian R2b) at Ramsbottom, Lancashire, England. 421–433 in Modern and ancient fluvial systems. COLLINSON, J D, and LEWIN, J (editors). *Special Publication of the International Association of Sedimentologists*, No. 6.

O'NIONS, R K, OXBURGH, E R, HAWKESWORTH, C J, and MACINTYRE, R M. 1973. New isotopic and stratigraphical evidence on the age of the Ingletonian: probable Cambrian of northern England. *Journal of the Geological Society of London*, Vol. 129, 445–452.

PARKINSON, D. 1926. The faunal succession in the Carboniferous Limestone and Bowland Shales at Clitheroe and Pendle Hill (Lancashire). *Quarterly Journal of the Geological Society of London*, Vol. 82, 188–249.

PARKINSON, D. 1935. The geology and topography of the limestone knolls in Bolland (Bowland), Lancs and Yorks. *Proceedings of the Geologists' Association*, Vol. 46, 97–120.

PARKINSON, D. 1936. The Carboniferous succession in the Slaidburn district, Yorkshire. *Quarterly Journal of the Geological Society of London*, Vol. 92, 294–331.

PARKINSON, D. 1944. The origin and structure of the lower Visean reef-knolls of the Clitheroe district, Lancashire. *Quarterly Journal of the Geological Society of London*, Vol. 99, 155–168.

PEARCE, J A. 1982. Trace element characteristics of lavas from destructive plate boundaries. 525–548 in *Orogenic andesites*. THORPE, R S (editor). (New York: Wiley.)

PEARCE, J A, HARRIS, N B W, and TINDLE, A G. 1984. Trace element discrimination diagrams for the tectonic interpretation of granitic rocks. *Journal of Petrology*, Vol. 25, 956–983.

PHARAOH, T C, ALLSOP, J M, HOLLIDAY, D W, MERRIMAN, R J, KIMBLE, G S, RUNDLE, C C, BREWER, T S, NOBLE, S R, and EVANS, C J. 1977. The Moorby microgranite: a deformed high level intrusion of Ordovician age in the concealed Caledonide basement of Lincolnshire. *Proceedings of the Yorkshire Geological Society*, Vol. 51, 329–341.

PHARAOH, T C, ALLSOP, J M, RUNDLE, C C, HOLLIDAY, D W, MERRIMAN, R J, and EVANS, C J. 1990. A pre-Carboniferous microgranite in the Claxby No. 1 Borehole, Lincolnshire, and its regional implications. *British Geological Survey Technical Report*, WA/90/80C.

PHARAOH, T C, BREWER, T S, and WEBB, PC. 1993. Subduction-related magmatism of late Ordovician age in eastern England. *Geological Magazine*, Vol. 130, 647–656.

PHARAOH, T C, ENGLAND, R W, and LEE, M K. 1995. The concealed Caledonide basement of Eastern England and the Southern North Sea — a review. *Studia Geophysica et Geodaetica*, Vol. 39, 330–346.

PHARAOH, T C, MERRIMAN, R J, WEBB, P C, and BECKINSALE, R D. 1987a.   The concealed Caledonides of eastern England: preliminary results of a multidisciplinary study.   *Proceedings of the Yorkshire Geological Society*, Vol. 46, 355–369.

PHARAOH, T C, WEBB, P C, THORPE, R S, and BECKINSALE, R D. 1987b.   Geochemical evidence for the tectonic setting of late Proterozoic volcanic suites in central England.   541–552 *in* Geochemistry and mineralization of Proterozoic volcanic suites. PHARAOH, T C, BECKINSALE, R D, and RICKARD, D (editors). *Special Publication of the Geological Society of London*, No 33.

PHILLIPS, J. 1836.   *Illustrations of the geology of Yorkshire*. Part 2 *The Mountain Limestone District*.   (London: John Murray.)

PHILLIPS, W. 1818. *A selection of facts from the best authorities, arranged so as to form an outline of the geology of England and Wales, with a map and sections of the strata.*

PICKERING, K T. 1989.   The destruction of Iapetus and Tornquist's Oceans.   *Geology Today*, Vol. 5, 160–166.

PICKERING, K T, BASSETT, M G, and SIVETER, D J. 1988.   Late Ordovician–early Silurian destruction of the Iapetus Ocean: Newfoundland, British Isles and Scandinavia — a discussion. *Transactions of the Royal Society of Edinburgh: Earth Sciences*, Vol. 79, 361–382.

PINFOLD, E S. 1958.   The search for oil in Lancashire.   *Liverpool and Manchester Geological Journal*, Vol, 106–123.

PLANT, J A, and JONES, D G (editors). 1989. *Metallogenic models and exploration criteria for buried carbonate-hosted ore deposits — a multidisciplinary study in eastern England.*   (Keyworth, Nottingham: British Geological Survey; London: The Institution of Mining and Metallurgy.)

PLANT, J A, and JONES, D G. (editors). 1999.   Development of regional exploration criteria for buried carbonate-hosted mineral deposits: A multidisciplinary study in northern England.   *British Geological Survey Technical Report*, WP/91/1C.

PLANT, J A, O'BRIEN, C, TARNEY, J, and HURDLEY, J. 1985. Geochemical criteria for the recognition of high heat production granites.   263–285 in *High heat production (HHP) granites, hydrothermal circulation and ore genesis*. (London: Institution of Mining and Metallurgy.)

PLAYFAIR, J. 1802.   *Illustrations of the Huttonian Theory of the Earth*. (London: Cadell and Davies; Edinburgh: William Creech.)

POOLE, E G, and WHITEMAN, A J. 1955.   Variations in thickness of the Collyhurst Sandstone in the Manchester area.   *Transactions of the Institution of Mining Engineers*, Vol. 114, 291–318.

POWELL, J H, COOPER, A H and BENFIELD, A C. 1992.   Geology of the country around Thirsk.   *Memoir of the British Geological Survey*, Sheet 52 (England and Wales).

RAMSBOTTOM, W H C. 1973.   Trangressions and regressions in the Dinantian: a new synthesis of British Dinantian stratigraphy. *Proceedings of the Yorkshire Geological Society*, Vol. 39, 567–607.

RAMSBOTTOM, W H C. 1977.   Major cycles of transgression and regression (mesothems) in the Namurian.   *Proceedings of the Yorkshire Geological Society*, Vol. 41, 261–291.

RAMSBOTTOM, W H C, CALVER, M A, EAGAR, R M C, HODSON, F, HOLLIDAY, D W, STUBBLEFIELD, C J, and WILSON, R B. 1978.   A correlation of Silesian rocks in the British Isles.   *Special Report of the Geological Society of London*, No. 10.

RASTALL, H. 1906.   The Ingletonian Series of West Yorkshire. *Proceedings of the Yorkshire Geological Society*, Vol. 16, 87–100.

RAWSON, P F, and RILEY, L A. 1982.   Latest Jurassic–early Cretaceous events and the 'Late-Cimmerian Unconformity' in the North Sea area.   *Bulletin of the American Association of Petroleum Geologists*, Vol. 66/12, 2628–2648.

RAYNER, D H. 1953.   The Lower Carboniferous rocks in the north of England: a review.   *Proceedings of the Yorkshire Geological Society*, Vol. 28, 231–315.

READ, W A. 1991.   The Millstone Grit (Namurian) of the southern Pennines viewed in the light of eustatically controlled sequence stratigraphy.   *Geological Journal*, Vol. 26, 157–165.

READING, H G. 1964.   A review of the factors affecting the sedimentation of the Millstone Grit (Namurian) in the central Pennines.   340–346 *in* Deltaic and shallow marine deposits. VAN STRAATEN, L M J V (editor). *Developments in Sedimentology*, Vol. 1. (Amsterdam: Elsevier.)

RILEY, N J. 1981.   Field meetings 1980: The Carboniferous of Slaidburn, Yorkshire, 7th June 1980.   *Proceedings of the Yorkshire Geological Society*, Vol. 41, 261–291.

RILEY, N J. 1990.   Stratigraphy of the Worston Shale Group (Dinantian), Craven Basin, north-west England.   *Proceedings of the Yorkshire Geological Society*, Vol. 48, 163–187.

RILEY, N J. 1993.   Dinantian (Lower Carboniferous) biostratigraphy and chronostratigraphy in the British Isles. *Journal of the Geological Society of London*, Vol. 150, 427–446.

ROLLIN, K E. 1987.   *Catalogue of geothermal data for the land area of the United Kingdom. Third revison: April 1987. Investigation of the geothermal potential of the UK.*   (Keyworth, Nottingham: British Geological Survey.)

ROSE, W C C, and DUNHAM, K C. 1977.   Geology and hematite deposits of south Cumbria.   *Economic Memoir of the British Geological Survey*, Sheet 58 and the southern part of sheet 48).

ROWE, J, BURLEY, S D, GAWTHORPE, R, COWAN, G, and HARDMAN, M 1993.   Palaeo-fluid flow in the east Irish Sea Basin and its margins.   358–362 in *Geofluids '93: International conference on fluid evolution, migration and interaction in rocks: extended abstracts British Gas*. (Torquay: British Gas.)

RUNDLE, C C. 1979.   Ordovician intrusions in the English Lake District.   *Journal of the Geological Society of London*, Vol. 136, 29–38.

RUSSELL, M, and PEARSON, M J. 1990.   Correlation of vitrinite reflectance with aromatic maturity parameters in the Pennine Carboniferous Basin, England.   *Mededelingen Rijks Geologische Dienst*, Vol. 45, 115–119.

SCOTESE, C R, and McKERROW, W S. 1991.   Ordovician plate tectonic reconstructions.   271–282 *in* Advances in Ordovician geology. BARNES, C R, and WILLIAMS, S H (editors). *Geological Survey of Canada Paper*, No. 90–99.

SCOTT, A. 1984.   Studies on the sedimentology, palaeontology and palaeoecology of the Middle Coal Measures (Westphalian B, Upper Carboniferous) at Swillington, Yorkshire. Part 1. Introduction.   *Transactions of the Leeds Geological Association*, Vol. 10, 1–16.

SHIPP, T. 1992.   The Permo-Trias of St Bees Headland.   62–68 in *Lakeland rocks and landscapes: a field guide*. DODD, M (editor). (Maryport: Ellenbank Press for the Cumberland Geological Society.)

SIMPSON, A. 1967.   The stratigraphy and tectonics of the Skiddaw Slates and the relationship of the overlying Borrowdale Volcanic Series in part of the Lake District.   *Geological Journal*, Vol. 5, 391–418.

SIMS, A P. 1988.   The evolution of a sand-rich basin-fill sequence in the Pendleian (Namurian E1c) of north-west England. Unpublished PhD thesis, University of Leeds.

SMITH, D B. 1980.   The evolution of the English Zechstein Basin.   7–34 in *The Zechstein Basin with emphasis on carbonate sequences*. FUCHTBAUR, H, and PERYT, T M (editors). *Contributions to Sedimentology*, Vol. 9.

SMITH, D B. 1989. The late Permian palaeogeography of north-east England. *Proceedings of the Yorkshire Geological Society*, Vol. 47 (Pt. 4), 285–312.

SMITH, D B, and TAYLOR, J C M. 1992. Permian. 87–94 *in* Atlas of palaeogeography and lithofacies. COPE, J C W, INGHAM, J K, and RAWSON, P F (editors). *Memoir of the Geological Society of London*, No. 13.

SMITH, E G, RHYS, G H, and GOOSSENS, R F. 1973. Geology of the country around East Retford, Worksop and Gainsborough. *Memoir of the Geological Survey of Great Britain*, Sheet 101 (England and Wales).

SMITH, I F. 1986. Mesozoic basins. 42–83 in *Geothermal energy — the potential in the United Kingdom*. DOWNING, R A, and GRAY, D A (editors). (London: HMSO for the British Geological Survey.)

SMITH, K, CRIPPS, A, and EVANS, C J. 1984. *The geothermal potential of Carboniferous rocks in the western Pennines — eastern Cheshire Basin region of north-west England. Investigation of the geothermal potential of the UK.* (Keyworth, Nottingham: British Geological Survey.)

SMITH, K, SMITH, N J P, and HOLLIDAY, D W. 1985. The deep geology of Derbyshire. *Geological Journal*, Vol. 20, 215–225.

SMITH, K, and SMITH, N J P. 1988. Geology of the East Midlands 5–11 in *Metallogenic models and exploration criteria for buried carbonate-hosted ore deposits — a multidisciplinary study in eastern England*. PLANT, J A, and JONES, D G (editors). (Keyworth, Nottingham: British Geological Survey; London: The Institute of Mining and Metallurgy.)

SMITH, N J P (compiler). 1985. Pre-Permian geology of the United Kingdom (South). Scale 1:1000 000. 2 maps commemorating the 150th Anniversary of the British Geological Survey. (Surrey: Cook Hammond and Kell, for the British Geological Survey on behalf of the Petroleum Engineering Division, Department of Energy.)

SMITH, N J P. 1987. The deep geology of central England: the prospectivity of the Palaeozoic rocks. 217–224 in *Petroleum geology of Northwest Europe*. BROOKS, J, and GLENNIE, K (editors). (London: Graham & Trotman.)

SMITH, N J P, and RUSHTON, A W A. 1993. Cambrian and Ordovician stratigraphy related to structure and seismic profiles in the western part of the English Midlands. *Geological Magazine*, Vol. 130, 665–671.

SMITH, W. 1821. *Geological map of Yorkshire*. 4 sheets. (London: J Cary.)

SOPER, N J. 1986. The Newer Granite problem: a geotectonic view. *Geological Magazine*, Vol. 123, 227–236.

SOPER, N J, ENGLAND, R W, SNYDER, D B, and RYAN, P D. 1992. The Iapetus suture zone in England, Scotland and eastern Ireland: a reconciliation of geological and deep seismic data. *Journal of the Geological Society of London*, Vol. 149, 697–700.

SOPER, N J, and HUTTON, D H W. 1984. Late Caledonian displacements in Britain: implications for a three-plate collision model. *Tectonics*, Vol. 3, 781–794.

SOPER, N J, and MOSELEY, F. 1978. Chapter 5. Structure. 45–67 *in* The geology of the Lake District. MOSELEY, F (editor). *Yorkshire Geological Society Occasional Publication*, No. 3.

SOPER, N J, and NUMAN, N M S. 1974. Structure and stratigraphy of the Borrowdale Volcanic rocks of the Kentmere area, English Lake District. *Geological Journal*, Vol. 9, 147–166.

SOPER, N J, WEBB, B C, and WOODCOCK, N J. 1987. Late Caledonian (Acadian) transpression in north west England: timings, geometry and geotectonic significance. *Proceedings of the Yorkshire Geological Society*, Vol. 46, 175–192.

SOPER, N J, and WOODCOCK, N H. 1990. Silurian collision and sediment dispersal patterns in southern Britain. *Geological Magazine*, Vol. 127, 527–542.

SORBY, H C. 1859. On the structure and origin of the Millstone Grit in South Yorkshire. *Proceedings of the Yorkshire Geological and Polytechnical Society*, Vol. 3, 669–675.

STEELE, R P. 1988. The Namurian sedimentary history of the Gainsborough Trough. 102–113 in *Sedimentation in a synorogenic basin complex: the Upper Carboniferous of Northwest Europe*. BESLY, B M, and KELLING, G (editors). (Glasgow: Blackie.)

STEVENSON, I P, and GAUNT, G D. 1971. Geology of the country around Chapel en le Frith. *Memoir of the Geological Survey of Great Britain*, Sheet 99 (England and Wales).

STRANK, A R E. 1982. Asbian and Holkerian foraminifera from the Beckermonds Scar Borehole. *Proceedings of the Yorkshire Geological Society*, Vol. 44, 103–108.

STRONG, G E. 1993. Aspects of the petrology and diagenesis of Sherwood Sandstone Group (Triassic) sandstones from the Kirkham and Weetoh Camp boreholes, near Preston, Lancashire, UK. 283–292 in Characterisation of fluvial and aeolian reservoirs. NORTH, C P, and PROSSER, D J (editors). *Special Publication of the Geological Society of London*, No. 73.

STRONG, G E, MILODOWSKI, A E, PEARCE, J M, KEMP, S J, PRIOR, S V, and MORTON, A C. 1994. The petrology and diagenesis of Permo-Triassic rocks of the Sellafield area, Cumbria. *Proceedings of the Yorkshire Geological Society*, Vol. 50, 77–89.

STUART, I A, and COWAN, G. 1991. The South Morecambe Gas Field, Blocks 110/2a, 110/3a, 110/8a, UK East Irish Sea. 527–541 in United Kingdom oil and gas fields. ABBOTTS, I L (editor). *Memoir of the Geological Society of London*, No. 14.

SUGGATE, R P. 1981. Coal ranks on the Alston Block, northeast England: a discussion. *Proceedings of the Yorkshire Geological Society*, Vol. 43, 451–455.

TEICHMULLER, M. 1987. Recent advances in coalification studies and their application to geology. 127–169 *in* Coal and coal-bearing strata: recent advances. SCOTT, A C (editor). *Special Publication of the Geological Society of London*, No. 32.

THOMAS, B M. 1984. Hydrocarbons, source rocks and maturity trends in the Northern Perth Basin. 391–404 in *Petroleum geochemistry and basin evaluation*. DEMAISON, G, and MURRIS, R J (editors). (Tulsa, Oklahoma: American Association of Petroleum Geologists.)

THOMAS, L J. 1986. Low-grade metamorphism and stable isotopic composition of alteration fluids, Lower Palaeozoic succession, English Lake District. Unpublished PhD thesis, University of St. Andrews.

THOMPSON, D B. 1991. Triassic rocks of the Cheshire Basin. 57–81 *in* Geology of the Manchester area. EAGAR, R M C, and BROADHURST, F M (compilers). GREENSMITH, J T (editor). *Geologists' Association Guide*, No. 7.

THOROGOOD, E J. 1990. Provenance of the Pre-Devonian sediments of England and Wales. *Journal of the Geological Society of London*, Vol. 147, 591–594.

THORPE, R S, BECKINSALE, R D, PATCHETT, P J, PIPER, J D A, DAVIES, G R, and EVANS, J A. 1984. Crustal growth and the late Precambrian–early Palaeozoic plate tectonic evolution of England and Wales. *Journal of the Geological Society of London*, Vol. 141, 521–536.

THORPE, R S, GASKARTH, J W, and HENNEY, P. 1993. Tectonic setting of Caledonian minor intrusions of the English Midlands. *Geological Magazine*, Vol. 130, 657–663.

TIDDEMAN, R H. 1889. On concurrent faulting and deposit in Carboniferous times in Craven, Yorkshire, with a note on

Carboniferous reefs. *Report of the British Association for the Advancement of Science* (Newcastle), 600–603.

TOGHILL, P. 1992.   The Shelveian event, a late Ordovician tectonic episode in Southern Britain (Eastern Avalonia). *Proceedings of the Geologists' Association*, Vol. 103, 31–35.

TONKS, L H, JONES, R C B, LLOYD, W, and SHERLOCK, R L. 1931. The geology of Manchester and the south-east Lancashire Coalfield. *Memoir of the Geological Survey*, Sheet 85 (England and Wales).

TORSVIK, T H, and TRENCH, A. 1991.   The Ordovician history of the Iapetus Ocean in Britain: new palaeomagnetic constraints. *Journal of the Geological Society of London*, Vol. 148, 423–425.

TRENCH, A, TORSVIK, T H, and McKERROW, W S. 1992.   The palaeogeographic evolution of Southern Britain during early Palaeozoic times: a reconciliation of palaeomagnetic and biogeographic evidence. *Tectonophysics*, Vol. 201, 75–82.

TROTTER, F M. 1953.   Exploratory borings in southwest Lancashire. *Transactions of the Institution of Mining Engineers*, Vol. 112, 261–281.

TROTTER, F M. 1954.   Reddened beds in the Coal Measures of Lancashire. *Bulletin of the Geological Survey*, No. 5, 61–80.

TURNER, J S. 1927.   The Lower Carboniferous succession in the western Pennines and the relations of the Pennine and Dent faults. *Proceedings of the Geologists' Association*, Vol. 38, 339–374.

TURNER, J S. 1935.   Structural geology of Stainmore, Westmorland, and notes on the late Palaeozoic (late Variscan) tectonics of the north of England. *Proceedings of the Geologists' Association*, Vol. 46, 121–151.

TURNER, J S. 1936.   The structural significance of the Rossendale Anticline. *Transactions of the Leeds Geological Association*, Vol. 5, 157–160.

TURNER, J S. 1949.   The deeper structure of central and northern England. *Proceedings of the Yorkshire Geological Society*, Vol. 27, 280–297.

TWIST, D, and HARMER, R E J. 1987.   Geochemistry of contrasting siliceous magmatic suites in the Bushveld Complex: Genetic aspects and the implications for tectonic discrimination diagrams. *Journal of Volcanology and Geothermal Research*, Vol. 32, 83–98.

UNDERHILL, J R, GAYER, R A, WOODCOCK, N H, DONNELLY, R, JOLLEY, E J, and STIMPSON, I. G. 1988.   The Dent Fault System, northern England — reinterpreted as a major oblique-slip fault zone. *Journal of the Geological Society of London*, Vol. 145, 303–316.

VAN HOORN, B. 1987.   Structural evolution, timing and tectonic style of the Sole Pit inversion. *Tectonophysics*, Vol. 137, 239–284.

WADGE, A. 1983.   Mineral reconnaissance in the Craven Basin. *BGS Mineral Reconnaissance Report*, No. 66.

WADGE, A J, BATESON, J H, and EVANS, A D. 1983.   Mineral reconnaissance surveys in the Craven Basin. *British Geological Survey Report*, Vol. 83/66, 1–100.

WADGE, A J, GALE, N H, BECKINSALE, R D, and RUNDLE, C C. 1978. A Rb-Sr isochron for the Shap Granite. *Proceedings of the Yorkshire Geological Society*, Vol. 42, 297–305.

WALKER, R G. 1966.   Shale Grit and Grindslow Shales: transition from turbidite to shallow water sediments in the Upper Carboniferous of northern England. *Journal of Sedimentary Petrology*, Vol. 36, 1, 90–114.

WARRINGTON, G. 1974.   Triassic.   145–160 in *The geology and mineral resources of Yorkshire*. RAYNER, D H, and HEMINGWAY, J E. (editors). (Leeds: W S Maney and Son Ltd for Yorkshire Geological Society.)

WARRINGTON, G, AUDLEY CHARLES, M G, ELLIOT, R E, EVANS, W B, IVIMEY-COOK, H C, KENT, P E, ROBINSON, P, SHOTTON, F W, and

TAYLOR, F M. 1980.   A correlation of Triassic rocks in the British Isles. *Special Report of the Geological Society of London*, No. 13.

WEBB, P C, and BROWN, G C. 1984.   *Lake District granites: heat production and related geochemistry. Investigation of the geothermal potential of the UK.*   (Keyworth, Nottingham: British Geological Survey.)

WEBB, P C, and BROWN, G C. 1989.   Geochemistry of igneous rocks.   95–12 in *Metallogenic models and exploration criteria for buried carbonate-hosted ore deposits — a multidisciplinary study in eastern England*. PLANT, J A, and JONES, D G (editors). (Keyworth, Nottingham: British Geological Survey; Institution of Mining and Metallurgy.)

WEBB, P C, and COOPER, A H. 1988.   Slump folds and gravity slide structures in a Lower Palaeozoic marginal basin sequence (the Skiddaw Group), NW England. *Journal of Structural Geology*, Vol. 10, 463–472.

WHETTON, J T, MYERS, J O, and WATSON, I J. 1956.   A gravimeter survey in the Craven district of north-west Yorkshire. *Proceedings of the Yorkshire Geological Society*, Vol. 30, 259–287.

WHITTAKER, A (editor). 1985.   *Atlas of onshore sedimentary basins in England and Wales: Post-Carboniferous tectonics and stratigraphy.* (Glasgow and London: Blackie.)

WILCOCKSON, W H (compiler). 1950.   *Sections of strata of the Coal Measures of Yorkshire* (3rd edition).   (Sheffield: Midland Institute of Mining Engineers.)

WILSON, A A, and CORNWELL, J D. 1982.   The Institute of Geological Sciences borehole at Beckermonds Scar, North Yorkshire. *Proceedings of the Yorkshire Geological Society*, Vol. 44, 59–88.

WILSON, A A, and EVANS, W B. 1990.   Geology of the country around Blackpool. *Memoir of the British Geological Survey*, Sheet 67 (England and Wales).

WILLS, L J. 1951.   *Palaeogeographical atlas.*   (London: Blackie.)

WILLS, L J. 1978.   A palaeogeological map of the Lower Palaeozoic Floor, below the cover of Upper Devonian, Carboniferous and later formations. *Memoir of the Geological Society of London*, No. 8.

WOODCOCK, N H, and GIBBONS, W. 1988.   Is the Welsh Borderland Fault System a terrane boundary? *Journal of the Geological Society of London*, Vol. 145, 915–933.

WRAY, D A. 1936.   *British regional geology: the Pennines and adjacent areas* (1st edition).   (London: HMSO for Geological Survey of Great Britain.)

WRAY, D A, and COPE, F W. 1948.   Geology of Southport and Formby. *Memoir of the Geological Survey of Great Britain*, Sheets 74 and 83. (England and Wales).

WRAY, D A, STEPHENS, J V, EDWARDS, W N, and BROMEHEAD, C E N. 1930.   The geology of the country around Huddersfield and Halifax. *Memoir of the Geological Survey*, Sheet 77 (England and Wales).

WRAY, D A, and TRUEMAN, A E. 1931.   The non-marine lamellibranchs of the Upper Carboniferous of Yorkshire and their zonal sequence. *Summary of Progress of the Geological Survey for 1930*, Part III, 70–72. (London: HMSO.)

WRIGHT, W B, SHERLOCK, R L, WRAY, D A, LLOYD, W, and TONKS, L H. 1927.   The geology of the Rossendale Anticline. *Memoir of the Geological Survey*, Sheet 76 (England and Wales).

ZIEGLER, P A. 1982.   *Geological atlas of Western and Central Europe.* (Amsterdam: Shell International Petroleum Maatschappij BV.)

ZIEGLER, P A. 1990.   *Geological atlas of Western and Central Europe* (2nd edition).   (Amsterdam: Shell International Petroleum Maatschappij BV.)

APPENDIX 1

Memoirs of the region

This Appendix contains a list of the 1:50 000 sheet memoirs for the region. Out-of-print memoirs are indicated by an asterisk. 'Old Series' memoirs are listed for those areas where no other sheet description is available. Photocopies of out-of-print BGS memoirs may be purchased from BGS Keyworth. See back cover for key to geological sheet numbers. Other information is available at BGS web site: www:bgs.ac.uk.

NEW SERIES (1:50 000)

Sheet	Date	Memoir title and authors
28, 37, and 47	1997	Geology of the west Cumbria district. Akhurst, M C, Chadwick, R A, Holliday, D W, McCormac, McMillan, A A, M, Millward, D and Young, B.
37*	1937	Geology of the country around Gosforth. Trotter, F M, Hollingworth, S E, Eastwood, T, and Rose, W C C.
38	1998	Geology of the country around Ambleside. Millward, D, Johnson, E W, Beddoe-Stephens, B, Young, B, Kneller, B C, Lee, M K, and Fortey, N J.
42	1998	Geology of the country around Northallerton. Frost, D V.
52	1992	Geology of the country around Thirsk. Powell, J H, Cooper, A H, and Benfield, A C.
59	1998	Geology of the country around Lancaster. Brandon, A, Aitkenhead, N, Crofts, R G, Ellison, R A, Evans, D J, and Riley, N J.
60	1988	Geology of the country around Settle. Arthurton, R S, Johnson, E W, and Mundy, D J C.
62	1993	Geology of the country around Harrogate. Cooper, A H, and Burgess, I C.
66	1990	Geology of the country around Blackpool. Wilson, A A, and Evans, W B.
67	1992	Geology of the country around Garstang. Aitkenhead, N, Bridge, D McC, Riley, N J, and Kimbell, S F.
68	1961	Geology of the country around Clitheroe and Nelson. Earp, J R, Magraw, D, Poole, E G, Land, D H, and Whiteman, A J.
69	1953	Geology of the country between Bradford and Skipton. Stephens, J V, Mitchell, G H, and Edwards, W.
70*	1950	Geology of the district north and east of Leeds. Edwards, W, Mitchell, G H, and Whitehead, T H.
74* and 83	1948	Geology of Southport and Formby. Wray, D A, and Wolverson Cope, F.
75*	1963	Geology of the country around Preston. Price, D, Wright, W B, Jones, R C B, Tonks, L H, and Whitehead, T H.
76*	1927	The geology of the Rossendale Anticline. Wright, W B, Sherlock, R L, Wray, D A, Lloyd, W, and Tonks, L H.
77*	1930	The geology of the country around Huddersfield and Halifax. Wray, D A, Stephens, J V, Edwards, W N, and Bromehead, C E N.
78*	1940	Geology of the country around Wakefield. Edwards, W, Wray, D A, and Mitchell, G H.
84*	1938	Wigan district. Jones, R B C, Tonks, L H, and Wright, W B.
85*	1931	The geology of Manchester and the south-east Lancashire Coalfield. Tonks, L H, Jones, R B C, Lloyd, W, and Sherlock, R L.
86*	1933	The geology of the country around Holmfirth and Glossop. Bromehead, C E N, Edwards, W, Wray, D A, and Stephens, J V.
87	1947	Geology of the country around Barnsley. Mitchell, G H, Stephens, J V, Bromehead, C E N, and Wray, D A.
96*	1923	Geology of Liverpool, with Wirral and part of the Flintshire Coalfield. Wedd, C B, Smith, B, Simmons, W C, and Wray, D A.
98*	1963	Geology of the country around Stockport and Knutsford. Taylor, B J, Price, R H, and Trotter, F M.
99	1971	Geology of the country around Chapel-en-le-Frith. Stevenson, I P, and Gaunt, G D.
100	1957	Geology of the country around Sheffield. Eden, R A, Stevenson, I P, and Edwards, W.

REGIONAL/ECONOMIC MEMOIRS

40, 41 and 50	1985	Geology of the Northern Pennine Orefield. Volume 2: Stainmore to Craven. Dunham, K C, and Wilson, A A.
58 and 48	1977	Geology and hematite deposits of South Cumbria. Rose, W C C, and Dunham, K C.

OLD SERIES

Sheet	Old series	Date	Memoir title and authors
39*	98 NE	1888	The geology of the country around Kendal, Sedburgh, Bowness and Tebay. Aveline, W T, and Hughes, T McK.
40*	97 NW	1891	The geology of the country around Mallerstang; with parts of Wensleydale, Swaledale and Arkendale. Dakyns, J R, Tiddeman, R H, Russel, R, Clough, C T, and Strahan, A.
41	97 NW	Not available	
49	97 SE	Not available	
50*	97 SW	1890	The geology of the country around Ingleborough with parts of Wensleydale and Wharfedale. Dakyns, J R, Tiddeman, R H, Gunn, W, and Strahan, A.
97*	80 NW	1882	The geology of the country around Prescot, Lancashire. Hull, E.

APPENDIX 2

Summary of principal boreholes

Outline records for the boreholes judged to be of particular significance in the elucidation of the subsurface geology of the region are given below. The list is selective and does not include all of the deeper boreholes. The full records are held in the National Geological Records Centre, British Geological Survey, Keyworth, Nottingham, NG12 5GG, Tel. 0115 936 3109, Fax 0115 936 3276.

All depths are given below Kelly Bushing or other reference level. The depths to the main stratigraphical boundaries is the interpretation of the authors of this book, and may differ in some instances from previously published accounts or from the interpretation on composite logs supplied to the British Geological Survey. Except for those indicated as currently held 'commercial-in-confidence', more details of these boreholes can be found in British Geological Survey records and in the publications cited.

The BGS reference number is a unique number assigned to each borehole. The first two letters of this reference refer to the 100 km grid square, the boundaries of which are indicated in Figure 53. The next two numbers define the 10 km grid square within this area (easting, northing). The following two letters define within which quarter the borehole lies (e.g. NW, SE etc.) and the final figure is the number of that borehole within that quarter assigned on a time sequential basis.

*	Organic maturation data available
C	Commercial-in-confidence
IGS	Institute of Geological Sciences
AOD	Above Ordnance Datum
m	metres

Aiskew Bank Farm *

BGS record number	SE28NE9
National Grid reference	^{42}6670 ^{48}8880
Surface or reference level	40.00 m AOD
Drilled by	IGS (BGS)
Date	1975
Published data source	Dunham and Wilson (1985) Wilson (1960)
Base Quaternary	45.20 m
Base Permo-Trias	96.45 m
Terminal depth	178.77 m in Arnsbergian sandstone

Alport-1 *

BGS record number	SK19SW1
National Grid reference	^{41}3600 ^{39}1000
Surface or reference level	295.00 m AOD
Drilled by	Steel Brothers Co. Ltd
Date	1939–1941
Published data source	Earp, Magraw, Poole, Land and Whiteman (1948), Gutteridge (1991) Hudson and Cotton (1945), Stevenson and Gaunt (1971)
Base Namurian	335.00 m
Terminal depth	778.80 m in Dinantian (Arundian)

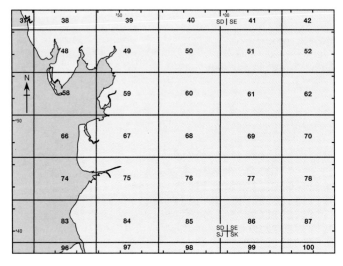

Figure 53 One-inch and 1:50 000 series geological maps of the region.

Beckermonds Scar *

BGS record number	SD88SE1
National Grid reference	^{38}6350 ^{48}0160
Surface or reference level	337.00 m AOD
Drilled by	IGS (BGS)
Date	1973
Published data source	Arthurton, Johnson and Mundy, (1988), Berridge (1982), Creaney (1982), Dunham and Wilson (1985), Strank (1982) Wilson and Cornwell, (1982)
Base Quaternary	1.60 m
Base Dinantian	267.88 m
Terminal depth	527.90 m in Ordovician Ingleton Group (Arenig)

Bickerstaff

BGS record number	SD40SW7
National Grid reference	^{34}4560 ^{40}2480
Surface or reference level	43.89 m AOD
Drilled by	D'arcy Brothers Exploration
Date	1944
Base Quaternary	6.70 m
Base Coal Measures	485.22 m
Terminal depth	579.40 m in Namurian

Boulsworth-1 * C

BGS record number	SD93SW14
National Grid reference	^{39}2685 ^{43}4790
Surface or reference level	429.40 m AOD
Drilled by	Continental Oil Co. Ltd
Date	1963
Base Namurian	1053.00 m
Base Dinantian	1889.67 m
Terminal depth	1922.89 m in Devonian

Brookhouse
BGS record number	SJ69SW55
National Grid reference	^{36}4470 ^{39}4130
Surface or reference level	33.58 m AOD
Drilled by	National Coal Board
Date	1980
Base Permo-Trias	639.00 m
Terminal depth	1436.60 m in Coal Measures

Comingo S2
BGS record number	SD86SW6
National Grid reference	^{38}4920 ^{46}3450
Surface or reference level	c. 300 m AOD
Drilled by	Comingo
Date	1968
Published data source	Arthurton, Johnson and Mundy (1988)
Base Quaternary	6.60 m
Base Dinantian	388.01 m
Terminal depth	426.35 m in ?Silurian

Crimple Beck
BGS record number	SE25SE42
National Grid reference	^{42}7280 ^{45}1860
Surface or reference level	132.00 m AOD
Drilled by	IGS (BGS)
Date	1982
Base Namurian	59.40 m
Terminal depth	188.50 m in Brigantian

Ellenthorpe-1
BGS record number	SE46NW7
National Grid reference	^{42}33000 ^{67}0300
Surface or reference level	18.30 m AOD
Drilled by	D'arcy Brothers Exploration Ltd
Date	1945-5
Published data source	Cooper and Burgess (1993)
Base Quaternary	38.00 m
Base Triassic	163.00 m
Base Permian	317.00 m
Terminal depth	335.26 m in Chadian–Arundian

Elswick-1 C
BGS record number	SD43NW15
National Grid reference	^{34}2380 ^{43}6965
Surface or reference level	20.00 m AOD
Drilled by	British Gas plc
Date	1990
Base Triassic	846.04 m
Base Permian	1596.04 m
Terminal depth	1615.85 m in Carboniferous siltstone

Farnham
BGS record number	SE35NW27
National grid reference	^{43}4690 ^{45}9960
Surface or reference level	42.00 m AOD
Drilled by	IGS (BGS)
Date	1979
Base Triassic	42.00 m
Terminal depth	322.20 m in Namurian (Chokierian) Upper Follifoot Grit

Fearnhead
BGS record number	SJ69SW50
National Grid reference	^{36}272 ^{39}020
Surface or reference level	10.06 m AOD
Drilled by	National Coal Board
Date	1977
Base Quaternary	22.00 m
Base Permo-Trias	641.00 m
Terminal depth	1412.86 m in Carboniferous

Fletcherbank-1
BGS record number	SD81NW3
National Grid reference	^{38}0530 ^{41}6440
Surface or reference level	243.52 m AOD
Drilled by	Steel Brothers Co. Ltd
Date	1958–59
Base Namurian	1376.22 m
Terminal depth	1680.97 m

Formby-1 *
BGS record number	SD30NW22
National Grid reference	^{33}1880 ^{40}8040
Surface or reference level	5.88 m AOD
Drilled by	D'arcy Exploration Co. Ltd BP Exploration Co. Ltd
Date	1940–47
Published data source	Wray and Wolverson (1948)
Base Quaternary	30.48 m
Base Permo-Trias	1793.66 m
Terminal depth	2340.75 m in Dinantian Worston Shale

Formby-4 *
BGS record number	SD20NE1
National Grid reference	^{32}8220 ^{40}7480
Surface or reference level	10.97 m AOD
Drilled by	D'arcy Exploration Co. Ltd
Date	1950
Base Quaternary	22.86 m
Base Permo-Trias	846.69 m
Terminal depth	1182.57 m in Dinantian Limestone Group

Formby-5
BGS record number	SD21SE1
National Grid reference	^{32}9730 ^{41}2460
Surface or reference level	9.75 m AOD
Drilled by	D'arcy Exploration Co. Ltd
Base Quaternary	39.62 m
Base Permo-Trias	1274.00 m
Terminal depth	1326.73 m in Namurian Millstone Grit

Gleaston Castle Farm
BGS record number	SD27SE51
National Grid reference	^{32}5490 ^{47}1850
Surface or reference level	43.89 m AOD
Drilled by	IGS (BGS)
Date	1971
Published data source	Rose and Dunham (1977)
Base Quaternary	7.30 m
Base Namurian	124.27 m
Terminal depth	165.36 m in Dinantian limestone

Harsley-1
BGS record number	SE49NW6
National Grid reference	^{44}2230 ^{49}8070
Surface or reference level	116.03 m AOD
Drilled by	Home Oil of Canada Ltd
Date	1965
Base Jurassic	73.00 m

Base Permo-Trias   706.00 m
Base Namurian   about 1060.00 m
Terminal depth   1081.68 m

Hesketh-1 C
BGS record number   SD42NW6
National Grid reference   [34]3001 [42]5197
Surface or reference level   12.50 m AOD
Drilled by   British Gas plc
Date   1990
Base Triassic   563.72 m
Base Permian   660.67 m
Base Namurian   963.00 m
Terminal depth   1295.73 m in Lower Bowland Shale
                             (Brigantian)

HeywoodD-1
BGS record number   SD80NW141
National Grid reference   [38]3850 [40]8980
Surface or reference level   120.02 m AOD
Drilled by   BP Development Ltd
Date   1984
Base Namurian   1441.00 m
Terminal depth   1619.00 m in Chatburn
                             Limestone (Asbian–Brigantian)

Holme Chapel-1 *
BGS record number   SD82NE68
National Grid reference   [38]6080 [42]8780
Surface or reference level   271.65 m AOD
Drilled by   Quintana Petroleum Corporation
Date   1974
Base Coal Measures   67.66 m
Base Namurian   1564.00 m
Base Dinantian   1968.00 m
Terminal depth   1982.32 m in purple slates

Humphrey Head
BGS record number   SD37SE1
National Grid reference   [33]8540 [47]4140
Surface or reference level   14.00 m AOD
Drilled by   IGS (BGS)
Date   1973
Base Permo-Trias   257.29 m
Terminal depth   272.10 m in ?Namurian

Kirklington
BGS record number   SE38SW38
National Grid reference   [43]2900 [48]0900
Surface or reference level   33.76 m AOD
Drilled by   National Coal Board
Date   1978
Base Permo-Trias   196.38 m
Terminal depth   298.48 m in ?Namurian
                             sandstone

Kirk Smeaton-1 C
BGS record number   SE51NW40
National Grid reference   [45]1142 [41]6097
Surface or reference level   37.70 m AOD
Drilled by   RTZ Oil and Gas Ltd
Date   1985
Base Permo-Trias   37.00 m
Base Coal Measures   999.00 m
Base Namurian   1591.00 m
Terminal depth   1636.00 m in Dinantian
                             limestone

Larkhill
BGS record number   SJ69NE22
National Grid reference   [36]8990 [39]6820
Surface or reference level   22.62 m AOD
Drilled by   National Coal Board
Date   1978
Base Quaternary   4.00 m
Base Permo-Trias   436.00 m
Terminal depth   1266.05 m in Coal Measures

Longford
BGS record number   SJ69SW51
National Grid reference   [36]0330 [39]0010
Surface or reference level   9.10 m AOD
Drilled by   National Coal Board
Date   1977
Base Quaternary   60.00 m
Base Permo-Trias   537.00 m
Terminal depth   1260.65 m in Coal Measures

Raydale *
BGS record number   SD98SW1
National Grid reference   [39]0260 [48]4740
Surface or reference level   267.90 m AOD
Drilled by   IGS (BGS)
Date   1973
Published data source   Creaney (1982)
                             Dunham (1974)
                             Dunham and Wilson, (1985)
Base Quaternary   5.18 m
Base Dinantian   495.05 m
Terminal depth   600.56 m in the Wensleydale
                             Granite

Roddlesworth-1 C
BGS record number   SD62SE6
National Grid reference   [36]5629 [42]1263
Surface or reference level   235.92 m AOD
Drilled by   Amoco (UK) Exploration Co. Ltd
Date   1987–88
Base Namurian   1276.52 m
Base Dinantian   2471.34 m
Terminal depth   2510.37 m in Devonian O.R.S.
                             (?Famennian)

Roosecote-1 *
BGS record number   SD26NW19
National Grid reference   [32]3040 [46]8660
Surface or reference level   37.49 m AOD
Drilled by   IGS (BGS)
Date   1970–71
Published data source   Rose and Dunham (1977)
Base Quaternary   35.80 m
Base Permo-Trias   158.13 m
Base Namurian   613.31 m
Terminal depth   800.88 m in Dinantian limestone

Sandhutton-1
BGS record number   SE38SE10
National Grid reference   [43]7985 [48]1575
Surface or reference level   3.30 m AOD
Drilled by   National Coal Board
Date   1978
Base Quaternary   27.00 m
Base Permo-Trias   386.67 m
Terminal depth   417.98 m in Carboniferous
                             (?Namurian)

Sawley-1 *
BGS record number	SE26NW15
National Grid reference	245104 650204
Surface or reference level	178.60 m AOD
Drilled by	D'arcy Exploration Co. Ltd
Date	1945
Published data source	Arthurton, Johnson and Mundy (1988), Dunham and Wilson (1985), Falcon and Kent (1960)
Base Namurian	383.42 m
Terminal depth	394.70 m in Dinantian limestone

Silverdale
BGS record number	SD87SW9
National Grid reference	384350 471330
Surface or reference level	427.00 m AOD
Drilled by	BGS
Date	1980
Published data source	Arthurton, Johnson and Mundy (1988), Dunham and Wilson (1985), Murray (1983)
Base Quaternary	0.40 m
Base Dinantian	191.00 m
Terminal depth	200.77 m in ?Silurian (?Ludlow)

South Kirkby-1
BGS record number	SE41SE59
National Grid reference	445460 410920
Surface or reference level	50.29 m AOD
Drilled by	Safari Oil Co.
Date	1967
Published data source	Whittaker, Holliday and Penn (1985)
Base Coal Measures	1256.00 m
Terminal depth	1406.58 m

Thistleton-1 C
BGS record number	SD33NE17
National Grid reference	339760 437000
Surface or reference level	22.86 m AOD
Drilled by	British Gas
Date	1987–88
Base Triassic	819.21 m
Base Permian	926.52 m
Base Namurian	2118.90 m (approx.)
Terminal depth	2140.24 m in Dinantian limestone.

Tholthorpe-1 *
BGS record number	SE46NE7
National Grid reference	446824 466891
Surface or reference level	63.00 m AOD
Drilled by	Home Oil of Canada Ltd
Date	1965
Base Quaternary	27.43 m
Base Permo-Trias	478.51 m
Terminal depth	929.59 m in Namurian

Upholland-1 *
BGS record number	SD50SW20
National Grid reference	350440 402900
Surface or reference level	83.80 m AOD

Drilled by	B.P. Exploration Co.
Date	1956
Published data source	Russell and Pearson (1991)
Base Quaternary	9.75 m
Base Coal Measures	?
Faulted zone	240.78 m–289.55 m
Faulted zone	606.52 m–643.10 m
Terminal depth	1523.00 m in Sabden Shales

Waters Farm
BGS record number	SD76NE11
National Grid reference	375370 467630
Surface or reference level	131.00 m AOD
Drilled by	BGS (IGS)
Date	1982
Published data source	Arthurton, Johnson and Mundy (1988)
Base Quaternary	7.15 m
Base Coal Measures	56.40 m
Terminal depth	200.00 m in Namurian

Weeton-1 *
BGS record number	SE24NE11
National Grid reference	429809 446385
Surface or reference level	50.83 m AOD
Drilled by	RTZ Oil and Gas Ltd
Date	1984
Base Namurian	590.00 m
Terminal depth	1979.28 m in Chadian

Wessenden-1 C
BGS record number	SE00NE7
National Grid reference	405460 406310
Surface or reference level	497.26 m AOD
Drilled by	Enterprise Oil plc
Date	1987–88
Published data source	Gutteridge (1991)
Base Namurian	489.48 m
Base Dinantian	1103.32 m
Terminal depth	1127.70 m in Lower Palaeozoic metamorphic rocks

Whitmoor-1
BGS record number	SD56SE1
National Grid reference	358744 463150
Surface or reference level	311.96 m AOD
Drilled by	Place Oil and Gas Co. (UK) Ltd
Date	1967
Base Namurian	1050.00 m
Terminal depth	1552.00 m in late Chadian

Winksley
BGS record number	SE27SE9
National Grid reference	425070 471510
Surface or reference level	134.00 m AOD
Drilled by	IGS (BGS)
Date	1976
Published data source	Dunham and Wilson (1985)
Base Coal Measures	29.70 m
Terminal depth	114.25 m in Namurian (Kinderscoutian)

INDEX

CROSS-SECTIONS AND MAPS

CROSS-SECTIONS

Regional cross-sections A–A′, B–B′, C–C′ and D–D′

MAPS

REGIONAL CROSS-SECTIONS

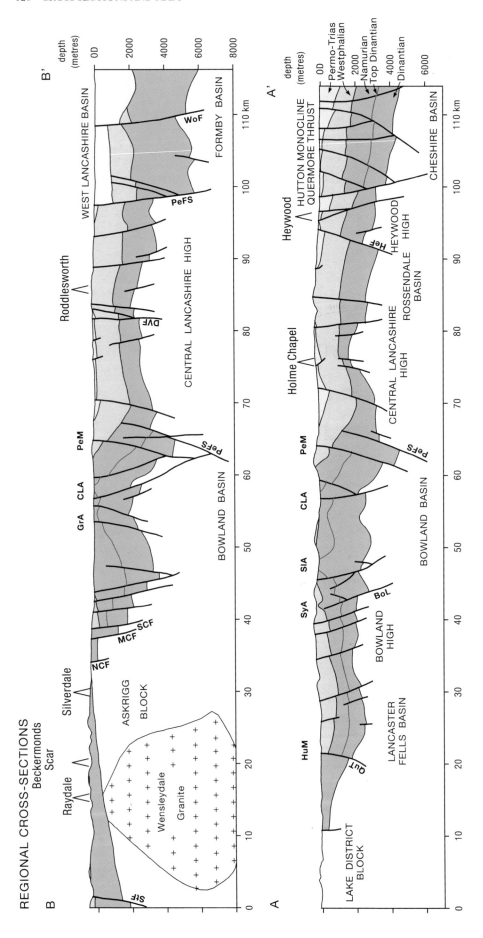

Regional cross-sections A–A', B–B', C–C' and D–D'.

AlF Alport Fault; BoL Bowland Line; CLA Clitheroe Anticline; DVF Darwen Valley Fault; ElA Ellenthorpe Anticline; GrA Grindleton Anticline; HaA Harrogate Anticline; HBF Herridge–Bradshaw Fault; HeF Heywood Fault; HoF Holme Fault; HuM Hutton Monocline; MCF Middle Craven Fault; MoCF Morley–Campsall Fault; NCF North Craven Fault; PeM Pendle Monocline; PeFS Pendle Fault System; QuT Quernmore Thrust; SCF South Craven Fault; SlA Slaidburn Anticline; StF Stockdale Fault; SyA Sykes Anticline; WoF Woodsford Fault.

REGIONAL CROSS-SECTIONS

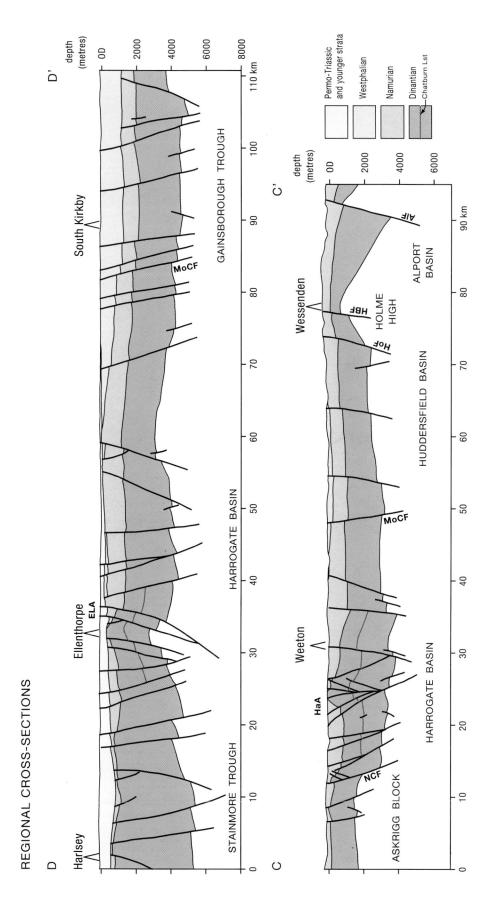

Regional cross-sections (*continued*).

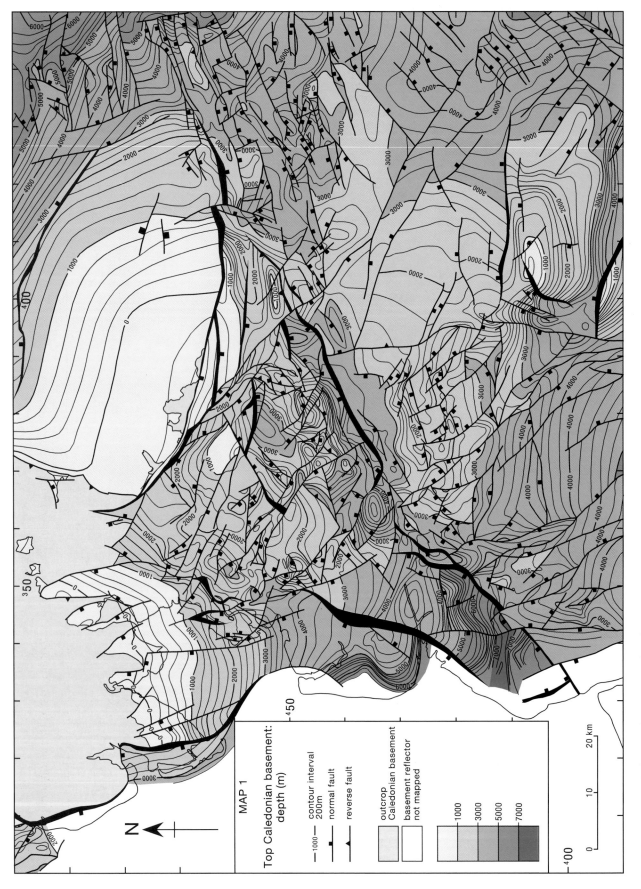

Map 1   Top Caledonian basement: depth.

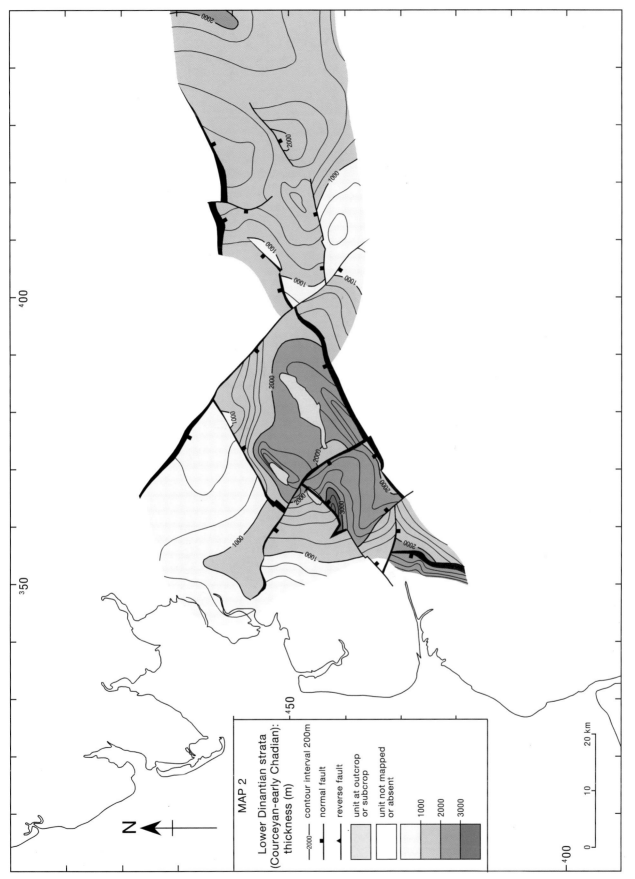

Map 2   Lower Dinantian strata (Courceyan–early Chadian): preserved thickness.

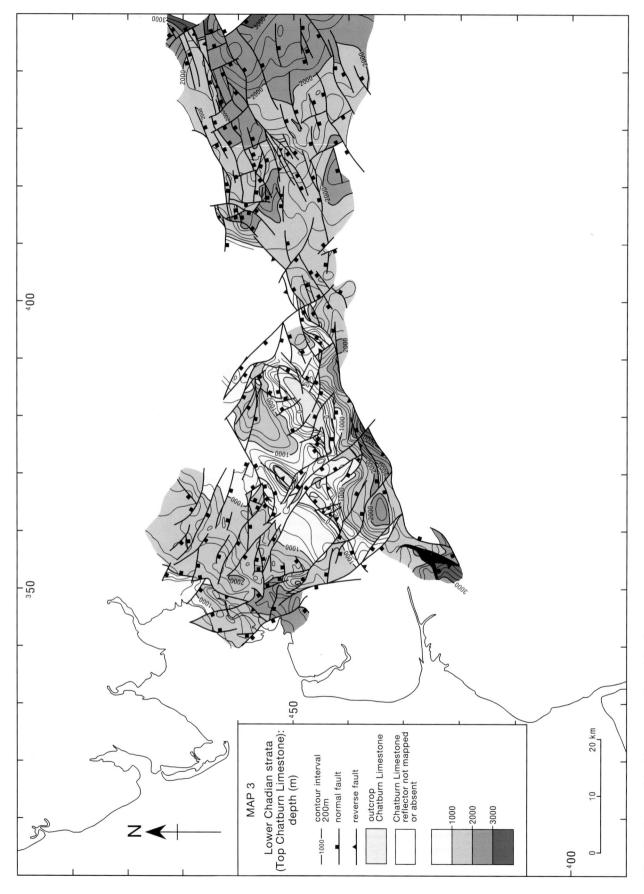

Map 3   Lower Chadian strata (Top Chatburn Limestone): depth.

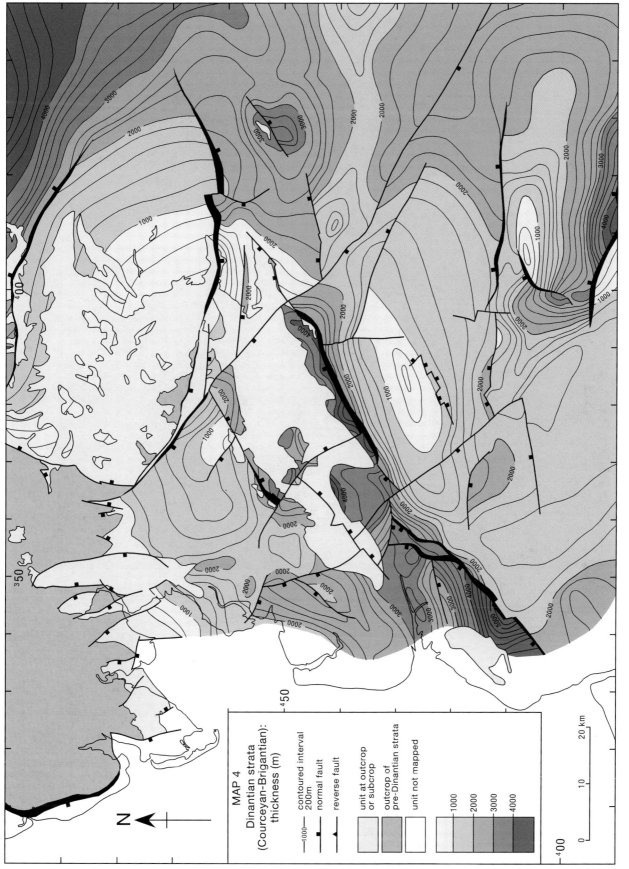

Map 4 Dinantian strata (Courceyan–Brigantian): thickness.

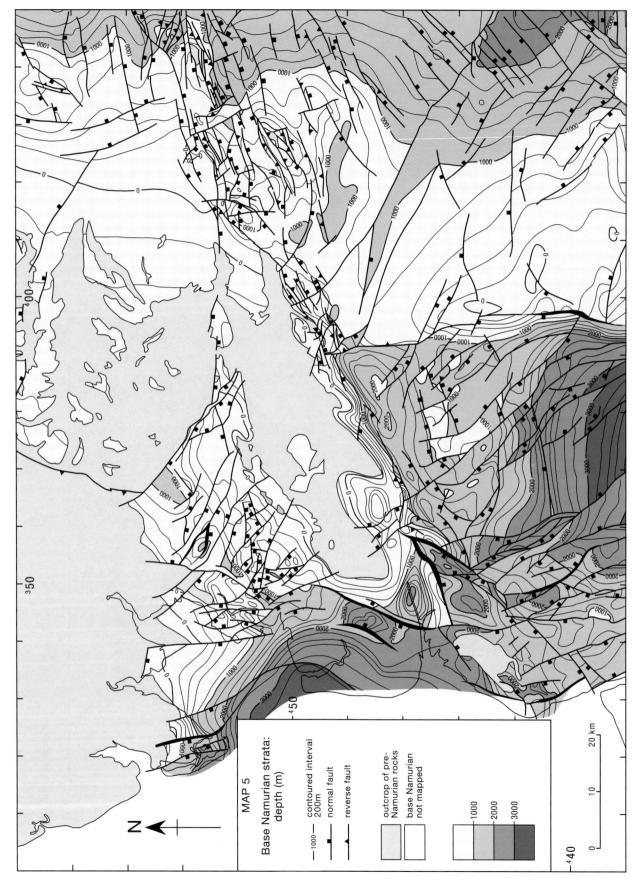

Map 5   Base Namurian strata: depth.

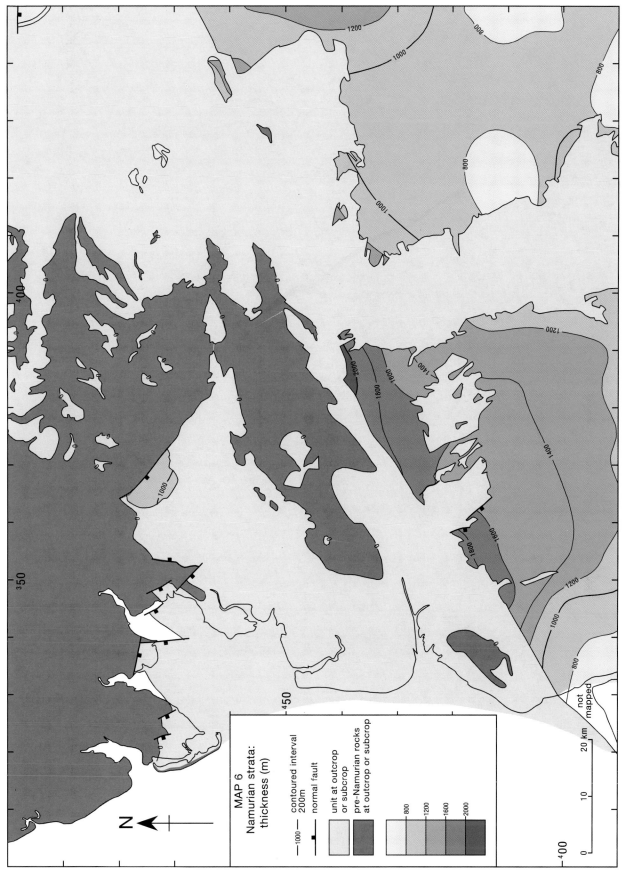

Map 6 Namurian strata: thickness.

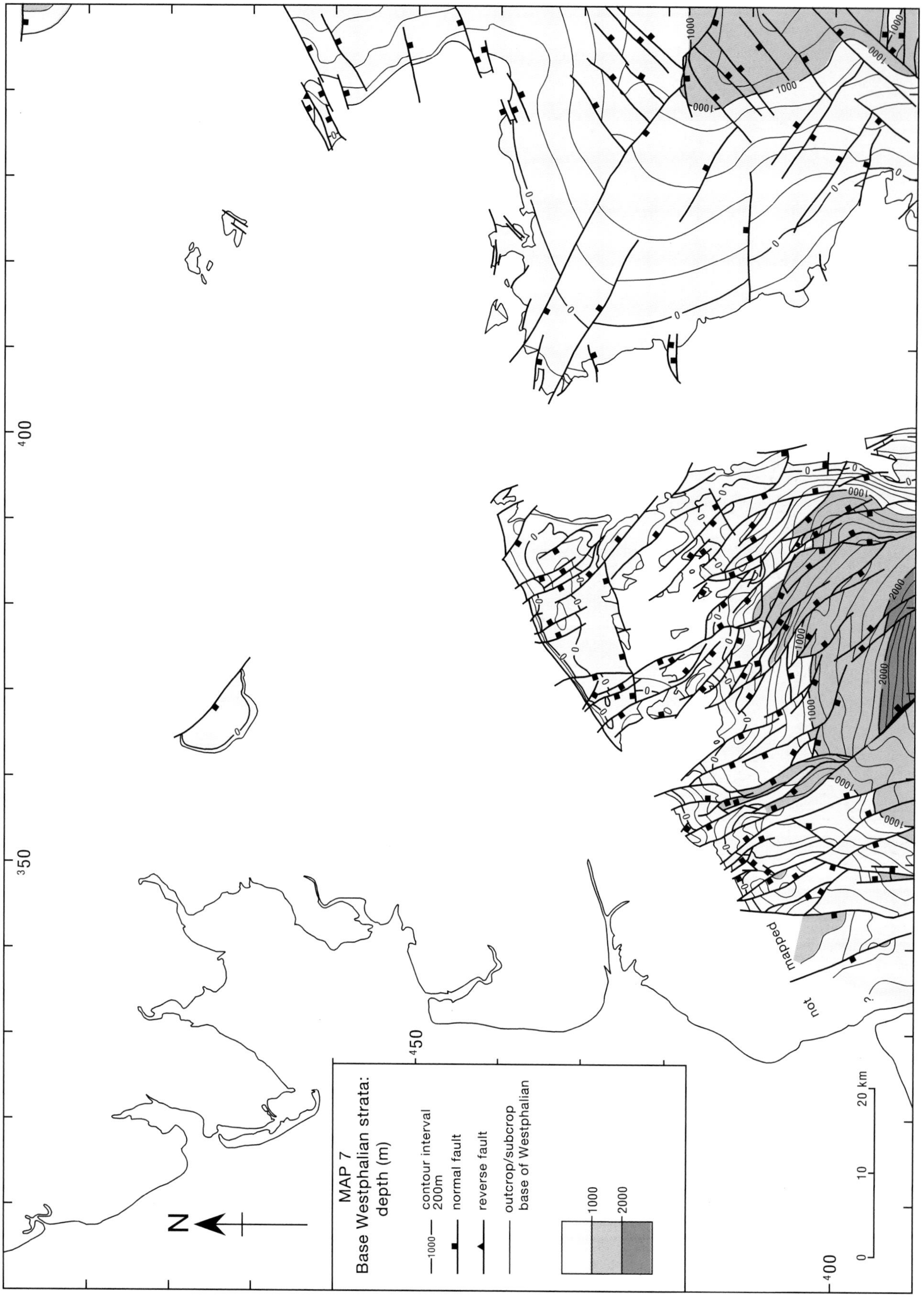

Map 7 Base Westphalian strata: depth.

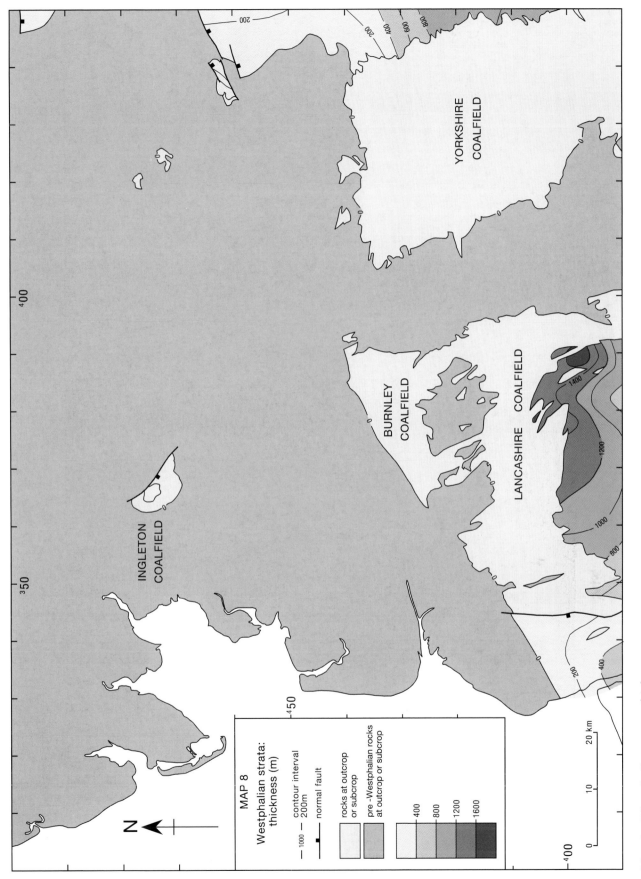

Map 8 Westphalian strata: thickness.

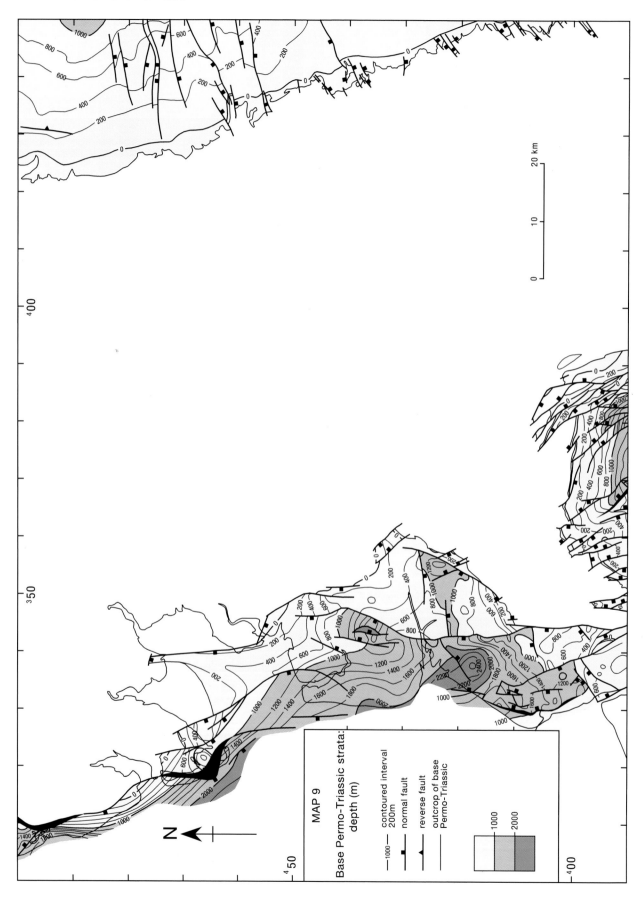

Map 9 Base Permo-Triassic strata: depth.

MAP 9

Base Permo-Triassic strata:
depth (m)

—1000— contoured interval
          200m
◼ normal fault
▲ reverse fault
        outcrop of base
        Permo-Triassic

1000
2000

20 km

N

BRITISH GEOLOGICAL SURVEY

Keyworth, Nottingham NG12 5GG
0115 936 3100

Murchison House, West Mains Road, Edinburgh EH9 3LA
0131 667 1000

London Information Office, Natural History Museum
Earth Galleries, Exhibition Road, London SW7 2DE
020 7589 4090

The full range of Survey publications is available through the Sales Desks at Keyworth and at Murchison House, Edinburgh, and in the BGS London Information Office in the Natural History Museum (Earth Galleries). The adjacent bookshop stocks the more popular books for sale over the counter. Most BGS books and reports can be bought from The Stationery Office and through Stationery Office agents and retailers. Maps are listed in the BGS Map Catalogue, and can be bought together with books and reports through BGS-approved stockists and agents as well as direct from BGS.

The British Geological Survey carries out the geological survey of Great Britain and Northern Ireland (the latter as an agency service for the government of Northern Ireland), and of the surrounding continental shelf, as well as its basic research projects. It also undertakes programmes of British technical aid in geology in developing countries as arranged by the Department for International Development and other agencies.

The British Geological Survey is a component body of the Natural Environment Research Council.

Published by The Stationery Office and available from:

The Publications Centre
(mail, telephone and fax orders only)
PO Box 276, London SW8 5DT
Telephone orders/General enquiries 0870 600 5522
Fax orders 0870 600 5533

www.tso-online.co.uk

The Stationery Office Bookshops
123 Kingsway, London WC2B 6PQ
020 7242 6393 Fax 020 7242 6412
68–69 Bull Street, Birmingham B4 6AD
0121 236 9696 Fax 0121 236 9699
33 Wine Street, Bristol BS1 2BQ
0117 926 4306 Fax 0117 929 4515
9–21 Princess Street, Manchester M60 8AS
0161 834 7201 Fax 0161 833 0634
16 Arthur Street, Belfast BT1 4GD
028 9023 8451 Fax 028 9023 5401
The Stationery Office Oriel Bookshop
18–19 High Street, Cardiff CF1 2BZ
029 2039 5548 Fax 029 2038 4347
71 Lothian Road, Edinburgh EH3 9AZ
0870 606 5566 Fax 0870 606 5588

The Stationery Office's Accredited Agents
(see Yellow Pages)

and through good booksellers